THE
SOUTHERN
EXPERIENCE
IN
SHORT FICTION

THE
SOUTHERN
EXPERIENCE
IN
SHORT FICTION

ALLEN F. STEIN
THOMAS N. WALTERS

North Carolina State University at Raleigh

SCOTT, FORESMAN AND COMPANY
Glenview, Illinois   London

Library of Congress Catalog Card No. 71-129219

Copyright © 1971 by Scott, Foresman and Company,
Glenview, Illinois 60025.
All Rights Reserved.
Philippines Copyright 1971 by Scott, Foresman and Company.
Printed in the United States of America.

Regional offices of Scott, Foresman and Company
are located in Dallas, Oakland, N. J., Palo Alto, and Tucker, Ga.

For Gale and Ellen

acknowledgments

"Barn Burning" Copyright 1939 and renewed 1967 by Estelle Faulkner and Jill Faulkner Summers. Reprinted from *Collected Stories of William Faulkner*, by permission of Random House, Inc.

"Old Red" (Copyright 1933 Charles Scribner's Sons; renewal copyright © 1960 Caroline Gordon) is reprinted by permission of Charles Scribner's Sons from *The Forest of the South* by Caroline Gordon.

"Long Black Song" From *Uncle Tom's Children* by Richard Wright. Copyright, 1938, by Richard Wright; renewed 1966 by Ellen Wright. Reprinted by permission of Harper & Row, Publishers, Inc.

"The Man Who Was Almost a Man" Reprinted by permission of The World Publishing Company from *Eight Men* by Richard Wright. Copyright © 1961, 1940 by Richard Wright.

"A Late Encounter with the Enemy" Copyright, 1953, by Flannery O'Connor. Reprinted from her volume, *A Good Man Is Hard to Find and Other Stories*, by permission of Harcourt Brace Jovanovich, Inc.

"The River" Copyright, 1953, by Flannery O'Connor. Reprinted from her volume, *A Good Man Is Hard to Find and Other Stories*, by permission of Harcourt Brace Jovanovich, Inc.

"Venus, Cupid, Folly and Time" From *Happy Families Are All Alike*, Copyright 1959 by Peter Taylor. Reprinted by permission of Astor-Honor, Inc. All Rights Reserved.

"To the Open Water" Copyright © 1959, 1960, 1961, 1962, 1963, 1964, 1965, 1966, 1967 by Jesse Hill Ford; and Sarah Davis Ford and Katherine Kieffer Musgrove, Trustees. From *Fishes, Birds & Sons of Men* by Jesse Hill Ford, by permission of Atlantic-Little, Brown and Co.

"Reunion" Reprinted by permission of G. P. Putnam's Sons from *The Lonesome Traveler and Other Stories* by John William Corrington. Copyright © 1967, 1968 by John William Corrington.

"The Retrievers" Reprinted by permission of G. P. Putnam's Sons from *The Lonesome Traveler and Other Stories* by John William Corrington. Copyright © 1967, 1968 by John William Corrington.

"Battle Royal" Copyright 1947 by Ralph Ellison. Reprinted from *Invisible Man*, by Ralph Ellison, by permission of Random House, Inc.

"Flying Home" Reprinted by permission of William Morris Agency, Inc., on behalf of author. Copyright © 1944 by Ralph Ellison.

"A Fresh Snow" From *The Last Husband*, Copyright 1962. Reprinted by permission of the author.

"The Sky Is Gray" Reprinted from *Bloodline* by Ernest J. Gaines. Copyright © 1963, 1964, 1968 by Ernest J. Gaines and used by permission of the publisher, The Dial Press.

"The Flim-Flam Man and the Tent Meeting" Reprinted with permission of The Macmillan Company from *The Ballad of the Flim-Flam Man* by Guy Owen. Copyright © by Guy Owen 1965.

"Texarkana Was a Crazy Town" From *Cold Ground Was My Bed Last Night*, Copyright 1964, by George P. Garrett. Reprinted by permission of the author and the University of Missouri Press.

"Neighbors" First published in *The Sewanee Review*, LXXIV, 2 (Spring 1966). Copyright 1966 by The University of the South. Reprinted by permission of *The Sewanee Review* and the estate of Diane Oliver.

"Where Is the Voice Coming From?" Reprinted by permission of Random House, Inc. Copyright © 1963 by Eudora Welty. Originally appeared in *The New Yorker*.

"The Soul's Sting" From *Phylon: Review of Race & Culture*, Vol. 30, Winter 1969. Reprinted by permission.

prefatory note

The Southern Experience in Short Fiction is an anthology comprised solely of stories about the South. It is meant for students who are interested in the South and its literature, and who want to study them in greater depth than most textbooks allow. As has frequently been noted, Southern literature in its concerns and techniques is frequently as different from the rest of American literature as the South often is from the nation at large. A collection of Southern stories, then, provides students across the country with an opportunity to view a unique part of America through its own writers and gives Southern students a chance to see their way of life depicted by those in their own region.

While we conceive of *The Southern Experience in Short Fiction* to be essentially a supplementary text for most courses in reading and composition, the diversity of themes and styles represented in this collection is so great that it would by no means be inadequate as the sole literary text for such courses. Indeed we have made a special effort to select stories that are not limited to merely regional concerns. Thus, the reader will find that most of the stories in this text are, like the selections by Faulkner, Ellison, Wright, and O'Connor, more than regional in their appeal.

We have included a general introduction which sets the tone for the text by describing those elements of Southern life with which writers frequently deal, and each story is followed by a short commentary, questions, and suggestions for writing. Neither the introduction nor the commentaries, questions, and suggestions are meant to be all-inclusive. Rather, they are geared to elicit thought and discussion, and we hope the instructor and students will see them merely as starting points.

AFS

TNW

contents

introduction

Why, when we speak of twentieth-century American literature, do we often speak of one of its major components as "Southern literature"? Rarely, if ever, do we hear of a "Northwestern" or "Northeastern" literature, or of a writer who is a "Pacific Coast Regionalist"; but we often hear writers called "Southern Regionalists." The chief reason for this singular emphasis on the Southern element in modern American literature is that to a far greater degree than is true of writers in other parts of the United States, Southern writers see themselves as part of a continuing pattern of regional life. Viewing themselves as part of a living tradition, many feel compelled to write of that tradition and of their relationship to it both as writers and as Southerners. Thus, the number of Southern writers in modern American literature is disproportionately large, and Southern literature is a nearly autonomous national literature within the larger body of American writing.

THE COMMON HERITAGE

Slavery

The American South is a relatively homogeneous society in that its two preponderant groups—white Protestants (largely of English, Scottish, and Irish ancestry) and black Protestants—share a common heritage: one of heroism and shame, accomplishment and frustration, love and hate. It is a heritage inextricably bound up in the land and in the economic and racial system which the land produced. That system was slavery.

Slavery defeated both master and chattel. It robbed the white man of his morality, for in depriving another man of his rights, he deprived himself of his own most precious birthright: his innocence and his human dignity. This was a loss so profound that no amount of heroism in a war to defend his way of life could ever redeem it. In addition to debilitating whites morally, slavery destroyed them financially. Not only was it economically unfeasible, but it led Southern whites into a war which destroyed their homeland and which confronted them with the need for rebuilding—a task for which, because of their dependence on slave labor, they had little training. Similarly, slavery robbed the black man of *his* birthright by denying him his identity as a man. However, unlike the white man, the black was not responsible for his loss, and for three hundred years had to endure quietly the indignities and deprivations forced upon him.

Violence

Further, slavery contributed to a syndrome of violence which still permeates Southern life. The Southern white's position was one of authority. The resultant sense of power, combined with the rugged outdoor life of most Southern males and with an inherent romantic disposition which derived from the early love of swashbuckling adventure stories such as those of Sir Walter Scott, which were widely read throughout the South, generated an emphasis on action and a chivalric code which, in turn, led the white man too readily to the assumption that he could force his will upon others, both black and white. Thus began a series of violent attempts at coercion which has still not run its course. Today there are still episodes of violence in which some whites who conceive themselves guardians of an ideal attack others—black or white—whose standards of conduct they find objectionable.

The black man, too, resorted to violence, though in his case violence was a response to the abuses visited upon him and his people. Consequently, through the eighteenth and nineteenth centuries, there were sporadic outbreaks of bloody slave rebellion, of the type chronicled by William Styron in *The Confessions of Nat Turner*. In our own time we see the increasing virulence of black militants who find that even a hundred years after emancipation they and other blacks have not been allowed to take their place in American life. Thus, violence begets violence, making Southern life and Southern literature frequently turbulent, intense, and disturbing.

Ties to the Land

As well as sharing a heritage of loss and violence, both white and black Southerners share a common bond with the land. Because the South has traditionally been agrarian, both races have been closely involved in farming, and even today they feel a kinship with the land. Southern literature reflects the belief of both races that man is most aware of what manhood entails and most aware of the deeper meaning of life when he has established a close relationship with the land, be it through planting and harvesting, or through camping and hunting. For these reasons, William Faulkner, in such a story as *The Bear,* has Ike McCaslin learn most tellingly of his Southern heritage and of himself when he is in the wilderness.

In addition to teaching the Southerner about his heritage and about himself, the land also serves him as a means of release from an increasingly crass and materialistic society. Often, Southern writers present characters who go back into the country for short stays in order to rescue their souls, which have been smothered by the concerns of modern urban society. Thus, Caroline Gordon's protagonist in "Old Red" must continually break away from the forces of social convention and get back to the essential—the relationship of man to the land.

Because of the kinship which the Southerner has with the land, it is understandable that he finds symbolic possibilities in nature. That is, he has an inbred propensity for seeing in natural objects significance for himself. Consequently, a crop failure, flood damage, or even a bird's song might be perceived as conveying a spiritual or moral lesson. In Robert Penn Warren's *All the King's Men,* the bayou country surrounding the town of Burden's Landing becomes for Jack Burden a symbol of the opportunities, dangers, and contradictions of Southern life.

THE CUMBERSOME BURDEN

The Past

Not surprisingly, people who are as aware of their heritage as are Southerners often find that history torments them. More specifically, many Southern whites are guilt-ridden over their forebears' mistreatment of black people. This sense of guilt takes many complex forms. It may cause the Southern white to be so preoccupied with the past and with the sense of guilt which has been transmitted to him that he becomes paralyzed. For example, Mr. Compson, in *The Sound and the Fury,* becomes a man who merely sips bourbon and philosophizes about guilt. Allen Tate, in his "Ode to the Confederate Dead," warns against this self-defeating attitude:

> What shall we say who have knowledge
> Carried to the heart? Shall we take the act
> To the grave? Shall we, more hopeful, set up the grave
> In the house? The ravenous grave?
>
> Leave now
> The shut gate and the decomposing wall.

Worse, though, is the response of those white Southerners who are so warped by their burden of guilt that they react violently, blindly attacking those about whom they feel guilty. Church bombings and cross burnings are obviously manifestations of guilt as well as of hatred. Eudora Welty describes this situation with particular force in her short story, "Where Is the Voice Coming From?" which is based largely on the assassination of Medgar Evers.

It is significant that some Southern whites, by grappling spiritually, and sometimes even physically, with their guilt, manage to use it, to force themselves—almost as a means of personal atonement—to attack injustice. The protagonist of George Garrett's story, "Texarkana Was A Crazy Town," finds himself avenging a black man by brutally beating a fellow white. It becomes apparent, though, that the protagonist is, in a sense, beating himself—striking at an inhumanity potentially his own.

Religion

The history of the South has not been the only cause of the guilt felt by the Southern white. Southern Protestantism, derived largely from Calvinism, has been a major force in making Southern whites, and blacks, uneasy about their spiritual states by impressing upon them a sense of human worthlessness. Moreover, the disasters of slavery, military defeat, and reconstruction have reinforced this Calvinistic view of man. It is this view which has made the Southerner see hardship as inevitable and, in fact, deserved. This sense of worthlessness and the sense that one must expect and endure the worst have too often led the Southerner to allow stupidity and injustice to perpetuate themselves. For instance, Tarwater, in Flannery O'Connor's novel *Wise Blood,* cannot survive in the modern world because of his fundamentalist reliance upon Calvinistic evangelism as a solution to human problems. On the other hand, it must be noted that for Tarwater, as for other Southerners, religion has provided not only solace but has inculcated a strong sense of responsibility which can be a liberating as well as a restrictive force.

The Family

We have seen, then, that his region's history and his religion have often served the Southerner both as a source of strength and as one of oppression. Serving in a similar fashion is the Southern emphasis upon maintaining close family ties. The family provides the Southerner with a sense of security, for he knows that it is made up of people like himself who understand him and his needs. The family also serves as a source of pride, for each Southern family has its collection of ancestral heroes who operate as abiding examples to be emulated. Thus, the family establishes standards against which one is measured. Southern writers reflect both the strengths and weaknesses of the Southern family relationship: there are characters who gain support and assurance from their family bonds, and there are those who react negatively to them, rebelling in ways which strain the traditional family unit. William Humphrey, in *The Ordways,* has his protagonist gain self-knowledge and inspiration from what he learns of his family and its history. However, Brick, in Tennessee Williams' drama, *Cat On A Hot Tin Roof,* has been damaged by the overbearing influence of his parents, Big Mama and Big Daddy. Certainly most people are closely bound to their families and familial traditions, and feel themselves to be either helped or damaged by these ties, but it is apparent that sensitive Southerners feel these ties more strongly than do most people from other regions.

Individualism

Another force bearing on the Southerner is his strongly romantic sense of individualism. Paradoxically, individualism has as strong an effect on the Southerner as the influence of the family. Growing out of an early reliance upon a chivalric code, the romantic ideal of man's singular and innate qualities becomes a chief motivating factor in the Southerner's life. He has benefitted by his belief that a man should be self-reliant, proud, generous, and strong, for, even in times of adversity, these qualities have enabled him to survive and to retain his honor. Conversely, these tenets of the code make it difficult for the Southerner to live in an increasingly complex society in which the individual is pressured to conform and to sacrifice some of his personal customs for the good of society at large. Thus, the Southerner who drives a pickup truck equipped with a rifle on a rack believes himself to be carrying out his manly responsibility of self-defense. But he does not realize that this individualistic excess makes him a potential public menace.

Nevertheless, the Southerner's refusal to relinquish his individualistic code under the pressures of society sometimes reveals him as a man maintaining his dignity against gross odds. In John William Corrington's story, "Reunion," the old soldiers refuse to demean themselves by taking part in a vulgar re-enactment of Pickett's charge. Their refusal throws them into conflict with the modern world, isolating them, but at the same time making the dignity and courage of these independent diehards apparent. Similarly, the protagonist of Jesse Hill Ford's story, "To The Open Water," is in rebellion against social restrictions and finds satisfaction in hunting alone under arduous circumstances. His excessively romantic view of his own power leads him to consider himself capable of vanquishing nature, thus making him a misfit in society and leading inevitably to his destruction.

SOUTHERN LITERATURE

As the frequent references to Southern literature in our discussion of the Southern way of life have indicated, Southern writers have been remarkably attuned to the customs and problems of their region. They have also been extremely conscious of what the nuances of Southern life have to say not only about the nature of the Southerner, but also about the nature of all men. Thus, when they write about individual responsibility, the sense of guilt, the ambivalence one feels toward one's family, and the human propensity for violence, they are writing of problems which are particularly relevant to Southern American life but which are applicable throughout the world.

From its beginnings, Southern literature has consistently held to certain basic themes. Thus, in the early nineteenth century such writers as Thomas Jefferson and John Taylor demonstrated the necessity of a system of government based on an agrarian order which would work to foster the fundamentally healthy relationship between man and the land. Similarly, such early Southern writers as William Gilmore Simms, John Pendleton Kennedy, and J. E. Cooke emphasized romance, the chivalric hero, and ties to family and region, all of which derive in part from Walter Scott. This romantic emphasis carries over into the courtly lyrics of Edward Coote Pinckney and Philip Pendleton Cooke. Around 1835, in the *Georgia Scenes* of Judge Augustus Baldwin Longstreet, we note for the first time in the American South, and indeed in America, an emphasis on the faithful depiction of local scenes. Longstreet's work had far-reaching effect, particularly in the South, giving impetus to a number of Southern humorists who wrote in a genre we speak of as the "Humor of the Old Southwest." (The "Old Southwest" consisted of Georgia, Tennessee, Mississippi, Alabama, Louisiana, and Arkansas.) The writers of this region portrayed the local life patterns of the South through the raucously humorous, frequently violent, escapades of such roving con-men and all-around hell-raisers as G. W. Harris' Sut Lovingood and J. J. Hooper's Simon Suggs.

The themes of nineteenth-century Southern literature—local scenes, the land, romanticism, chivalry, family ties—have been explored by the Southern writers of the twentieth century, who are generally more sophisticated than their forebears. Modern Southern writers have tied these themes to such modern Southern concerns as the regional sense of guilt derived from slavery and religion, the awareness of the dangers of extreme individualism, and the increasingly complex questions of violence and race relations. Not only have modern Southern writers explored these problems, but they have shown how they may be overcome. Thus, William Faulkner's *The Sound and the Fury* and Robert Penn Warren's *All The King's Men,* even while exploring questions of Southern guilt, corruption, and decadence, suggest how such problems may be overcome through acceptance, endurance, and faith. Similarly, Ralph Ellison, despite his anger as a black man over the injustice he and his people have suffered, offers a means of ameliorating the racial situation, one in which the black man asserts his manhood and blackness, compelling the white man's respect and thus making America's democratic principles meaningful for both black and white.

The answers found by Southern writers are applicable not only to American Southerners, but to all men. All modern men struggle with questions of doubt and faith, guilt and innocence, freedom and restraint; in their wrestling with these problems, modern Southern writers perform a service for all men as they move through defeat and error to point to awareness, courage, and honor. Thus, despite his local preoccupations, the Southern regionalist has been, through the past decades, a regional universalist.

WILLIAM FAULKNER
barn burning

The store in which the Justice of the Peace's court was sitting smelled of cheese. The boy, crouched on his nail keg at the back of the crowded room, knew he smelled cheese, and more: from where he sat he could see the ranked shelves close-packed with the solid, squat, dynamic shapes of tin cans whose labels his stomach read, not from the lettering which meant nothing to his mind but from the scarlet devils and the silver curve of fish—this, the cheese which he knew he smelled and the hermetic meat which his intestines believed he smelled coming intermittent gusts momentary and brief between the other constant one, the smell and sense just a little of fear because mostly of despair and grief, the old fierce pull of blood. He could not see the table where the Justice sat and before which his father and his father's enemy (*our enemy* he thought in that despair; *ourn! mine and hisn both! He's my father!*) stood, but he could hear them, the two of them that is, because his father had said no word yet:

"But what proof have you, Mr. Harris?"

"I told you. The hog got into my corn. I caught it up and sent it back to him. He had no fence that would hold it. I told him so, warned him. The next time I put the hog in my pen. When he came to get it I gave him enough wire to patch up his pen. The next time I put the hog up and kept it. I rode down to his house and saw the wire I gave him still rolled on to the spool in his yard. I told him he could have the hog when he paid me a dollar pound fee. That evening a nigger came with the dollar and got the hog. He was a strange nigger. He said, 'He say to tell you wood and hay kin burn.' I said, 'What?' 'That whut he say to tell you,' the nigger said. 'Wood and hay kin burn.' That night my barn burned. I got the stock out but I lost the barn."

"Where is the nigger? Have you got him?"

"He was a strange nigger, I tell you. I don't know what became of him."

"But that's not proof. Don't you see that's not proof?"

"Get that boy up here. He knows." For a moment the boy thought too that the man meant his older brother until Harris said, "Not him. The little one. The boy," and, crouching, small for his age, small and wiry like his father, in patched and faded jeans even too small for him, with straight, uncombed, brown hair and eyes gray and wild as storm scud, he saw the men between himself and the table part and become a lane of grim faces, at the end of which he saw the Justice, a shabby, collarless, graying man in spectacles, beckoning him. He felt no floor under his bare feet; he seemed to walk beneath the palpable weight of the grim turning faces. His father, stiff in his black Sunday coat donned not for the trial but for the moving, did not even look at him. *He aims for me to lie,* he thought, again with that frantic grief and despair. *And I will have to do hit.*

"What's your name, boy?" the Justice said.

"Colonel Sartoris Snopes," the boy whispered.

"Hey?" the Justice said. "Talk louder. Colonel Sartoris? I reckon anybody named for Colonel Sartoris in this country can't help but tell the truth, can they?" The boy said nothing. *Enemy! Enemy!* he thought; for a moment he could not even see, could not see that the Justice's face was kindly nor discern that his voice was troubled when he spoke to the man named Harris: "Do you want me to question this boy?" But he could hear, and during those subsequent long seconds while there was absolutely no sound in the crowded little room save that of quiet and intent breathing it was as if he had swung outward at the end of a grape vine, over a ravine, and at the top of the swing had been caught in a prolonged instant of mesmerized gravity, weightless in time.

"No!" Harris said violently, explosively. "Damnation! Send him out of here!" Now time, the fluid world, rushed beneath him again, the voices coming to him again through the smell of cheese and sealed meat, the fear and despair and the old grief of blood:

"This case is closed. I can't find against you, Snopes, but I can give you advice. Leave this country and don't come back to it."

His father spoke for the first time, his voice cold and harsh, level, without emphasis: "I aim to. I don't figure to stay in a country among people who . . ." he said something unprintable and vile, addressed to no one.

"That'll do," the Justice said. "Take your wagon and get out of this country before dark. Case dismissed."

His father turned, and he followed the stiff black coat, the wiry figure walking a little stiffly from where a Confederate provost's man's musket ball had taken him in the heel on a stolen horse thirty years ago, followed the two backs now, since his older brother had appeared from somewhere in the crowd, no taller than the father but thicker, chewing tobacco steadily, between the two lines of grim-faced men and out of the store and across the worn gallery and down the sagging steps and among the dogs and half-grown boys in the mild May dust, where as he passed a voice hissed:

"Barn burner!"

Again he could not see, whirling; there was a face in a red haze, moonlike, bigger than the full moon, the owner of it half again his size, he leaping in the red haze toward the face, feeling no blow, feeling no shock when his head struck the earth, scrabbling up and leaping again, feeling no blow this time either and tasting no blood, scrabbling up to see the other boy in full flight and himself already leaping into pursuit as his father's hand jerked him back, the harsh, cold voice speaking above him: "Go get in the wagon."

It stood in a grove of locusts and mulberries across the road. His two hulking sisters in their Sunday dresses and his mother and her sister in calico and sunbonnets were already in it, sitting on and among the sorry residue of the dozen and more movings which even the boy could remember—the battered stove, the broken beds and chairs, the clock inlaid with mother-of-pearl, which would not run, stopped at some fourteen minutes past two o'clock of a dead and forgotten day and time, which had been his mother's dowry. She was crying, though when she saw him she drew her sleeve across her face and began to descend from the wagon. "Get back," the father said.

"He's hurt. I got to get some water and wash his . . ."

"Get back in the wagon," his father said. He got in too, over the tail-gate. His father mounted to the seat where the older brother already sat and struck the gaunt mules two savage blows with the peeled willow, but without heat. It was not even sadistic; it was exactly that same quality which in later years would cause his descendants to over-run the engine before putting a motor car into motion, striking and reining back in the same movement. The wagon went on, the store with its quiet crowd of grimly watching men dropped behind; a curve in the road hid it. *Forever* he thought. *Maybe he's done satisfied now, now that he has* . . . stopping himself, not to say it aloud even to himself. His mother's hand touched his shoulder.

"Does hit hurt?" she said.

"Naw," he said. "Hit don't hurt. Lemme be."

"Can't you wipe some of the blood off before hit dries?"

"I'll wash tonight," he said. "Lemme be, I tell you."

The wagon went on. He did not know where they were going. None of them ever did or ever asked, because it was always somewhere, always a house of sorts waiting for them a day or two days or even three days away. Likely his father had already arranged to make a crop on another farm before he . . . Again he had to stop himself. He (the father) always did. There was something about his wolflike independence and even courage when the advantage was at least neutral which impressed strangers, as if they got from his latent ravening ferocity not so much a sense of dependability as a feeling that his ferocious conviction in the rightness of his own actions would be of advantage to all whose interest lay with his.

That night they camped in a grove of oaks and beeches where a spring ran. The nights were still cool and they had a fire against it, of a rail lifted from a nearby fence and cut into lengths—a small fire, neat, niggard almost, a shrewd fire; such fires were his father's habit and custom always, even in freezing weather. Older, the boy might have remarked this and wondered why not a big one; why should not a man who had not only seen the waste and extravagance of war, but who had in his blood an inherent voracious prodigality with material not his own, have burned everything in sight? Then he might have gone a step farther and thought that that was the reason: that niggard blaze was the living fruit of nights passed during those four years in the woods hiding from all men, blue or gray, with his strings of horses (captured horses, he called them). And older still, he might have divined the true reason: that the element of fire spoke to some deep mainspring of his father's being, as the element of steel or of powder spoke to other men, as the one weapon for the preservation of integrity, else breath were not worth the breathing, and hence to be regarded with respect and used with discretion.

But he did not think this now and he had seen those same niggard blazes all his life. He merely ate his supper beside it and was already half asleep over his iron plate when his father called him, and once more he followed the stiff back, the stiff and ruthless limp, up the slope and on to the starlit road where, turning, he could see his father against the stars but without face or depth—a shape black, flat, and bloodless as though cut from tin in the iron folds of the frockcoat which had not been made for him, the voice harsh like tin and without heat like tin:

"You were fixing to tell them. You would have told him." He didn't answer. His father struck him with the flat of his hand on the side of the head, hard but without heat, exactly as he had struck the two mules at the store, exactly as he would strike either of them with any stick in order to kill a horse fly, his voice still without heat or anger: "You're getting to be a man. You got to learn. You got to learn to stick to your own blood or you ain't going to have any blood to stick to you. Do you think either of them, any man there this morning, would? Don't you know all they wanted was a chance to get at me because they knew I had them beat? Eh?" Later, twenty years later, he was to tell himself, "If I had said they wanted only truth, justice, he would have hit me again." But now he said nothing. He was not crying. He just stood there. "Answer me," his father said.

"Yes," he whispered. His father turned.

"Get on to bed. We'll be there tomorrow."

Tomorrow they were there. In the early afternoon the wagon stopped before a paintless two-room house identical almost with the dozen others it had stopped before even in the boy's ten years, and again, as on the other dozen occasions, his mother and aunt got down and began to unload the wagon, although his two sisters and his father and brother had not moved.

"Likely hit ain't fitten for hawgs," one of the sisters said.

"Nevertheless, fit it will and you'll hog it and like it," his father said. "Get out of them chairs and help your Ma unload."

The two sisters got down, big, bovine, in a flutter of cheap ribbons; one of them drew from the jumbled wagon bed a battered lantern, the other a worn broom. His father handed the reins to the older son and began to climb stiffly over the wheel. "When they get unloaded, take the team to the barn and feed them." Then he said, and at first the boy thought he was still speaking to his brother: "Come with me."

"Me?" he said.

"Yes," his father said. "You."

"Abner," his mother said. His father paused and looked back—the harsh level stare beneath the shaggy, graying, irascible brows.

"I reckon I'll have a word with the man that aims to begin tomorrow owning me body and soul for the next eight months."

They went back up the road. A week ago—or before last night, that is —he would have asked where they were going, but not now. His father had struck him before last night but never before had he paused afterward to explain why; it was as if the blow and the following calm, outrageous voice still rang, repercussed, divulging nothing to him save the terrible handicap of being young, the light weight of his few years, just heavy enough to prevent his soaring free of the world as it seemed to be ordered but not heavy enough to keep him footed solid in it, to resist it and try to change the course of its events.

Presently he could see the grove of oaks and cedars and the other flowering trees and shrubs where the house would be, though not the house yet. They walked beside a fence massed with honeysuckle and Cherokee roses and came to a gate swinging open between two brick pillars, and now, beyond a sweep of drive, he saw the house for the first time and at that instant he forgot his father and the terror and despair both, and even when he remembered his father again (who had not stopped) the terror and despair did not return. Because, for all the twelve movings, they had sojourned until now in a poor country, a land of small farms and fields and houses, and he had never seen a house like this before. *Hit's big as a courthouse* he thought quietly, with a surge of peace and joy whose reason he could not have thought into words, being too young for that: *They are safe from him. People whose lives are a part of this peace and dignity are beyond his touch, he no more to them than a buzzing wasp: capable of stinging for a little moment but that's all; the spell of this peace and dignity rendering even the barns and stable and cribs which belong to it impervious to the puny flames he might contrive* . . . this, the peace and joy, ebbing for an instant as he looked again at the stiff black back, the stiff and implacable limp of the figure which was not dwarfed by the house, for the reason that it had never looked big anywhere and which now, against the serene columned backdrop, had more than ever that impervious quality of something cut ruthlessly from tin, depthless, as though, sidewise to the sun, it would cast no shadow. Watching him, the boy remarked the absolutely undeviating course which his father held and saw the stiff foot come squarely down in a pile of fresh droppings where a horse had stood in the drive and which his father could have avoided by a simple change of stride. But it ebbed only for a moment, though he could not have thought this into words either, walking on in the spell of the house, which he could even want but without envy, without sorrow, certainly never with that ravening and jealous rage which unknown to him walked in the ironlike black coat before him. *Maybe he will feel it too. Maybe it will even change him now from what maybe he couldn't help but be.*

They crossed the portico. Now he could hear his father's stiff foot as it came down on the boards with clocklike finality, a sound out of all proportion to the displacement of the body it bore and which was not dwarfed either by the white door before it, as though it had attained to a sort of vicious and ravening minimum not to be dwarfed by anything—the flat, wide, black hat, the formal coat of broadcloth which had once been black but which had now the friction-glazed greenish cast of the bodies of old house flies, the lifted sleeve which was too large, the lifted hand like a curled claw. The door opened so promptly that the boy knew the Negro must have been watching them all the time, an old man with neat grizzled hair, in a linen jacket, who stood barring the door with his body, saying, "Wipe yo foots, white man, fo you come in here. Major ain't home nohow."

"Get out of my way, nigger," his father said, without heat too, flinging the door back and the Negro also and entering, his hat still on his head. And now the boy saw the prints of the stiff foot on the doorjamb and saw them appear on the pale rug behind the machinelike deliberation of the foot which seemed to bear (or transmit) twice the weight which the body compassed. The Negro was shouting "Miss Lulu! Miss Lulu!" somewhere behind them, then the boy, deluged as though by a warm wave by a suave turn of carpeted stair and a pendant glitter of chandeliers and a mute gleam of gold frames, heard the swift feet and saw her too, a lady—perhaps he had never seen her like before either—in a gray, smooth gown with lace at the throat and an apron tied at the waist and the sleeves turned back, wiping cake or biscuit dough from her hands with a towel as she came up the hall, looking not at his father at all but at the tracks on the blond rug with an expression of incredulous amazement.

"I tried," the Negro cried. "I tole him to . . ."

"Will you please go away?" she said in a shaking voice. "Major de Spain is not at home. Will you please go away?"

His father had not spoken again. He did not speak again. He did not even look at her. He just stood stiff in the center of the rug, in his hat, the shaggy iron-gray brows twitching slightly above the pebble-colored eyes as he appeared to examine the house with brief deliberation. Then with the same deliberation he turned; the boy watched him pivot on the good leg and saw the stiff foot drag round the arc of the turning, leaving a final long and fading smear. His father never looked at it, he never once looked down at the rug. The Negro held the door. It closed behind them, upon the hysteric and indistinguishable woman-wail. His father stopped at the top of the steps and scraped his boot clean on the edge of it. At the gate he stopped again. He stood for a moment, planted stiffly on the stiff foot, looking back at the house. "Pretty and white, ain't it?" he said. "That's sweat. Nigger sweat. Maybe it ain't white enough yet to suit him. Maybe he wants to mix some white sweat with it."

Two hours later the boy was chopping wood behind the house within which his mother and aunt and the two sisters (the mother and aunt, not the two girls, he knew that; even at this distance and muffled by walls the flat loud voices of the two girls emanated an incorrigible idle inertia) were setting up the stove to prepare a meal, when he heard the hooves and saw the linen-clad man on a fine sorrel mare, whom he recognized even before he saw the rolled rug in front of the Negro youth following on a fat bay carriage horse—a suffused, angry face vanishing, still at full gallop, beyond the corner of the house where his father and brother were sitting in the two tilted chairs; and a moment later, almost before he could have put the axe down, he heard the hooves again and watched the sorrel mare go back out of the yard, already galloping again. Then his father began to shout one of the sisters' names, who presently emerged backward from the kitchen door dragging the rolled rug along the ground by one end while the other sister walked behind it.

"If you ain't going to tote, go on and set up the wash pot," the first said.

"You, Sarty!" the second shouted, "Set up the wash pot!" His father appeared at the door, framed against that shabbiness, as he had been against that other bland perfection, impervious to either, the mother's anxious face at his shoulder.

"Go on," the father said. "Pick it up." The two sisters stooped, broad, lethargic; stooping, they presented an incredible expanse of pale cloth and a flutter of tawdry ribbons.

"If I thought enough of a rug to have to git hit all the way from France I wouldn't keep hit where folks coming in would have to tromp on hit," the first said. They raised the rug.

"Abner," the mother said. "Let me do it."

"You go back and git dinner," his father said. "I'll tend to this."

From the woodpile through the rest of the afternoon the boy watched them, the rug spread flat in the dust beside the bubbling wash-pot, the two sisters stooping over it with that profound and lethargic reluctance, while the father stood over them in turn, implacable and grim, driving them though never raising his voice again. He could smell the harsh homemade lye they were using; he saw his mother come to the door once and look toward them with an expression not anxious now but very like despair; he saw his father turn, and he fell to with the axe and saw from the corner of his eye his father raise from the ground a flattish fragment of field stone and examine it and return to the pot, and this time his mother actually spoke: "Abner. Abner. Please don't. Please, Abner."

Then he was done too. It was dusk; the whippoorwills had already begun. He could smell coffee from the room where they would presently eat the cold food remaining from the mid-afternoon meal, though when he entered the house he realized they were having coffee again probably because there was a fire on the hearth, before which the rug now lay spread over the backs of the two chairs. The tracks of his father's foot were gone. Where they had been were now long, water-cloudy scoriations resembling the sporadic course of a lilliputian mowing machine.

It still hung there while they ate the cold food and then went to bed, scattered without order or claim up and down the two rooms, his mother in one bed, where his father would later lie, the older brother in the other, himself, the aunt, and the two sisters on pallets on the floor. But his father was not in bed yet. The last thing the boy remembered was the depthless, harsh silhouette of the hat and coat bending over the rug and it seemed to him that he had not even closed his eyes when the silhouette was standing over him, the fire almost dead behind it, the stiff foot prodding him awake. "Catch up the mule," his father said.

When he returned with the mule his father was standing in the black door, the rolled rug over his shoulder. "Ain't you going to ride?" he said.

"No. Give me your foot."

He bent his knee into his father's hand, the wiry, surprising power flowed smoothly, rising, he rising with it, on to the mule's bare back (they had owned a saddle once; the boy could remember it though not when or where) and with the same effortlessness his father swung the rug up in front of him. Now in the starlight they retraced the afternoon's path, up the dusty road rife with honeysuckle, through the gate and up the black tunnel of the drive to the lightless house, where he sat on the mule and felt the rough warp of the rug drag across his thighs and vanish.

"Don't you want me to help?" he whispered. His father did not answer and now he heard again that stiff foot striking the hollow portico with that wooden and clocklike deliberation, that outrageous overstatement of the weight it carried. The rug, hunched, not flung (the boy could tell that even in the darkness) from his father's shoulder struck the angle of wall and floor with a sound unbelievably loud, thunderous, then the foot again, unhurried and enormous; a light came on in the house and the boy sat, tense, breathing steadily and quietly and just a little fast, though the foot itself did not increase its beat at all, descending the steps now; now the boy could see him.

"Don't you want to ride now?" he whispered. "We kin both ride now," the light within the house altering now, flaring up and sinking. *He's coming down the stairs now,* he thought. He had already ridden the mule up beside the horse block; presently his father was up behind him and he doubled the reins over and slashed the mule across the neck, but before the animal could begin to trot the hard, thin arm came around him, the hard, knotted hand jerking the mule back to a walk.

In the first red rays of the sun they were in the lot, putting plow gear on the mules. This time the sorrel mare was in the lot before he heard it at all, the rider collarless and even bareheaded, trembling, speaking in a shaking voice as the woman in the house had done, his father merely looking up once before stooping again to the hame he was buckling, so that the man on the mare spoke to his stooping back:

"You must realize you have ruined that rug. Wasn't there anybody here, any of your women . . ." he ceased, shaking, the boy watching him, the older brother leaning now in the stable door, chewing, blinking slowly and steadily at nothing apparently. "It cost a hundred dollars. But you never had a hundred dollars. You never will. So I'm going to charge you twenty bushels of corn against your crop. I'll add it in your contract and when you come to the commissary you can sign it. That won't keep Mrs. de Spain quiet but maybe it will teach you to wipe your feet off before you enter her house again."

Then he was gone. The boy looked at his father, who still had not spoken or even looked up again, who was now adjusting the logger-head in the hame.

"Pap," he said. His father looked at him—the inscrutable face, the shaggy brows beneath which the gray eyes glinted coldly. Suddenly the boy went toward him, fast, stopping as suddenly. "You done the best you could!" he cried. "If he wanted hit done different why didn't he wait and tell you how? He won't git no twenty bushels! He won't git none! We'll gether hit and hide hit! I kin watch . . ."

"Did you put the cutter back in the straight stock like I told you?"

"No, sir," he said.

"Then go do it."

That was Wednesday. During the rest of that week he worked steadily, at what was within his scope and some which was beyond it, with an industry that did not need to be driven nor even commanded twice; he had this from his mother, with the difference that some at least of what he did he liked to do, such as splitting wood with the half-size axe which his mother and aunt had earned, or saved money somehow, to present him with at Christmas. In company with the two older women (and on one afternoon, even one of the sisters), he built pens for the shoat and the cow which were a part of his father's contract with the landlord, and one afternoon, his father being absent, gone somewhere on one of the mules, he went to the field.

They were running a middle buster now, his brother holding the plow straight while he handled the reins, and walking beside the straining mule, the rich black soil shearing cool and damp against his bare ankles, he thought *Maybe this is the end of it. Maybe even that twenty bushels that seems hard to have to pay for just a rug will be a cheap price for him to stop forever and always from being what he used to be;* thinking, dreaming now, so that his brother had to speak sharply to him to mind the mule: *Maybe he even won't collect the twenty bushels. Maybe it will all add up and balance and vanish—corn, rug, fire; the terror and grief, the being pulled two ways like between two teams of horses—gone, done with for ever and ever.*

Then it was Saturday; he looked up from beneath the mule he was harnessing and saw his father in the black coat and hat. "Not that," his father said. "The wagon gear." And then, two hours later, sitting in the wagon bed behind his father and brother on the seat, the wagon accomplished a final curve, and he saw the weathered paintless store with its tattered tobacco and patent-medicine posters and the tethered wagons and saddle animals below the gallery. He mounted the gnawed steps behind his father and brother, and there again was the lane of quiet, watching faces for the three of them to walk through. He saw the man in spectacles sitting at the plank table and he did not need to be told this was a Justice of the Peace; he sent one glare of fierce, exultant, partisan defiance at the man in collar and cravat now, whom he had seen but twice before in his life, and that on a galloping horse, who now wore on his face an expression not of rage but of amazed unbelief which the boy could not have known was at the incredible circumstance of being sued by one of his own tenants, and came and stood against his father and cried at the Justice: "He ain't done it! He ain't burnt . . ."

"Go back to the wagon," his father said.

"Burnt?" the Justice said. "Do I understand this rug was burned too?"

"Does anybody here claim it was?" his father said. "Go back to the wagon." But he did not, he merely retreated to the rear of the room, crowded as that other had been, but not to sit down this time, instead, to stand pressing among the motionless bodies, listening to the voices:

"And you claim twenty bushels of corn is too high for the damage you did to the rug?"

"He brought the rug to me and said he wanted the tracks washed out of it. I washed the tracks out and took the rug back to him."

"But you didn't carry the rug back to him in the same condition it was in before you made the tracks on it."

His father did not answer, and now for perhaps half a minute there was no sound at all save that of breathing, the faint, steady suspiration of complete and intent listening.

"You decline to answer that, Mr. Snopes?" Again his father did not answer. "I'm going to find against you, Mr. Snopes. I'm going to find that you were responsible for the injury to Major de Spain's rug and hold you liable for it. But twenty bushels of corn seems a little high for a man in your circumstances to have to pay. Major de Spain claims it cost a hundred dollars. October corn will be worth about fifty cents. I figure that if Major de Spain can stand a ninety-five dollar loss on something he paid cash for, you can stand a five-dollar loss you haven't earned yet. I hold you in damages to Major de Spain to the amount of ten bushels of corn over and above your contract with him, to be paid to him out of your crop at gathering time. Court adjourned."

It had taken no time hardly, the morning was but half begun. He thought they would return home and perhaps back to the field, since they were late, far behind all other farmers. But instead his father passed on behind the wagon, merely indicating with his hand for the older brother to follow with it, and crossed the road toward the blacksmith shop opposite, pressing on after his father, overtaking him, speaking, whispering up at the harsh, calm face beneath the weathered hat: "He won't git no ten bushels neither. He won't git one. We'll . . ." until his father glanced for an instant down at him, the face absolutely calm, the grizzled eyebrows tangled above the cold eyes, the voice almost pleasant, almost gentle: "You think so? Well, we'll wait till October anyway."

The matter of the wagon—the setting of a spoke or two and the tightening of the tires—did not take long either, the business of the tires accomplished by driving the wagon into the spring branch behind the shop and letting it stand there, the mules nuzzling into the water from time to time, and the boy on the seat with the idle reins, looking up the slope and through the sooty tunnel of the shed where the slow hammer rang and where his father sat on an upended cypress bolt, easily, either talking or listening, still sitting there when the boy brought the dripping wagon up out of the branch and halted it before the door.

"Take them on to the shade and hitch," his father said. He did so and returned. His father and the smith and a third man squatting on his heels inside the door were talking, about crops and animals; the boy, squatting too in the ammoniac dust and hoof-parings and scales of rust, heard his father tell a long and unhurried story out of the time before the birth of the older brother even when he had been a professional horse-trader. And then his father came up beside him where he stood before a tattered last year's circus poster on the other side of the store, gazing rapt and quiet at the scarlet horses, the incredible poisings and convolutions of tulle and tights and the painted leers of comedians, and said, "It's time to eat."

But not at home. Squatting beside his brother against the front wall, he watched his father emerge from the store and produce from a paper sack a segment of cheese and divide it carefully and deliberately into three with his pocket knife and produce crackers from the same sack. They all three squatted on the gallery and ate, slowly, without talking; then in the store again, they drank from a tin dipper tepid water smelling of the cedar bucket and of living beech trees. And still they did not go home. It was a horse lot this time, a tall rail fence upon and along which men stood and sat and out of which one by one horses were led, to be walked and trotted and then cantered back and forth along the road while the slow swapping and buying went on and the sun began to slant westward, they—the three of them—watching and listening, the older brother with his muddy eyes and his steady, inevitable tobacco, the father commenting now and then on certain of the animals, to no one in particular.

It was after sundown when they reached home. They ate supper by lamplight, then, sitting on the doorstep, the boy watched the night fully accomplished, listening to the whippoorwills and the frogs, when he heard his mother's voice: "Abner! No! No! Oh, God. Oh, God. Abner!" and he rose, whirled, and saw the altered light through the door where a candle stub now burned in a bottle neck on the table and his father, still in the hat and coat, at once formal and burlesque as though dressed carefully for some shabby and ceremonial violence, emptying the reservoir of the lamp back into the five-gallon kerosene can from which it had been filled, while the mother tugged at his arm until he shifted the lamp to the other hand and flung her back, not savagely or viciously, just hard, into the wall, her hands flung out against the wall for balance, her mouth open and in her face the same quality of hopeless despair as had been in her voice. Then his father saw him standing in the door.

"Go to the barn and get that can of oil we were oiling the wagon with," he said. The boy did not move. Then he could speak.

"What . . ." he cried. "What are you . . ."

"Go get that oil," his father said. "Go."

Then he was moving, running, outside the house, toward the stable: this the old habit, the old blood which he had not been permitted to choose for himself, which had been bequeathed him willy nilly and which had run for so long (and who knew where, battening on what of outrage and savagery and lust) before it came to him. *I could keep on,* he thought. *I could run on and on and never look back, never need to see his face again. Only I can't. I can't,* the rusted can in his hand now, the liquid sploshing in it as he ran back to the house and into it, into the sound of his mother's weeping in the next room, and handed the can to his father.

"Ain't you going to even send a nigger?" he cried. "At least you sent a nigger before!"

This time his father didn't strike him. The hand came even faster than the blow had, the same hand which had set the can on the table with almost excruciating care flashing from the can toward him too quick for him to follow it, gripping him by the back of his shirt and on to tiptoe before he had seen it quit the can, the face stooping at him in breathless and frozen ferocity, the cold, dead voice speaking over him to the older brother who leaned against the table, chewing with that steady, curious, sidewise motion of cows:

"Empty the can into the big one and go on. I'll ketch up with you."

"Better tie him up to the bedpost," the brother said.

"Do like I told you," the father said. Then the boy was moving, his bunched shirt and the hard, bony hand between his shoulder-blades, his toes just touching the floor, across the room and into the other one, past the sisters sitting with spread heavy thighs in the two chairs over the cold hearth, and to where his mother and aunt sat side by side on the bed, the aunt's arms about his mother's shoulders.

"Hold him," the father said. The aunt made a startled movement. "Not you," the father said. "Lennie. Take hold of him. I want to see you do it." His mother took him by the wrist. "You'll hold him better than that. If he gets loose don't you know what he is going to do? He will go up yonder." He jerked his head toward the road. "Maybe I'd better tie him."

"I'll hold him," his mother whispered.

"See you do then." Then his father was gone, the stiff foot heavy and measured upon the boards, ceasing at last.

Then he began to struggle. His mother caught him in both arms, he jerking and wrenching at them. He would be stronger in the end, he knew that. But he had no time to wait for it. "Lemme go!" he cried. "I don't want to have to hit you!"

"Let him go!" the aunt said. "If he don't go, before God, I am going up there myself!"

"Don't you see I can't?" his mother cried. "Sarty! Sarty! No! No! Help me, Lizzie!"

Then he was free. His aunt grasped at him but it was too late. He whirled, running, his mother stumbled forward on to her knees behind him, crying to the nearer sister: "Catch him, Net! Catch him!" But that was too late too, the sister (the sisters were twins, born at the same time, yet either of them now gave the impression of being, encompassing as much living meat and volume and weight as any other two of the family) not yet having begun to rise from the chair, her head, face, alone merely turned, presenting to him in the flying instant an astonishing expanse of young female features untroubled by any surprise even, wearing only an expression of bovine interest. Then he was out of the room, out of the house, in the mild dust of the starlit road and the heavy rifeness of honeysuckle, the pale ribbon unspooling with terrific slowness under his running feet, reaching the gate at last and turning in, running, his heart and lungs drumming, on up the drive toward the lighted house, the lighted door. He did not knock, he burst in, sobbing for breath, incapable for the moment of speech; he saw the astonished face of the Negro in the linen jacket without knowing when the Negro had appeared.

"De Spain!" he cried, panted. "Where's . . ." then he saw the white man too emerging from a white door down the hall. "Barn!" he cried. "Barn!"

"What?" the white man said. "Barn?"

"Yes!" the boy cried. "Barn!"

"Catch him!" the white man shouted.

But it was too late this time too. The Negro grasped his shirt, but the entire sleeve, rotten with washing, carried away, and he was out that door too and in the drive again, and had actually never ceased to run even while he was screaming into the white man's face.

Behind him the white man was shouting, "My horse! Fetch my horse!" and he thought for an instant of cutting across the park and climbing the fence into the road, but he did not know the park nor how high the vine-massed fence might be and he dared not risk it. So he ran on down the drive, blood and breath roaring; presently he was in the road again though he could not see it. He could not hear either: the galloping mare was almost upon him before he heard her, and even then he held his course, as if the very urgency of his wild grief and need must in a moment more find him wings, waiting until the ultimate instant to hurl himself aside and into the weed-choked roadside ditch as the horse thundered past and on, for an instant in furious silhouette against the stars, the tranquil early summer night sky, which, even before the shape of the horse and rider vanished, stained abruptly and violently upward: a long, swirling roar incredible and soundless, blotting the stars, and he springing up and into the road again, running again, knowing it was too late yet still running even after he heard the shot and, an instant later, two shots, pausing now without knowing he had ceased to run, crying "Pap! Pap!", running again before he knew he had begun to run, stumbling, tripping over something and scrabbling up again without ceasing to run, looking backward over his shoulder at the glare as he got up, running on among the invisible trees, panting, sobbing, "Father! Father!"

At midnight he was sitting on the crest of a hill. He did not know it was midnight and he did not know how far he had come. But there was no glare behind him now and he sat now, his back toward what he had called home for four days anyhow, his face toward the dark woods which he would enter when breath was strong again, small, shaking steadily in the chill darkness, hugging himself into the remainder of his thin, rotten shirt, the grief and despair now no longer terror and fear but just grief and despair. *Father. My father,* he thought. "He was brave!" he cried suddenly, aloud but not loud, no more than a whisper: "He was! He was in the war! He was in Colonel Sartoris' cav'ry!" not knowing that his father had gone to that war a private in the fine old European sense, wearing no uniform, admitting the authority of and giving fidelity to no man or army or flag, going to war as Malbrouck himself did: for booty—it meant nothing and less than nothing to him if it were enemy booty or his own.

The slow constellations wheeled on. It would be dawn and then sun-up after a while and he would be hungry. But that would be tomorrow and now he was only cold, and walking would cure that. His breathing was easier now and he decided to get up and go on, and then he found that he had been asleep because he knew it was almost dawn, the night almost over. He could tell that from the whippoorwills. They were everywhere now among the dark trees below him, constant and inflectioned and ceaseless, so that, as the instant for giving over to the day birds drew nearer and nearer, there was no interval at all between them. He got up. He was a little stiff, but walking would cure that too as it would the cold, and soon there would be the sun. He went on down the hill, toward the dark woods within which the liquid silver voices of the birds called unceasing—the rapid and urgent beating of the urgent and quiring heart of the late spring night. He did not look back.

afterword

"Barn Burning" depicts an aspect of Southern life with which Faulkner frequently deals, the tendency of Southerners to become involved in violent conflicts. Faulkner sees these conflicts as deriving, in great part, from the extremely rigid commitments that Southerners are capable of making to the things in which they believe. Thus, loyalty to his region, to his family, or even to his own self-image can make the Southerner resort to violence if he conceives the objects of his loyalty to be threatened. The historical pattern of decisive, individual action, which is part of the Southern heritage, also contributes to the incidence of conflict and violence. Faulkner, then, sees as motivating many of his fellow Southerners the same attitude which Wilber J. Cash saw as pushing them up the slopes of Gettysburg, the conviction that "nothing living could cross them and get away with it." In "Barn Burning," Faulkner deals with problems that arise from loyalty and action: what happens when an individual with strong convictions is at odds with the society around him; and, conversely, what happens when one who lacks such conviction finds himself in the midst of a people unswervingly devoted to a common cause.

The barn-burner, Abner Snopes, who drags his family from town to town, leaving behind him memories of hatred and destruction, is a man whose commitment to his sense of dignity keeps him from living peaceably in any society. Essentially, Snopes's unyielding pride has made him less a man than an embodiment of a dark force of destruction. Bitter because others are wealthier and more successful than he and are, consequently, able to exercise some control over him, Snopes reacts violently, expressing himself in the only way he knows—arson. Faulkner explains that "the element of fire spoke to some deep mainspring of [Ab's] being, as the element of steel or of powder spoke to other men, as the one weapon for the preservation of integrity, else breath were not worth breathing. . . ." Ab's conflict with society initiates a terrible internal conflict for his son, Colonel Sartoris, who must ascertain whether his loyalty lies with his father or with society at large. In reaching his decision, the boy goes through a difficult time, achieving emotional growth through adversity.

William Faulkner lived nearly all his life in the university town of Oxford, Mississippi. Although he completed neither his high-school nor his college education, he attended the public school and, for a brief period, the university in his home town. During World War I, he served in the Canadian Royal Air Force, but he never went overseas. After the war, he worked at a variety of jobs in Oxford, New Orleans, and New York. While in New Orleans, where he met Sherwood Anderson and other writers, he wrote two novels, *Mosquitos* and *Soldier's Pay,* neither of lasting significance. Settling in Oxford, Faulkner began in earnest the pursuit of a literary career which was to stretch over more than forty years. His efforts brought him international fame, made him a commanding personality among writers, eliciting both their admiration and emulation, and, in 1949, won him the Nobel Prize for Literature. Nearly all of his novels and short stories are set in an imaginary Mississippi county which he called Yoknapatawpha. Among his most distinguished novels are *The Sound and the Fury* (1929), *As I Lay Dying* (1930), *Light in August* (1932), *Absalom, Absalom!* (1936), *The Wild Palms* and *Old Man* (1939), and *The Reivers* (1962). Three of his novels form a trilogy about the Snopes clan: *The Hamlet* (1940), *The Town* (1957), and *The Mansion* (1959). His collections of short stories include *Idyll In The Desert* (1931), *These 13* (1931), *Doctor Martino and Other Stories* (1934), *Go Down, Moses and Other Stories* (1942), *Collected Stories of William Faulkner* (1950), and *Big Woods* (1955).

questions for general discussion

1. Faulkner's prose style is one of his unique attributes. Is he verbose needlessly or does his style contribute effectively to the establishment of character, tone, and theme?

2. What is the function of the sisters in the story? Why are these apparently unimportant characters even mentioned at all?

3. What kinds of images does Faulkner use in describing Ab Snopes and his immediate environment? How do these images compare with the imagery employed in describing other characters and scenes in the story?

4. Describe in detail the ways Faulkner varies the pace or tempo of the story. What is Faulkner's purpose in making some of the scenes long and slow and others more tightly compressed and fast-moving?

5. What does Faulkner gain by presenting Abner as a man who walks with a limp?

6. What is the significance, near the end of the story, of Sarty's thought, *"Father. My father. . . .* He was brave! . . . He was! He was in the war"?

7. Comment on the symbols in the story.

suggestions for writing

1. Write a theme in which you make a case for Abner as an admirable character.

2. Comment on Faulkner's selection of settings for the different scenes.

3. Discuss "Barn Burning" as a story of initiation. Into what awareness is Colonel Sartoris initiated?

4. Discuss the effectiveness of the third-person point of view in "Barn Burning." Point out what effects are gained or lost through this method.

5. Discuss the various conflicts in the story and their implications.

CAROLINE GORDON
old red

1

When the door had closed behind his daughter, Mister Maury went to the window and stood a few moments looking out. The roses that had grown in a riot all along that side of the fence had died or been cleared away, but the sun lay across the garden in the same level lances of light that he remembered. He turned back into the room. The shadows had gathered until it was nearly all in gloom. The top of his minnow bucket just emerging from the duffel bag glinted in the last rays of the sun. He stood looking down at his traps all gathered neatly in a heap at the foot of the bed. He would leave them like that. Even if they came in here sweeping and cleaning up—it was only in hotels that a man was master of his own room—even if they came in here cleaning up, he would tell them to leave all his things exactly as they were. It was reassuring to see them all there together, ready to be taken up in the hand, to be carried down and put into a car, to be driven off to some railroad station at a moment's notice.

As he moved toward the door, he spoke aloud, a habit that was growing on him:

"Anyhow, I won't stay but a week. . . . I ain't going to stay but a week, no matter what they say. . . ."

Downstairs in the dining room they were already gathered at the supper table, his white-haired, shrunken mother-in-law, his tall sister-in-law who had the proud carriage of the head, the aquiline nose, but not the spirit of his dead wife, his lean, blond new son-in-law, his black-eyed daughter who, but that she was thin, looked so much like him, all of them gathered there waiting for him, Alexander Maury. It occurred to him that this was the first time he had sat down in the bosom of the family for some years. They were always writing saying that he must make a visit this summer or certainly next fall. ". . . all had a happy Christmas together but missed you. . . ." They had even made the pretext that he ought to come up to inspect his new son-in-law. As if he hadn't always known exactly the kind of young man Sarah would marry! What was the boy's name? Stephen, yes, Stephen. He must be sure and remember that.

He sat down, and shaking out his napkin spread it over his capacious paunch and tucked it well up under his chin in the way his wife had never allowed him to do. He let his eyes rove over the table and released a long sigh.

"Hot batter bread," he said, "and ham. Merry Point ham. I sure am glad to taste them one more time before I die."

The old lady was sending the little Negro girl scurrying back to the kitchen for a hot plate of batter bread. He pushed aside the cold plate and waited. She had bridled when he spoke of the batter bread and a faint flush had dawned on her withered cheeks. Vain she had always been as a peacock, of her housekeeping, her children, the animals on her place, anything that belonged to her. And she went on, even at her advanced age, making her batter bread, smoking her hams according to that old recipe she was so proud of; but who came here now to this old house to eat or to praise?

He helped himself to a generous slice of batter bread, buttered it, took the first mouthful and chewed it slowly. He shook his head.

"There ain't anything like it," he said. "There ain't anything else like it in this world."

His dark eyes roving the table fell on his son-in-law. "You like batter bread?" he inquired.

Stephen nodded, smiling. Mister Maury, still masticating slowly, regarded his face, measured the space between the eyes—his favorite test for man, horse, or dog. Yes, there was room enough for sense between the eyes. But how young the boy looked! And infected already with the fatal germ, the *cacoëthes scribendi.*[1] Well, their children would probably escape. It was like certain diseases of the eye, skipped every other generation. His own father had had it badly all his life. He could see him now sitting at the head of the table spouting his own poetry—or Shakespeare's—while the children watched the preserve dish to see if it was going around. He, Aleck Maury, had been lucky to be born in the generation he had. He had escaped that at least. A few translations from Heine in his courting days, a few fragments from the Greek, but no, he had kept clear of that on the whole. . . .

The eyes of his sister-in-law were fixed on him. She was smiling faintly. "You don't look much like dying, Aleck. Florida must agree with you."

The old lady spoke from the head of the table. "I can't see what you do with yourself all winter long. Doesn't time hang heavy on your hands?"

Time, he thought, time! They were always mouthing the word and what did they know about it? Nothing in God's world! He saw time suddenly, a dull, leaden-colored fabric depending from the old lady's hands, from the hands of all of them, a blanket that they pulled about, now this way, now that, trying to cover up their nakedness. Or they would cast it on the ground and creep in among the folds, finding one day a little more tightly rolled than another, but all of it everywhere the same dull gray substance. But time was a banner that whipped before him always in the wind. He stood on tiptoe to catch at the bright folds, to strain them to his bosom. They were bright and glittering. But

---

[1] *Cacoëthes scribendi:* Itch for writing.

they whipped by so fast and were whipping always ever faster. The tears came into his eyes. Where, for instance, had this year gone? He could swear he had not wasted a minute of it, for no man living, he thought, knew better how to make each day a pleasure to him. Not a minute wasted and yet here it was already May! If he lived to the Biblical three score and ten, which was all he ever allowed himself in his calculations, he had before him only nine more Mays. Only nine more Mays out of all eternity, and they wanted him to waste one of them sitting on the front porch at Merry Point!

The butter plate which had seemed to swim in a glittering mist was coming solidly to rest upon the white tablecloth. He winked his eyes rapidly and laying down his knife and fork squared himself about in his chair to address his mother-in-law:

"Well, ma'am, you know I'm a man that always likes to be learning something. Now this year I learned how to smell out fish." He glanced around the table, holding his head high and allowing his well-cut nostrils to flutter slightly with his indrawn breaths. "Yes, sir," he said, "I'm probably the only white man in this country knows how to smell out feesh."

There was a discreet smile on the faces of the others. Sarah was laughing outright. "Did you have to learn how or did it just come to you?" she asked.

"I learned it from an old nigger woman," her father said. He shook his head reminiscently. "It's wonderful how much you can learn from niggers. But you have to know how to handle them. I was half the winter wooing that old Fanny. . . ."

He waited until their laughter had died down. "We used to start off every morning from the same little cove and we'd drift in there together at night. I noticed how she always brought in a good string, so I says to her, 'Fanny, you just lemme go 'long with you.' But she wouldn't have nothing to do with me. I saw she was going to be a hard nut to crack, but I kept right on. Finally I began giving her presents. . . ."

Laura was regarding him fixedly, a queer look on her face.

"What sort of presents did you give her, Aleck?"

He made his tones hearty in answer. "I gave her a fine string of fish one day and I gave her fifty cents. And finally I made her a present of a Barlow knife. That was when she broke down. She took me with her that morning. . . ."

"Could she really smell fish?" the old lady asked curiously.

"You ought to 'a' seen her," Mister Maury said. "She'd sail over that lake like a hound on the scent. She'd row right along and then all of a sudden she'd stop rowing." He bent over, wrinkling his nose and peering into the depths of imaginary water. " 'Thar they are, White Folks, thar they are. Cain't you smell 'em?' "

Stephen was leaning forward, eyeing his father-in-law intently. "Could you?" he asked.

"I got so I could smell feesh," Mister Maury told him. "I could smell out the feesh, but I couldn't tell which kind they were. Now Fanny could row over a bed and tell just by the smell whether it was bass or bream. But she'd been at it all her life." He paused, sighing. "You can't just pick these things up.

You have to give yourself to them. Who was it said 'Genius is an infinite capacity for taking pains'?"

Sarah was rising briskly. Her eyes sought her husband's across the table. She was still laughing. "Sir Izaak Walton," she said, "we'd better go in the other room. Mandy wants to clear the table."

The two older ladies remained in the dining room. Mister Maury walked across the hall to the sitting room, accompanied by Steve and Sarah. He lowered himself cautiously into the most solid-looking of the rocking chairs that were drawn up around the fire. Steve was standing on the hearthrug, back to the fire, gazing abstractedly off across the room.

Mister Maury glanced up at him curiously. "What are you thinking about, feller?" he asked.

Steve looked down. He smiled, but his gaze was still contemplative. "I was thinking about the sonnet," he said, "in the form in which it first came to England."

Mister Maury shook his head, "Wyatt and Surrey," he said. "Hey, nonny, nonny. . . . You'll have hardening of the liver long before you're my age." He looked past Steve's shoulder at the picture that hung over the mantel shelf: Cupid and Psyche holding between them a fluttering veil and running along a rocky path toward the beholder. "Old Merry Point," he said; "it don't change much, does it?"

He settled himself more solidly in his chair. His mind veered from the old house to his own wanderings in brighter places. He regarded his daughter and son-in-law affably.

"Yes, sir," he said, "this winter in Florida was valuable to me just for the acquaintances I made. Take my friend, Jim Barbee. Just to live in the same hotel with that man is an education." He paused, smiling reminiscently into the fire. "I'll never forget the first time I saw him. He came up to me there in the lobby of the hotel. 'Professor Maury!' he says, 'You been hearin' about me for twenty years and I been hearin' about you for twenty years. And now we've done met!' "

Sarah had sat down in the little rocking chair by the fire. She leaned toward him now, laughing. "They ought to have put down a cloth of gold for the meeting," she said.

Mister Maury shook his head. "Nature does that in Florida," he said. "I knew right off the reel it was him. There were half a dozen men standing around. I made 'em witness. 'Jim Barbee,' I says, 'Jim Barbee of Maysville or I'll eat my hat!' "

"Why is he so famous?" Sarah asked.

Mister Maury took out his knife and cut a slice from a plug of tobacco. When he had offered a slice to his son-in-law and it had been refused, he put the plug back in his pocket. "He's a man of imagination," he said slowly. "There ain't many in this world."

He took a small tin box out of his pocket and set it on the little table that held the lamp. Removing the top he tilted the box so that they could see its contents: an artificial lure, a bug with a dark body and a red, bulbous head, a hook protruding from what might be considered its vitals.

"Look at her," he said, "ain't she a killer?"

Sarah leaned forward to look and Steve, still standing on the hearthrug, bent above them. The three heads ringed the light.

Mister Maury disregarded Sarah and addressed himself to Steve. "She takes nine strips of rind," he said, "nine strips just thick enough." He marked off the width of the strips with his two fingers on the table, then picking up the lure and cupping it in his palm he moved it back and forth quickly so that the painted eyes caught the light.

"Look at her," he said, "look at the wicked way she sets forward."

Sarah was poking at the lure with the tip of her finger.

"Wanton," she said, "simply wanton. What does he call her?"

"This is his Devil Bug," Mister Maury said. "He's the only man in this country makes it. I myself had the idea thirty years ago and let it slip by me the way I do with so many of my ideas." He sighed, then elevating his tremendous bulk slightly above the table level and continuing to hold Stephen with his gaze he produced from his coat pocket the oilskin book that held his flies. He spread it open on the table and began to turn the pages. His eyes sought his son-in-law's as his hand paused before a gray, rather draggled-looking lure.

"Old Speck," he said. "I've had that fly for twenty years. I reckon she's taken five hundred pounds of fish in her day. . . ."

The fire burned lower. A fiery coal rolled from the grate and fell onto the hearthrug. Sarah scooped it up with a shovel and threw it among the ashes. In the circle of the lamplight the two men still bent over the table looking at the flies. Steve was absorbed in them but he spoke seldom. It was her father's voice that rising and falling filled the room. He talked a great deal, but he had a beautiful speaking voice. He was telling Steve now about Little West Fork, the first stream ever he put a fly in. "My first love," he kept calling it. It sounded rather pretty, she thought, in his mellow voice. "My first love . . ."

2

When Mister Maury came downstairs the next morning the dining room was empty except for his daughter, Sarah, who sat dawdling over a cup of coffee and a cigarette. Mister Maury sat down opposite her. To the little Negro girl who presented herself at his elbow he outlined his wants briefly. "A cup of coffee and some hot batter bread just like we had last night." He turned to his daughter. "Where's Steve?"

"He's working," she said, "he was up at eight and he's been working ever since."

Mister Maury accepted the cup of coffee from the little girl, poured half of it into his saucer, set it aside to cool. "Ain't it wonderful," he said, "the way a man can sit down and work day after day? When I think of all the work I've done in my time. . . . Can he work *every* morning?"

"He sits down at his desk every morning," she said, "but of course he gets more done some mornings than others."

Mister Maury picked up the saucer, found the coffee cool enough for his taste. He sipped it slowly, looking out of the window. His mind was already busy with his day's program. No water—no running water—nearer than West Fork three miles away. He couldn't drive a car and Steve was going to be busy writing all morning. There was nothing for it but a pond. The Willow Sink. It was not much but it was better than nothing. He pushed his chair back and rose.

"Well," he said, "I'd better be starting."

When he came downstairs with his rod a few minutes later the hall was still full of the sound of measured typing. Sarah sat in the dining room in the same position in which he had left her, smoking. Mister Maury paused in the doorway while he slung his canvas bag over his shoulders. "How you ever going to get anything done if you don't take advantage of the morning hours?" he asked. He glanced at the door opposite as if it had been the entrance to a sick chamber.

"What's he writing about?" he inquired in a whisper.

"It's an essay on John Skelton."

Mister Maury looked out at the new green leaves framed in the doorway. "John Skelton," he said. "God Almighty!"

He went through the hall and stepped down off the porch onto the ground that was still moist with spring rains. As he crossed the lower yard he looked up into the branches of the maples. Yes, the leaves were full grown already even on the late trees. The year, how swiftly, how steadily it advanced! He had come to the far corner of the yard. Grown up it was in pokeberry shoots and honeysuckle, but there was a place to get through. The top strand of wire had been pulled down and fastened to the others with a ragged piece of rope. He rested his weight on his good leg and swung himself over onto the game one. It gave him a good, sharp twinge when he came down on it. It was getting worse all the time, that leg, but on the other hand he was learning better all the time how to handle it. His mind flew back to a dark, startled moment, that day when the cramp first came on him. He had been sitting still in the boat all day long and that evening when he had stood up to get out his leg had failed him utterly. He had pitched forward among the reeds, had lain there a second, face downwards, before it came to him what had happened. With the realization came a sharp picture of his faraway youth: Uncle Quent lowering himself ponderously out of the saddle after a hard day's hunting had fallen forward in exactly the same way, into a knot of yowling little Negroes. He had got up and cursed them all out of the lot. It had scared the old boy to death, coming down like that. The black dog he had had on his shoulder all that fall. But he himself had never lost one day's fishing on account of his leg. He had known from the start how to handle it. It meant simply that he was slowed down that much. It hadn't really made much difference in fishing. He didn't do as much wading but he got around just about as well on the whole. Hunting, of course, had had to go. You couldn't walk all day shooting birds, dragging a game leg. He had just given it up right off the reel, though it was a shame when a man was as good a shot as he was. That day he was out with Tom Kensington last November, the only day he got out during the season. Nine shots he'd had and he'd bagged nine birds. Yes, it was a shame. But a man couldn't do everything. He had to limit himself. . . .

He was up over the little rise now. The field slanted straight down before him to where the pond lay, silver in the morning sun. A Negro cabin was perched halfway up the opposite slope. A woman was hanging out washing on a line stretched between two trees. From the open doorway little Negroes spilled down the path toward the pond. Mister Maury surveyed the scene, spoke aloud:

"Ain't it funny now? Niggers always live in the good places."

He stopped under a wild cherry tree to light his pipe. It had been hot crossing the field, but the sunlight here was agreeably tempered by the branches. And that pond down there was fringed with willows. His eyes sought the bright disk of the water, then rose to where the smoke from the cabin chimney lay in a soft plume along the crest of the hill.

When he stooped to pick up his rod again it was with a feeling of sudden, keen elation. An image had risen in his memory, an image that was familiar but came to him infrequently of late and that only in moments of elation: the wide field in front of his uncle's old house in Albemarle, on one side the dark line of undergrowth that marked the Rivanna River, on the other the blue of Peters' Mountain. They would be waiting there in that broad plain when they had the first sight of the fox. On that little rise by the river, loping steadily, not yet alarmed. The sun would glint on his bright coat, on his quick-turning head as he dove into the dark of the woods. There would be hullabaloo after that and shouting and riding. Sometimes there was the tailing of the fox—that time old Whisky was brought home on a mattress! All of that to come afterward, but none of it ever like that first sight of the fox there on the broad plain between the river and the mountain.

There was one fox, they grew to know him in time, to call him affectionately by name. Old Red it was who showed himself always like that there on the crest of the hill. "There he goes, the damn' impudent scoundrel!" . . . Uncle Quent would shout and slap his thigh and yell himself hoarse at Whisky and Mag and the pups, but they would have already settled to their work. They knew his course, every turn of it by heart. Through the woods and then down across the fields again to the river. Their hope was always to cut him off before he could circle back to the mountain. If he got in there among those old field pines it was all up. But he always made it. Lost 'em every time and then dodged through to his hole in Pinnacle Rock. . . . A smart fox, Old Red. . . .

He descended the slope and paused in the shade of a clump of willows. The little Negroes who squatted, dabbling in the water, watched him out of round eyes as he unslung his canvas bag and laid it on a stump. He looked down at them gravely.

"D'you ever see a white man that could conjure?" he asked.

The oldest boy laid the brick he was fashioning out of mud down on a plank. He ran the tip of his tongue over his lower lip to moisten it before he spoke. "Naw suh."

"I'm the man," Mister Maury told him. "You chillun better quit that playin' and dig me some worms."

He drew his rod out of the case, jointed it up and laid it down on a stump. Taking out his book of flies he turned the pages, considering. "Silver Spinner," he said aloud. "They ought to take that . . . in May. Naw, I'll just give Old Speck a chance. It's a long time now since we had her out."

The little Negroes had risen and were stepping quietly off along the path toward the cabin, the two little boys hand in hand, the little girl following, the baby astride her hip. They were pausing now before a dilapidated building that might long ago have been a hen-house. Mister Maury shouted at them. "Look under them old boards. That's the place for worms." The biggest boy was turning around. His treble "Yassuh" quavered over the water. Then their voices died away. There was no sound except the light turning of the willow boughs in the wind.

Mister Maury walked along the bank, rod in hand, humming: "Bangum's gone to the wild boar's den . . . *Bangum's* gone to the wild boar's den . . ." He stopped where a white, peeled log protruded six or seven feet into the water. The pond made a little turn here. Two lines of willows curving in framed the whole surface of the water. He stepped out squarely upon the log, still humming. The line rose smoothly, soared against the blue and curved sweetly back upon the still water. His quick ear caught the little whish that the fly made when it clove the surface, his eye followed the tiny ripples of its flight. He cast again, leaning a little backward as he did sometimes when the mood was on him. Again and again his line soared out over the water. His eye rested now and then on his wrist. He noted with detachment the expert play of the muscles, admired each time the accuracy of his aim. It occurred to him that it was four days now since he had wet a line. Four days. One whole day packing up, parts of two days on the train and yesterday wasted sitting there on that front porch with the family. But the abstinence had done him good. He had never cast better than he was casting this morning.

There was a rustling along the bank, a glimpse of blue through the trees. Mister Maury leaned forward and peered around the clump of willows. A hundred yards away Steve, hatless, in an old blue shirt and khaki pants, stood jointing up a rod.

Mister Maury backed off his log and advanced along the path. He called out cheerfully, "Well, feller, do any good?"

Steve looked up. His face had lightened for a moment, but the abstracted expression stole over it again when he spoke. "Oh, I fiddled with it," he said, "all morning, but I didn't do much good."

Mister Maury nodded sympathetically. *"Minerva invita erat,"*[2] he said; "you can do nothing unless Minerva perches on the roof-tree. Why, I been castin' here all morning and not a strike. But there's a boat tied up over on the other side. What say we get in it and just drift around?" He paused, looking at the rod Steve had finished jointing up. "I brought another rod along," he said. "You want to use it?"

Steve shook his head. "I'm used to this one."

An expression of relief came over Mister Maury's face. "That's right," he said, "a man always does better with his own rod."

The boat was only a quarter full of water. They heaved her over and dumped it out, then dragged her down to the bank. The little Negroes had come up, bringing a can of worms. Mister Maury threw them each a nickel and set the can in the bottom of the boat. "I always like to have a few worms handy," he told Steve, "ever since I was a boy." He lowered himself ponderously into the bow and Steve pushed off and dropped down behind him.

The little Negroes still stood on the bank staring. When the boat was a little distance out on the water the boldest of them spoke: "Yo reckon 'at ole jawnboat going to hold you up, Cap'm?"

Mister Maury turned his head to call over his shoulder. "Go 'way, boy, ain't I done tole you I's a conjure?"

The boat dipped ominously. Steve changed his position a little and she settled to the water. Sitting well forward Mister Maury made graceful casts, now to this side, now to that. Steve, in the stern, made occasional casts, but he laid his rod down every now and then to paddle, though there was really no use in it. The boat drifted well enough with the wind. At the end of half an hour seven sizable bass lay on the bottom of the boat. Mister Maury had caught five of them. He reflected that perhaps he really ought to change places with Steve. The man in the bow certainly had the best chance at the fish. "But no," he thought, "it don't make any difference. He don't hardly know where he is now."

He stole a glance over his shoulder at the young man's serious, abstracted face. It was like that of a person submerged. Steve seemed to float up to the surface every now and then, his expression would lighten, he would make some observation that showed he knew where he was, then he would sink again. If you asked him a question he answered punctiliously, two minutes later. Poor boy, dead to the world and would probably be that way the rest of his life! A pang of pity shot through Mister Maury, and on the heels of it a gust of that black fear that occasionally shook him. It was he, not Steve, that was the queer one! The world was full of people like this boy, all of them walking around with their heads so full of this and that they hardly knew where they were going. There was hardly anybody—there was *nobody* really in the whole world like him. . . .

Steve, coming out of his abstraction, spoke politely. He had heard that Mister Maury was a fine shot. Did he like to fish better than hunt?

---

[2] *Minerva invita erat:* Minerva was unwilling.

Mister Maury reflected. "Well," he said, "they's something about a covey of birds rising up in front of you . . . they's something. And a good dog. Now they ain't anything in this world that I like better than a good bird dog." He stopped and sighed. "A man has got to come to himself early in life if he's going to amount to anything. Now I was smart, even as a boy. I could look around me and see all the men of my family, Uncle Jeems, Uncle Quent, my father, every one of 'em weighed two hundred by the time he was fifty. You get as heavy on your feet as all that and you can't do any good shooting. But a man can fish as long as he lives. . . . Why, one place I stayed last summer there was an old man ninety years old had himself carried down to the river every morning. . . . Yes, sir, a man can fish as long as he can get down to the water's edge. . . ."

There was a little plop to the right. He turned just in time to see the fish flash out of the water. He watched Steve take it off the hook and drop it on top of the pile in the bottom of the boat. Eight bass that made and two bream. The old lady would be pleased. "Aleck always catches me fish," she'd say.

The boat glided on over the still water. There was no wind at all now. The willows that fringed the bank might have been cut out of paper. The plume of smoke hung perfectly horizontal over the roof of the Negro cabin. Mister Maury watched it stream out in little eddies and disappear into the bright blue.

He spoke softly: "Ain't it wonderful . . . ain't it wonderful now that a man of my gifts can content himself a whole morning on this here little old pond?"

3

Mister Maury woke with a start. He realized that he had been sleeping on his left side again. A bad idea. It always gave him palpitations of the heart. It must be that that had waked him up. He had gone to sleep almost immediately after his head hit the pillow. He rolled over, cautiously, as he always did since that bed in Leesburg had given down with him, and lying flat on his back stared at the opposite wall.

The moon rose late. It must be at its height now. That patch of light was so brilliant he could almost discern the pattern of the wall paper. It hung there, wavering, bitten by the shadows into a semblance of a human figure, a man striding with bent head and swinging arms. All the shadows in the room seemed to be moving toward him. The protruding corner of the washstand was an arrow aimed at his heart, the clumsy old-fashioned dresser was a giant towering above him.

They had put him to sleep in this same room the night after his wife died. In the summer it had been, too, in June, and there must have been a full moon, for the same giant shadows had struggled there with the same towering monsters. It would be like that here on this wall every full moon, for the pieces of furniture would never change their position, had never been changed, probably, since the house was built.

He turned back on his side. The wall before him was dark, but he knew every flower in the pattern of the wall paper, interlacing pink roses with thrusting up between every third cluster the enormous, spreading fronds of ferns. The wall paper in the room across the hall was like that too. The old lady slept there, and in the room next to his own, Laura, his sister-in-law, and in the east bedroom downstairs the young couple. He and Mary had slept there when they were first married, when they were the young couple in the house.

He tried to remember Mary as she must have looked the day he first saw her, the day he arrived from Virginia to open his school in the old office that used to stand there in the corner of the yard. He could see Mister Allard plainly, sitting there under the sugar tree with his chair tilted back, could discern the old lady—young she had been then!—hospitably poised in the doorway, could hear her voice: "Well, here are two of your pupils to start with. . . ." He remembered Laura, a shy child of nine hiding her face in her mother's skirts, but Mary was only a shadow in the dark hall. He could not even remember how her voice had sounded. "Professor Maury," she would have said and her mother would have corrected her with "Cousin Aleck. . . ."

That day a year later when she was getting off her horse at the stile blocks. . . . She had turned as she walked across the lawn to look back at him. Her white sunbonnet had fallen back on her shoulders, her eyes meeting his had been wide and startled. He had gone on and had hitched both the horses before he leaped over the stile to join her. But he had known in that moment that she was the woman he was going to have. He could not remember all the rest of it, only that moment stood out. He had won her. She had become his wife, but the woman he had won was not the woman he had sought. It was as if he had had her only in that moment there on the lawn. As if she had paused there only for that one moment, and was ever after retreating before him down a devious, a dark way that he would never have chosen.

The death of the first baby had been the start of it, of course. It had been a relief when she took so definitely to religion. Before that there had been those sudden, unaccountable forays out of some dark lurking place that she had. Guerrilla warfare and trying to the nerves, but that had been only at the first. For many years they had been two enemies contending in the open. . . . Toward the last she had taken mightily to prayer. He would wake often to find her kneeling by the side of the bed in the dark. It had gone on for years. She had never given up hope. . . .

Ah, a stout-hearted one, Mary! She had never given up hope of changing him, of making him over into the man she thought he ought to be. Time and again she almost had him. And there were long periods, of course, during which he had been worn down by the conflict, one spring when he himself said, when she had told all the neighbors that he was too old now to go fishing any more. . . . But he had made a comeback. She had had to resort to stratagem. His lips curved in a smile, remembering the trick.

It had come over him suddenly, a general lassitude, an odd faintness in the mornings, the time when his spirits ordinarily were always at their highest. He had sat there looking out of the window at the woods glistening with spring rain; he had not even taken his gun down to shoot a squirrel.

Remembering Uncle Quent's last days, he had been alarmed, had decided finally that he must tell her so that they might begin preparations for the future—he had shuddered at the thought of eventual confinement, perhaps in some institution. She had looked up from her sewing, unable to repress a smile.

"You think it's your mind, Aleck. . . . It's coffee. . . . I've been giving you a coffee substitute every morning. . . ."

They had laughed together over her cleverness. He had not gone back to coffee, but the lassitude had worn off. She had gone back to the attack with redoubled vigor. In the afternoons she would stand on the porch calling after him as he slipped down to the creek, "Now, don't stay long enough to get that cramp. You remember how you suffered last time. . . ." He would have forgotten all about the cramp until that moment, but it would hang over him then through the whole afternoon's sport, and it would descend upon him inevitably when he left the river and started for the house.

Yes, he thought with pride. She was wearing him down—he didn't believe there was a man living who could withstand her a lifetime!—she was wearing him down and would have had him in another few months, another year certainly. But she had been struck down just as victory was in her grasp. The paralysis had come on her in the night. It was as if a curtain had descended, dividing their life sharply into two parts. In the bewildered year and a half that followed he had found himself forlornly trying to reconstruct the Mary he had known. The pressure she had so constantly exerted upon him had become for him a part of her personality. This new, calm Mary was not the woman he had loved all these years. She had lain there—heroically they all said—waiting for death. And lying there, waiting, all her faculties engaged now in defensive warfare, she had raised as it were her lifelong siege; she had lost interest in his comings and goings, had once even encouraged him to go out for an afternoon's sport. He felt a rush of warm pity. Poor Mary! She must have realized toward the last that she had wasted herself in conflict; she had spent her arms and her strength against an inglorious foe when all the time the real, the invincible adversary waited. . . .

He turned over on his back again. The moonlight was waning, the contending shadows paler now and retreating toward the door. From across the hall came the sound of long, sibilant breaths, ending each one on a little upward groan. The old lady . . . she would maintain till her dying day that she did not snore. He fancied that he could hear from the next room Laura's light, regular breathing, and downstairs were the young couple asleep in each other's arms. . . .

All of them quiet and relaxed now, but they had been lively enough at dinner time! It had started with the talk about Aunt Sally Crenfew's funeral Tuesday. Living as he had for some years away from women of his family he had forgotten the need to be cautious. He had spoken up before he thought:

"But that's the day Steve and I were going to Barker's Mill. . . ."

Sarah had cried out at the idea. "Barker's Mill!" she had said, "right on the Crenfew land . . . well, if not on the very farm in the very next field." It would be a scandal if he, Professor Maury, known by everybody to be in the neighborhood, could not spare one afternoon, one insignificant summer afternoon from his fishing long enough to attend the funeral of his cousin, the cousin of all of them, the oldest lady in the whole family connection. . . .

She had got him rattled; he had fallen back upon technicalities:

"I'm not a Crenfew. I'm a Maury. Aunt Sally Crenfew is no more kin to me than a catfish. . . ."

An unlucky crack, that about the catfish. Glancing around the table he had caught the same look in every eye. He had felt a gust of the same fright that had shaken him there on the pond. That look! Sooner or later you met it in every human eye. The thing was to be up and ready, ready to run for your life at a moment's notice. Yes, it had always been like that. It always would be. His fear of them was shot through suddenly with contempt. It was as if Mary was there laughing at them with him. *She* knew that none of them could have survived what he had survived, could have paid the price for freedom that he had paid. . . .

Sarah had come to a full stop. He had to say something. He shook his head:

"You think we just go fishing to have a good time. The boy and I hold high converse on that pond. . . . I'm starved for intellectual companionship, I tell you. In Florida I never see anybody but niggers. . . ."

They had all laughed out at that. "As if you didn't *prefer* the society of niggers," Sarah said scornfully.

The old lady had been moved to anecdote:

"I remember when Aleck first came out here from Virginia, Cousin Sophy said: 'Professor Maury is so well educated. Now Cousin Cave Maynor is dead, who is there in this neighborhood for him to associate with?' 'Well,' I said, 'I don't know about that. He seems perfectly satisfied now with Ben Hooser. They're off to the creek together every evening soon as school is out.' "

Ben Hooser. . . . He could see now the wrinkled face, overlaid with that ashy pallor of the aged Negro, the shrewd, smiling eyes, the pendulous lower lip that dropping away showed always some of the rotten teeth. A fine nigger, Ben, and on to a lot of tricks, the only man really that he'd ever cared to take fishing with him. . . .

But the first real friend of his bosom had been old Uncle Teague, back in Virginia. Once a week, or more likely every ten days, he fed the hounds on the carcass of a calf that had had time to get pretty high. They would drive the spring wagon out into the lot, he, a boy of ten, beside Uncle Teague on the driver's seat. The hounds would come in a great rush and rear their slobbering jowls against the wagon wheels. Uncle Teague would wield his whip, chuckling while he threw the first hunk of meat to Old Mag, his favorite.

"Dey goin' run on dis," he'd say, "dey goin' run like a shadow. . . ."

He shifted his position again, cautiously. People, he thought . . . people

. . . so bone ignorant, all of them. Not one person in a thousand realized that a fox hound remains at heart a wild beast and must kill and gorge, and then when he is ravenous kill and gorge again. . . . Or that the channel cat is a night feeder. . . . Or . . . his daughter had told him once that he ought to set all his knowledges down in a book. "Why?" he had asked. "So everybody else can know as much as I do?"

If he allowed his mind to get active, really active, he would never get any sleep. He was fighting an inclination now to get up and find a cigarette. He relaxed again upon his pillows, deliberately summoned pictures up before his mind's eye. Landscapes—and streams. He observed their outlines, watched one flow into another. The Black River into West Fork, that in turn into Spring Creek and Spring Creek into the Withlicoochee. Then they were all flowing together, merging into one broad plain. He watched it take form slowly: the wide field in front of Hawkwood, the Rivanna River on one side, on the other Peters' Mountain. They would be waiting there till the fox showed himself on that little rise by the river. The young men would hold back till Uncle Quent had wheeled Old Filly, then they would all be off pell-mell across the plain. He himself would be mounted on Jonesboro. Blind as a bat, but she would take anything you put her at. That first thicket on the edge of the woods. They would break there, one half of them going around, the other half streaking it through the woods. He was always of those going around to try to cut the fox off on the other side. No, he was down off his horse. He was coursing with the fox. He could hear the sharp, pointed feet padding on the dead leaves, see the quick head turned now and then over the shoulder.

The trees kept flashing by, one black trunk after another. And now it was a ragged mountain field and the sage grass running before them in waves to where a narrow stream curved in between the ridges. The fox's feet were light in the water. He ran steadily, head down. The hounds' baying was louder now. Old Mag knew the trick. She had stopped to give tongue by the big rock, and now they had all leaped the gulch and were scrambling up through the pines. But the fox's feet were already hard on the mountain path. He ran slowly now, past the big boulder, past the blasted pine to where the shadow of the Pinnacle Rock was black across the path. He ran on and the shadow rose and swayed to meet him. Its cool touch was on his hot tongue, his heaving flanks. He had slipped in under it. He was sinking down, panting, in black dark, on moist earth while the hounds' baying filled the bowl of the valley and reverberated from the mountainside.

afterword

"Old Red" reveals Caroline Gordon's emotional attachment to the land of her birth and its way of life. Aware of the weaknesses of the South, seeing it as at times derelict in carrying out its responsibilities, Miss Gordon nevertheless admires and loves it for the grace, gentility, and love of beauty of which it is frequently capable. In "Old Red," in the novel, *Aleck Maury, Sportsman,* and in other works in which she deals with the gentler sides of the Southern scene, Miss Gordon describes a way of life which, for all its shortcomings, provides a measure of freedom and contentment which is increasingly vulnerable to the encroachments of modern society.

Like Old Red, the freedom-loving fox he remembers from his youth, Mr. Maury gamely fights to continue his close relationship with nature. Recalling better days when a gentleman could hunt and fish without hindrance; he refuses to yield to the incursions of time and social necessity. His refusal appears to reveal a limitation in his character, by making him seem unwilling to give of himself to others, but it is also a triumph, for only a man with the fullest commitment to his individual perception of human fulfillment could be so steadfast.

Miss Gordon was born in 1895 in Kentucky, and she grew up in Clarksville, Tennessee, where her father was a school teacher. Her first novel, *Penhally,* appeared in 1931. In 1934, *Aleck Maury, Sportsman* appeared; in 1937, *None Shall Look Back* was published; and in 1956, *The Malefactors* appeared. Settings for her novels range from Kentucky through Tennessee to North Carolina. Miss Gordon was a Guggenheim fellow in 1932, and she won the O. Henry Prize in 1934. In 1924, she married the poet and teacher, Allen Tate, with whom, in 1950, she published an anthology of stories, *The House of Fiction.*

questions for general discussion

1. Comment on the various attitudes towards family relationships revealed in the story.

2. What effects are achieved by the prose rhythms created in the last paragraph of the story?

3. What is Mr. Maury seeking in his life?

4. Comment on the way the past is employed in the story.

5. What symbols does Miss Gordon use in the story?

suggestions for writing

1. Discuss the theme of freedom in conflict with repression as it relates to this story.

2. What is the author's attitude toward Mr. Maury? How does she manipulate the reader's attitudes?

3. Discuss Mr. Maury's strengths and weaknesses.

4. Compare and contrast Mr. Maury with Stephen, his son-in-law.

5. What aspects of Mr. Maury's character are revealed in the episode in which we learn of Mr. Maury's game leg and his subsequent decision not to hunt?

6. Comment on Mr. Maury's racial attitudes as revealed in the episode concerning how he learned to smell fish.

RICHARD WRIGHT
long black song

1

Go t sleep, baby
Papas gone t town
Go t sleep, baby
The suns goin down
Go t sleep, baby
Yo candys in the sack
Go t sleep, baby
Papas comin back . . .

Over and over she crooned, and at each lull of her voice she rocked the
wooden cradle with a bare black foot. But the baby squalled louder, its wail
drowning out the song. She stopped and stood over the cradle, wondering
what was bothering it, if its stomach hurt. She felt the diaper; it was dry. She
lifted it up and patted its back. Still it cried, longer and louder. She put it back
into the cradle and dangled a string of red beads before its eyes. The little
black fingers clawed them away. She bent over, frowning, murmuring:
"Whut's the mattah, chile? Yuh wan some watah?" she held a dripping gourd
to the black lips, but the baby turned its head and kicked its legs. She stood a
moment, perplexed. Whuts wrong wid that chile? She ain never carried on like
this this tima day. She picked it up and went to the open door. "See the sun,
baby?" she asked, pointing to a big ball of red dying between the branches of
trees. The baby pulled back and strained its round black arms and legs against
her stomach and shoulders. She knew it was tired; she could tell by the halting
way it opened its mouth to draw in air. She sat on a wooden stool, unbuttoned
the front of her dress, brought the baby closer and offered it a black teat.
"Don baby wan suppah?" It pulled away and went limp, crying softly,
piteously, as though it would never stop. Then it pushed its fingers against her
breasts and wailed. Lawd, chile, whut yuh wan? Yo ma cant hep yuh less she
knows whut yuh wan. Tears gushed; four white teeth flashed in red gums; the
little chest heaved up and down and round black fingers stretched floorward.
Lawd, chile, whuts wrong wid yuh? She stooped slowly, allowing her body to
be guided by the downward tug. As soon as the little fingers touched the floor

the wail quieted into a broken sniffle. She turned the baby loose and watched it crawl toward a corner. She followed and saw the little fingers reach for the tail-end of an old eight-day clock. "Yuh wan tha ol clock?" She dragged the clock into the center of the floor. The baby crawled after it, calling, "Ahh!" Then it raised its hands and beat on the top of the clock Bink! Bink! Bink! "Naw, yuhll hurt yo hands!" She held the baby and looked around. It cried and struggled. "Wait, baby!" she fetched a small stick from the top of a rickety dresser. "Here," she said, closing the little fingers about it. "Beat wid this, see?" She heard each blow landing squarely on top of the clock Bang! Bang! Bang! And with each bang the baby smiled and said, "Ahh!" Mabbe thall keep you quiet erwhile. Mabbe Ah kin git some res now. She stood in the doorway. Lawd, tha chiles a pain! She mus be teethin. Er something . . .

She wiped sweat from her forehead with the bottom of her dress and looked out over the green fields rolling up the hillsides. She sighed, fighting a feeling of loneliness. Lawd, its sho hard t pass the days wid Silas gone. Been mos a week now since he took the wagon outta here. Hope ain nothin wrong. He must be buyin a heapa stuff there in Colwata t be stayin all this time. Yes; maybe Silas would remember and bring that five-yard piece of red calico she wanted. Oh, Lawd! Ah *hope* he don fergit it!

She saw green fields wrapped in the thickening gloam. It was as if they had left the earth, those fields, and were floating slowly skyward. The afterglow lingered, red, dying, somehow tenderly sad. And far away, in front of her, earth and sky met in a soft swoon of shadow. A cricket chirped, sharp and lonely; and it seemed she could hear it chirping long after it had stopped. Silas ought c mon soon. Ahm tireda staying here by mahsef.

Loneliness ached in her. She swallowed, hearing Bang! Bang! Bang! Tom been gone t war mos a year now. N tha ol wars over n we ain heard nothin yit. Lawd, don let Tom be dead! She frowned into the gloam and wondered about that awful war so far away. They said it was over now. Yeah, Gawd had to stop em fo they killed everybody. She felt that merely to go so far away from home was a kind of death in itself. Just to go that far away was to be killed. Nothing good could come from men going miles across the sea to fight. N how come they wanna kill each other? How come they wanna make blood? Killing was not what men ought to do. Shucks! she thought.

She sighed, thinking of Tom, hearing Bang! Bang! Bang! She saw Tom, saw his big black smiling face; her eyes went dreamily blank, drinking in the red afterglow. Yes, God; it could have been Tom instead of Silas who was having her now. Yes; it could have been Tom she was loving. She smiled and asked herself, Lawd, Ah wondah how would it been wid Tom? Against the plush sky she saw a white bright day and a green cornfield and she saw Tom walking in his overalls and she was with Tom and he had his arm about her waist. She remembered how weak she had felt feeling his fingers sinking into the flesh of her hips. Her knees had trembled and she had had a hard time trying to stand up and not just sink right there to the ground. Yes; that was what Tom had wanted her to do. But she had held Tom up and he had held her up; they had held each other up to keep from slipping to the ground there in the green cornfield. Lawd! Her breath went and she passed her tongue over her lips. But that was not as exciting as that winter evening when the grey skies were sleeping and she and Tom were coming home from church down dark Lover's Lane. She felt the tips of her teats tingling and touching the front of her dress as she remembered how he had crushed her against him and hurt her. She had closed her eyes and was smelling the acrid scent of dry October leaves and had gone weak in his arms and had felt she could not breathe any more and had torn away and run, run home. And the sweet ache which had frightened her then was stealing back to her loins now with the silence and the cricket calls and the red afterglow and Bang! Bang! Bang! Lawd, Ah wondah how would it been wid Tom?

She stepped out on the porch and leaned against the wall of the house. Sky sang a red song. Fields whispered a green prayer. And song and prayer were dying in silence and shadow. Never in all her life had she been so much alone as she was now. Days were never so long as these days; and nights were never so empty as these nights. She jerked her head impatiently, hearing Bang! Bang! Bang! Shucks! she thought. When Tom had gone something had ebbed so slowly that at first she had not noticed it. Now she felt all of it as though the feeling had no bottom. She tried to think just how it had happened. Yes; there had been all her life the long hope of white bright days and the deep desire of dark black nights and then Tom had gone. Bang! Bang! Bang! There had been laughter and eating and singing and the long gladness of green corn-fields in summer. There had been cooking and sewing and sweeping and the deep dream of sleeping grey skies in winter. Always it had been like that and she had been happy. But no more. The happiness of those days and nights, of those green cornfields and grey skies had started to go from her when Tom had gone to war. His leaving had left an empty black hole in her heart, a black hole that Silas had come in and filled. But not quite. Silas had not quite filled that hole. No; days and nights were not as they were before.

She lifted her chin, listening. She had heard something, a dull throb like she had heard that day Silas had called her outdoors to look at the airplane. Her eyes swept the sky. But there was no plane. Mabbe its behin the house? She stepped into the yard and looked upward through paling light. There were only a few big wet stars trembling in the east. Then she heard the throb again. She turned, looking up and down the road. The throb grew louder, droning; and she heard Bang! Bang! Bang! There! A car! Wondah whuts a car doin coming out here? A black car was winding over a dusty road, coming toward her. Mabbe some white mans bringing Silas home wida loada goods? But, Lawd, Ah *hope* its no trouble! The car stopped in front of the house and a white man got out. Wondah whut he wans? She looked at the car, but could not see Silas. The white man was young; he wore a straw hat and had no coat. He walked toward her with a huge black package under his arm.

"Well, howre yuh today, Aunty?"

"Ahm well. How yuh?"

"Oh, so-so. Its sure hot today, hunh?"

She brushed her hand across her forehead and sighed.

"Yeah; it is kinda warm."

"You busy?"

"Naw, Ah ain doin nothin."

"Ive got something to show you. Can I sit here, on your porch?"

"Ah reckon so. But, Mistah, Ah ain got no money."

"Haven't you sold your cotton yet?"

"Silas gone t town wid it now."

"Whens he coming back?"

"Ah don know. Ahm waiting fer im."

She saw the white man take out a handkerchief and mop his face. Bang!
Bang! Bang! He turned his head and looked through the open doorway, into
the front room.

"Whats all that going on in there?"

She laughed.

"Aw, thas jus Ruth."

"Whats she doing?"

"She beatin tha ol clock."

"Beating a *clock?*"

She laughed again.

"She wouldn't go t sleep so Ah give her tha ol clock t play wid."

The white man got up and went to the front door; he stood a moment
looking at the black baby hammering on the clock. Bang! Bang! Bang!

"But why let her tear your clock up?"

"It ain no good."

"You could have it fixed."

"We ain got no money t be fixin no clocks."

"Havent you got a clock?"

"Naw."

"But how do you keep time?"

"We git erlong widout time."

"But how do you know when to get up in the morning?"

"We jus git up, thas all."

"But how do you know what time it is when you get up?"

"We git up wid the sun."

"And at night, how do you tell when its night?"

"It gits dark when the sun goes down."

"Havent you ever had a clock?"

She laughed and turned her face toward the silent fields.

"Mistah, we don need no clock."

"Well, this beats everything! I don't see how in the world anybody can live
without time."

"We jus don need no time, Mistah."

The white man laughed and shook his head; she laughed and looked at him.
The white man was funny. Jus like lil boy. Astin how do Ah know when t git
up in the mawnin! She laughed again and mused on the baby, hearing Bang!
Bang! Bang! She could hear the white man breathing at her side; she felt his

eyes on her face. She looked at him; she saw he was looking at her breasts. *Hes jus lika lil boy. Acks like he cant understand nothin!*

"But you need a clock," the white man insisted. "That's what Im out here for. Im selling clocks and graphophones. The clocks are made right into the graphophones, a nice sort of combination, hunh? You can have music and time all at once. Ill show you . . ."

"Mistah, we don need no clock!"

"You dont have to buy it. It wont cost you anything just to look."

He unpacked the big black box. She saw the strands of his auburn hair glinting in the afterglow. His back bulged against his white shirt as he stooped. He pulled out a square brown graphophone. She bent forward, looking. *Lawd, but its pretty!* She saw the face of a clock under the horn of the graphophone. The gilt on the corners sparkled. The color in the wood glowed softly. It reminded her of the light she saw sometimes in the baby's eyes. Slowly she slid a finger over a beveled edge; she wanted to take the box into her arms and kiss it.

"Its eight o'clock," he said.

"Yeah?"

"It only costs fifty dollars. And you dont have to pay for it all at once. Just five dollars down and five dollars a month."

She smiled. The white man was just like a little boy. *Jus like a chile.* She saw him grinding the handle of the box.

There was a sharp, scratching noise; then she moved nervously, her body caught in the ringing coils of music.

When the trumpet of the Lord shall sound . . .

She rose on circling waves of white bright days and dark black nights.

. . . and time shall be no more . . .

Higher and higher she mounted.

And the morning breaks . . .

Earth fell far behind, forgotten.

. . . eternal, bright and fair . . .

Echo after echo sounded.

When the saved of the earth shall gather . . .

Her blood surged like the long gladness of summer.

. . . over the other shore . . .

Her blood ebbed like the deep dream of sleep in winter.

And when the roll is called up yonder . . .

She gave up, holding her breath.

I'll be there . . .

A lump filled her throat. She leaned her back against a post, trembling, feeling the rise and fall of days and nights, of summer and winter; surging, ebbing, leaping about her, beyond her, far out over the fields to where earth and sky lay folded in darkness. She wanted to lie down and sleep, or else leap up and shout. When the music stopped she felt herself coming back, being let down slowly. She sighed. It was dark now. She looked into the doorway. The baby was sleeping on the floor. Ah gotta git up n put that chile t bed, she thought.

"Wasnt that pretty?"

"It wuz pretty, awright."

"When do you think your husbands coming back?"

"Ah don know, Mistah."

She went into the room and put the baby into the cradle. She stood again in the doorway and looked at the shadowy box that had lifted her up and carried her away. Crickets called. The dark sky had swallowed up the earth, and more stars were hanging, clustered, burning. She heard the white man sigh. His face was lost in shadows. She saw him rub his palms over his forehead. Hes jus lika lil boy.

"Id like to see your husband tonight," he said. "I've got to be in Lilydale at six o'clock in the morning and I wont be back through here soon. I got to pick up my buddy over there and we're heading North."

She smiled into the darkness. He was just like a little boy. A little boy selling clocks.

"Yuh sell them things alla time?" she asked.

"Just for the summer," he said. "I go to school in winter. If I can make enough money out of this Ill go to Chicago to school this fall **. . .**"

"Whut yuh gonna be?"

"*Be?* What do you mean?"

"Whut yuh goin t school fer?"

"Im studying science."

"Whuts tha?"

"Oh, er . . ." He looked at her. "Its about why things are as they are."

"Why things is as they *is?*"

"Well, its something like that."

"How come yuh wanna study tha?"

"Oh, you wouldn't understand."

She sighed.

"Naw, Ah guess Ah wouldnt."

"Well, I reckon Ill be getting along," said the white man. "Can I have a drink of water?"

"Sho. But we ain got nothin but well-watah, n yuhll have t come n git."

"Thats all right."

She slid off the porch and walked over the ground with bare feet. She heard the shoes of the white man behind her, falling to the earth in soft whispers. It was dark now. She led him to the well, groped her way, caught the bucket and let it down with a rope; she heard a splash and the bucket grew heavy. She drew it up, pulling against its weight, throwing one hand over the other, feeling the cool wet of the rope on her palms.

"Ah don git watah outa here much," she said, a little out of breath. "Silas gits the watah mos of the time. This buckets too heavy fer me."

"Oh, wait! Ill help!"

His shoulder touched hers. In the darkness she felt his warm hands fumbling for the rope.

"Where is it?"

"Here."

She extended the rope through the darkness. His fingers touched her breasts.

"Oh!"

She said it in spite of herself. He would think she was thinking about that. And he was a white man. She was sorry she had said that.

"Wheres the gourd?" he asked. "Gee, its dark!"

She stepped back and tried to see him.

"Here."

"I cant see!" he said, laughing.

Again she felt his fingers on the tips of her breasts. She backed away, saying nothing this time. She thrust the gourd out from her. Warm fingers met her cold hands. He had the gourd. She heard him drink; it was the faint, soft music of water going down a dry throat, the music of water in a silent night. He sighed and drank again.

"I was thirsty," he said. "I hadnt had any water since noon."

She knew he was standing in front of her; she could not see him, but she felt him. She heard the gourd rest against the wall of the well. She turned, then felt his hands full on her breasts. She struggled back.

"Naw, Mistah!"

"Im not going to hurt you!"

White arms were about her, tightly. She was still. But hes a *white* man. A *white* man. She felt his breath coming hot on her neck and where his hands held her breasts the flesh seemed to knot. She was rigid, poised; she swayed backward, then forward. She caught his shoulders and pushed.

"Naw, naw . . . Mistah, Ah cant do that!"

She jerked away. He caught her hand.

"Please . . ."

"Lemme go!"

She tried to pull her hand out of his and felt his fingers tighten. She pulled harder, and for a moment they were balanced, one against the other. Then he was at her side again, his arms about her.

"I wont hurt you! I wont hurt you . . ."

She leaned backward and tried to dodge his face. Her breasts were full against him; she gasped, feeling the full length of his body. She held her head far to one side; she knew he was seeking her mouth. His hands were on her breasts again. A wave of warm blood swept into her stomach and loins. She felt his lips touching her throat and where he kissed it burned.

"Naw, naw . . ."

Her eyes were full of the wet stars and they blurred, silver and blue. Her knees were loose and she heard her own breathing; she was trying to keep from falling. But hes a *white* man! A *white* man! Naw! Naw! And still she would not let him have her lips; she kept her face away. Her breasts hurt where they were crushed against him and each time she caught her breath she held it and while she held it it seemed that if she would let it go it would kill her. Her knees were pressed hard against his and she clutched the upper parts of his arms, trying to hold on. Her loins ached. She felt her body sliding.

"Gawd . . ."

He helped her up. She could not see the stars now; her eyes were full of the feeling that surged over her body each time she caught her breath. He held her close, breathing into her ear; she straightened, rigidly, feeling that she had to straighten or die. And then her lips felt his and she held her breath and dreaded ever to breathe again for fear of the feeling that would sweep down over her limbs. She held tightly, hearing a mounting tide of blood beating against her throat and temples. Then she gripped him, tore her face away, emptied her lungs in one long despairing gasp and went limp. She felt his hand; she was still, taut, feeling his hand, then his fingers. The muscles in her legs flexed and she bit her lips and pushed her toes deep into the wet dust by the side of the well and tried to wait and tried to wait until she could wait no longer. She whirled away from him and a streak of silver and blue swept across her blood. The wet ground cooled her palms and knee-caps. She stumbled up and ran, blindly, her toes flicking warm, dry dust. Her numbed fingers grabbed at a rusty nail in the post at the porch and she pushed ahead of hands that held her breasts. Her fingers found the door-facing; she moved into the darkened room, her hands before her. She touched the cradle and turned till her knees hit the bed. She went over, face down, her fingers trembling in the crumpled folds of his shirt. She moved and moved again and again, trying to keep ahead of the warm flood of blood that sought to catch her. A liquid metal covered her and she rode on the curve of white bright days and dark black nights and the surge of the long gladness of summer and the ebb of the deep dream of sleep in winter till a high red wave of hotness drowned her in a deluge of silver and blue and boiled her blood and blistered her flesh *bangbangbang* . . .

"Yuh bettah go," she said.

She felt him standing by the side of the bed, in the dark. She heard him clear his throat. His belt-buckle tinkled.

"Im leaving that clock and graphophone," he said.

She said nothing. In her mind she saw the box glowing softly, like the light in the baby's eyes. She stretched out her legs and relaxed.

"You can have it for forty instead of fifty. Ill be by early in the morning to see if your husbands in."

She said nothing. She felt the hot skin of her body growing steadily cooler.

"Do you think hell pay ten on it? Hell only owe thirty then."

She pushed her toes deep into the quilt, feeling a night wind blowing through the door. Her palms rested lightly on top of her breasts.

"Do you think hell pay ten on it?"

"Hunh?"

"Hell pay ten, wont he?"

"Ah don know," she whispered.

She heard his shoe hit against a wall; footsteps echoed on the wooden porch. She started nervously when she heard the roar of his car; she followed the throb of the motor till she heard it when she could hear it no more, followed it till she heard it roaring faintly in her ears in the dark and silent room. Her hands moved on her breasts and she was conscious of herself, all over; she felt the weight of her body resting heavily on shucks. She felt the presence of fields lying out there covered with night. She turned over slowly and lay on her stomach, her hands tucked under her. From somewhere came a creaking noise. She sat upright, feeling fear. The wind sighed. Crickets called. She lay down again, hearing shucks rustle. Her eyes looked straight up in the darkness and her blood sogged. She had lain a long time, full of a vast peace, when a far away tinkle made her feel the bed again. The tinkle came through the night; she listened, knowing that soon she would hear the rattle of Silas' wagon. Even then she tried to fight off the sound of Silas' coming, even then she wanted to feel the peace of night filling her again; but the tinkle grew louder and she heard the jangle of a wagon and the quick trot of horses. Thas Silas! She gave up and waited. She heard horses neighing. Out of the window bare feet whispered in the dust, then crossed the porch, echoing in soft booms. She closed her eyes and saw Silas come into the room in his dirty overalls as she had seen him come in a thousand times before.

"Yuh sleep, Sarah?"

She did not answer. Feet walked across the floor and a match scratched. She opened her eyes and saw Silas standing over her with a lighted lamp. His hat was pushed far back on his head and he was laughing.

"Ah reckon yuh thought Ah waznt never comin back, hunh? Cant yuh wake up? See, Ah got that red cloth yuh wanted . . ." He laughed again and threw the red cloth on the mantel.

"Yuh hongry?" she asked.

"Naw, Ah kin make out till mawnin." Shucks rustled as he sat on the edge of the bed. "Ah got two hundred n fifty fer mah cotton."

"Two hundred n fifty?"

"Nothin different! N guess whut Ah done?"

"Whut?"

"Ah bought ten mo acres o land. Got em from ol man Burgess. Paid im a hundred n fifty dollahs down. Ahll pay the rest next year ef things go erlong awright. Ahma have t git a man t hep me nex spring . . ."

"Yuh mean hire somebody?"

"Sho, hire somebody! Whut yuh think? Ain tha the way the white folks do? Ef yuhs gonna git anywheres yuhs gotta do just like they do." He paused. "Whut yuh ben doin since Ah been gone?"

"Nothin. Cookin, cleanin, n . . ."

"How Ruth?"

"She awright." She lifted her head. "Silas, yuh git any lettahs?"

"Naw. But Ah heard Tom wuz in town."

"In *town?*"

She sat straight up.

"Yeah, thas whut the folks wuz sayin at the sto."

"Back from the war?"

"Ah ast erroun t see ef Ah could fin im. But Ah couldnt."

"Lawd, Ah wish hed c mon home."

"Them white folks sho's glad the wars over. But things wuz kinda bad there in town. Everywhere Ah looked wuznt nothin but black n white soljers. N them white folks beat up a black soljer yestiddy. He was jus in from France. Wuz still wearin his soljers suit. They claimed he sassed a white woman . . ."

"Who wuz he?"

"Ah don know. Never saw im befo."

"Yuh see An Peel?"

"Naw."

"Silas!" she said reprovingly.

"Aw, Sarah, Ah jus couldn't git out there."

"Whut else yuh bring sides the cloth?"

"Ah got yuh some high-top shoes." He turned and looked at her in the dim light of the lamp. "Woman, ain yuh glad Ah bought yuh some shoes n cloth?" He laughed and lifted his feet to the bed. "Lawd, Sarah, yuhs sho sleepy, ain you?"

"Bettah put tha lamp out, Silas . . ."

"Aw . . ." He swung out of the bed and stood still for a moment. She watched him, then turned her face to the wall.

"Whuts that by the windah?" he asked.

She saw him bending over and touching the graphophone with his fingers.

"Thasa graphophone."

"Where yuh git it from?"

"A man lef it here."

"When he bring it?"

"Today."

"But how come he t leave it?"

"He says hell be out here in the mawnin t see ef yuh wans t buy it."

He was on his knees, feeling the wood and looking at the gilt on the edges of the box. He stood up and looked at her.

"Yuh ain never said yuh wanted one of these things."

She said nothing.

"Where wuz the man from?"

"Ah don know."

"He white?"

"Yeah."

He put the lamp back on the mantel. As he lifted the globe to blow out the flame, his hand paused.

"Whos hats this?"

She raised herself and looked. A straw hat lay bottom upwards on the edge of the mantel. Silas picked it up and looked back to the bed, to Sarah.

"Ah guess its the white mans. He must a lef it . . ."

"Whut he doin *in our room?*"

"He wuz talkin t me bout that graphophone."

She watched him go to the window and stoop again to the box. He picked it up, fumbled with the price-tag and took the box to the light.

"Whut this thing cos?"

"Forty dollahs."

"But its marked fifty here."

"Oh, Ah means he said fifty . . ."

He took a step toward the bed.

"Yuh lyin t me!"

"Silas!"

He heaved the box out of the front door; there was a smashing, tinkling noise as it bounded off the front porch and hit the ground. "Whut in hell yuh lie t me fer?"

"Yuh broke the box!"

"Ahma break yo Gawddam neck ef yuh don stop lyin t me!"

"Silas, Ah ain lied t yuh!"

"Shut up, Gawddammit! Yuh did!"

He was standing by the bed with the lamp trembling in his hand. She stood on the other side, between the bed and the wall.

"How come yuh tell me tha thing cos *forty* dollahs when it cos *fifty?*"

"Thas whut he tol me."

"How come he take *ten* dollahs off fer yuh?"

"He ain took nothin off fer me, Silas!"

"Yuh lyin t me! N yuh lied t me bout Tom, too!"

She stood with her back to the wall, her lips parted, looking at him silently, steadily. Their eyes held for a moment. Silas looked down, as though he were about to believe her. Then he stiffened.

"Whos this?" he asked, picking up a short yellow pencil from the crumpled quilt.

She said nothing. He started toward her.

"Yuh wan me t take mah raw-hide whip n make yuh talk?"

"Naw, naw, Silas! Yuh wrong! He wuz figgerin wid tha pencil!"

He was silent a moment, his eyes searching her face.

"Gawddam yo black soul t hell, don yuh try lyin t me! Ef yuh start layin wid white men Ahll hosswhip yuh t a incha yo life. Shos theres a Gawd in Heaven Ah will! From sunup t sundown Ah works mah guts out t pay them white trash bastards whut Ah owe em, n then Ah comes n fins they been in mah house! Ah cant go into their houses, n yuh know Gawddam well Ah cant! They don have no mercy on no black folks; wes jus like dirt under their feet! Fer ten years Ah slaves lika dog t git mah farm free, givin ever penny Ah kin t em, n then Ah comes n fins they been in mah house . . ." He was speechless with outrage. "Ef yuh wans t eat at mah table yuhs gonna keep them white trash bastards out, yuh hear? Tha white ape kin come n git tha damn box n Ah ain gonna pay im a cent! He had no bisness leavin it here, n yuh had no bisness lettin im! Ahma tell tha sonofabitch something when he comes out here in the mawnin, so hep me Gawd! Now git back in tha bed!"

She slipped beneath the quilt and lay still, her face turned to the wall. Her heart thumped slowly and heavily. She heard him walk across the floor in his bare feet. She heard the bottom of the lamp as it rested on the mantel. She stiffened when the room darkened. Feet whispered across the floor again. The shucks rustled from Silas' weight as he sat on the edge of the bed. She was still, breathing softly. Silas was mumbling. She felt sorry for him. In the darkness it seemed that she could see the hurt look on his black face. The crow of a rooster came from far away, came so faintly that it seemed she had not heard it. The bed sank and the shucks cried out in dry whispers; she knew Silas had stretched out. She heard him sigh. Then she jumped because he jumped. She could feel the tenseness of his body; she knew he was sitting bolt upright. She felt his hands fumbling jerkily under the quilt. Then the bed heaved amid a wild shout of shucks and Silas' feet hit the floor with a loud boom. She snatched herself to her elbows, straining her eyes in the dark, wondering what was wrong now. Silas was moving about, cursing under his breath.

"Don wake Ruth up!" she whispered.

"Eh yuh say one mo word t me Ahma slap yuh inter a black spasm!"

She grabbed her dress, got up and stood by the bed, the tips of her fingers touching the wall behind her. A match flared in yellow flame; Silas' face was caught in a circle of light. He was looking downward, staring intently at a white wad of cloth balled in his hand. His black cheeks were hard, set; his lips were tightly pursed. She looked closer; she saw that the white cloth was a man's handkerchief. Silas' fingers loosened; she heard the handkerchief hit the floor softly, damply. The match went out.

"Yuh little bitch!"

Her knees gave. Fear oozed from her throat to her stomach. She moved in the dark toward the door, struggling with the dress, jamming it over her head. She heard the thick skin of Silas' feet swish across the wooden planks.

"Ah got mah raw-hide whip n Ahm takin yuh t the barn!"

She ran on tiptoe to the porch and paused, thinking of the baby. She shrank as something whined through air. A red streak of pain cut across the small of her back and burned its way into her body, deeply.

"Silas!" she screamed.

She grabbed for the post and fell in dust. She screamed again and crawled out of reach.

"Git t the barn, Gawddammit!"

She scrambled up and ran through the dark, hearing the baby cry. Behind her leather thongs hummed and feet whispered swiftly over the dusty ground.

"Cmere, yuh bitch! Cmere, Ah say!"

She ran to the road and stopped. She wanted to go back and get the baby, but she dared not. Not as long as Silas had that whip. She stiffened, feeling that he was near.

"Yuh jus as well c mon back n git yo beatin!"

She ran again, slowing now and then to listen. If she only knew where he was she would slip back into the house and get the baby and walk all the way to Aunt Peel's.

"Yuh ain comin back in mah house till Ah beat yuh!"

She was sorry for the anger she knew he had out there in the field. She had a bewildering impulse to go to him and ask him not to be angry; she wanted to tell him that there was nothing to be angry about; that what she had done did not matter; that she was sorry; that after all she was his wife and still loved him. But there was no way she could do that now; if she went to him he would whip her as she had seen him whip a horse.

"Sarah! Sarah!"

His voice came from far away. Ahm goin git Ruth. Back through dust she sped, going on her toes, holding her breath.

"Saaaarah!"

From far off his voice floated over the fields. She ran into the house and caught the baby in her arms. Again she sped through dust on her toes. She did not stop till she was so far away that his voice sounded like a faint echo falling from the sky. She looked up; the stars were paling a little. Mus be gittin near mawnin. She walked now, letting her feet sink softly into the cool dust. The baby was sleeping; she could feel the little chest swelling against her arm. She looked up again; the sky was solid black. Its gittin near mawnin. Ahma take Ruth t An Peels. N mabbe Ahll fin Tom . . . But she could not walk all that distance in the dark. Not now. Her legs were tired. For a moment a memory of surge and ebb rose in her blood; she felt her legs straining, upward. She sighed. Yes, she would go to the sloping hillside back of the garden and wait until morning. Then she would slip away. She stopped, listened. She heard a faint, rattling noise. She imagined Silas' kicking or throwing the smashed graphophone. Hes mad! Hes sho mad! Aw, Lawd! . . . She stopped stock still, squeezing the baby till it whimpered. What would happen when that white man came out in the morning? She had forgotten him. She would have to head him off and tell him. Yeah, cause Silas jus mad ernuff t kill! Lawd, hes mad ernuff t kill!

3

She circled the house widely, climbing a slope, groping her way, holding the baby high in her arms. After awhile she stopped and wondered where on the slope she was. She remembered there was an elm tree near the edge; if she could find it she would know. She groped farther, feeling with her feet. Ahm gittin los! And she did not want to fall with the baby. Ahma stop here, she thought. When morning came she would see the car of the white man from this hill and she would run down the road and tell him to go back; and then there would be no killing. Dimly she saw in her mind a picture of men killing and being killed. White men killed the black and black men killed the white. White men killed the black men because they could, and the black men killed the white men to keep from being killed. And killing was blood. Lawd, Ah wish Tom wuz here. She shuddered, sat on the ground and watched the sky for signs of morning. Mabbe Ah oughta walk on down the road? Naw . . . Her legs were tired. Again she felt her body straining. Then she saw Silas holding the white man's handkerchief. She heard it hit the floor, softly, damply. She was sorry for what she had done. Silas was as good to her as any black man could be to a black woman. Most of the black women worked in the fields as croppers. But Silas had given her her own home, and that was more than many others had done for their women. Yes, she knew how Silas felt. Always he had said he was as good as any white man. He had worked hard and saved his money and bought a farm so he could grow his own crops like white men. Silas hates white folks! Lawd, he sho hates em!

The baby whimpered. She unbuttoned her dress and nursed her in the dark. She looked toward the east. There! A tinge of gray hovered. It wont be long now. She could see ghostly outlines of trees. Soon she would see the elm, and by the elm she would sit till it was light enough to see the road.

The baby slept. Far off a rooster crowed. Sky deepened. She rose and walked slowly down a narrow, curving path and came to the elm tree. Standing on the edge of a slope, she saw a dark smudge in a sea of shifting shadows. That was her home. Wondah how come Silas didnt light the lamp? She shifted the baby from her right hip to her left, sighed, struggled against sleep. She sat on the ground again, caught the baby close and leaned against the trunk of a tree. Her eye-lids drooped and it seemed that a hard cold hand caught hold of her right leg or was it her left leg? she did not know which—and began to drag her over a rough litter of shucks and when she strained to see who it was that was pulling her no one was in sight but far ahead was darkness and it seemed that out of the darkness some force came and pulled her like a magnet and she went sliding along over a rough bed of screeching shucks and it seemed that a wild fear made her want to scream but when she opened her mouth to scream she could not scream and she felt she was coming to a wide black hole and again she made ready to scream and then it was too late for she was already over the wide black hole falling falling falling . . .

She awakened with a start and blinked her eyes in the sunshine. She found she was clutching the baby so hard that it had begun to cry. She got to her feet, trembling from fright of the dream, remembering Silas and the white man and Silas' running her out of the house and the white man's coming. Silas was standing in the front yard; she caught her breath. Yes, she had to go and head that white man off! Naw! She could not do that, not with Silas standing there with that whip in his hand. If she tried to climb any of those slopes he would see her surely. And Silas would never forgive her for something like that. If it were anybody but a white man it would be different.

Then, while standing there on the edge of the slope looking wonderingly at Silas striking the whip against his overall-leg—and then, while standing there looking—she froze. There came from the hills a distant throb. Lawd! The baby whimpered. She loosened her arms. The throb grew louder, droning. Hes comin fas! She wanted to run to Silas and beg him not to bother the white man. But he had that whip in his hand. She should not have done what she had done last night. This was all her fault. Lawd, ef anything happens t im its mah blame . . . Her eyes watched a black car speed over the crest of a hill. She should have been out there on the road instead of sleeping here by the tree. But it was too late now. Silas was standing in the yard; she saw him turn with a nervous jerk and sit on the edge of the porch. He was holding the whip stiffly. The car came to a stop. A door swung open. A white man got out. Thas im! She saw another white man in the front seat of the car. N thats his buddy . . . The white man who had gotten out walked over the ground, going to Silas. They faced each other, the white man standing up and Silas sitting down; like two toy men they faced each other. She saw Silas point the whip to the smashed graphophone. The white man looked down and took a quick step backward. The white man's shoulders were bent and he shook his head from left to right. Then Silas got up and they faced each other again; like two dolls, a white doll and a black doll, they faced each other in the valley below. The white man pointed his finger into Silas' face. Then Silas' right arm went up; the whip flashed. The white man turned, bending, flinging his hands to shield his head. Silas' arm rose and fell, rose and fell. She saw the white man crawling in dust, trying to get out of reach. She screamed when she saw the other white man get out of the car and run to Silas. Then all three were on the ground, rolling in dust, grappling for the whip. She clutched the baby and ran. Lawd! Then she stopped, her mouth hanging open. Silas had broken loose and was running toward the house. She knew he was going for his gun.

Running, she stumbled and fell. The baby rolled in the dust and bawled. She grabbed it up and ran again. The white men were scrambling for their car. She reached level ground, running. Hell be killed! Then again she stopped. Silas was on the front porch, aiming a rifle. One of the white men was climbing into the car. The other was standing, waving his arms shouting at Silas. She tried to scream, but choked; and she could not scream till she heard a shot ring out.

"Silas!"

One of the white men was on the ground. The other was in the car. Silas was aiming again. The car started, running in a cloud of dust. She fell to her knees and hugged the baby close. She heard another shot, but the car was roaring over the top of the southern hill. Fear was gone now. Down the slope she ran. Silas was standing on the porch, holding his gun and looking at the fleeing car. Then she saw him go to the white man lying in dust and stoop over him. He caught one of the man's legs and dragged the body into the middle of the road. Then he turned and came slowly back to the house. She ran, holding the baby, and fell at his feet.

"Silas!"

4

"Git up, Sarah!"

His voice was hard and cold. She lifted her eyes and saw blurred black feet. She wiped tears away with dusty fingers and pulled up. Something took speech from her and she stood with bowed shoulders. Silas was standing still, mute; the look on his face condemned her. It was as though he had gone far off and had stayed a long time and had come back changed even while she was standing there in the sunshine before him. She wanted to say something, to give herself. She cried.

"Git the chile up, Sarah!"

She lifted the baby and stood waiting for him to speak, to tell her something to change all this. But he said nothing. He walked toward the house. She followed. As she attempted to go in, he blocked the way. She jumped to one side as he threw the red cloth outdoors to the ground. The new shoes came next. Then Silas heaved the baby's cradle. It hit the porch and a rocker splintered; the cradle swayed for a second, then fell to the ground, lifting a cloud of brown dust against the sun. All of her clothes and the baby's clothes were thrown out.

"Silas!"

She cried, seeing blurred objects sailing through the air and hearing them hit softly in the dust.

"Git yo things n go!"

"Silas!"

"Ain no use yuh sayin *nothin* now!"

"But theyll kill yuh!"

"There ain nothin Ah kin do. N there ain nothin yuh kin do. Yuh done done too Gawddam much awready. Git yo things n go!"

"Theyll kill yuh, Silas!"

He pushed her off the porch.

"GIT YO THINGS N GO T AN PEELS!"

"Les *both* go, Silas!"

"Ahm stayin here till they come back!"

She grabbed his arm and he slapped her hand away. She dropped to the edge of the porch and sat looking at the ground.

"Go way," she said quietly. "Go way fo they comes. Ah didnt mean no harm . . ."

"Go way fer whut?"

"Theyll *kill* yuh . . ."

"It don make no difference." He looked out over the sun-filled fields. "Fer ten years Ah slaved mah life out t git mah farm free . . ." His voice broke off. His lips moved as though a thousand words were spilling silently out of his mouth, as though he did not have breath enough to give them sound. He looked to the sky, and then back to the dust. "Now, its all gone. *Gone* . . . Ef Ah run erway, Ah ain got nothin. Ef Ah stay n fight, Ah ain got nothin. It dont make no difference which way Ah go. Gawd! Gawd, Ah wish all them white folks wuz dead! *Dead,* Ah tell yuh! Ah wish Gawd would kill em *all!*"

She watched him run a few steps and stop. His throat swelled. He lifted his hands to his face; his fingers trembled. Then he bent to the ground and cried. She touched his shoulders.

"Silas!"

He stood up. She saw he was staring at the white man's body lying in the dust in the middle of the road. She watched him walk over to it. He began to talk to no one in particular; he simply stood over the dead white man and talked out of his life, out of a deep and final sense that now it was all over and nothing could make any difference.

"The white folks ain never gimme a chance! They ain never give no black man a chance! There ain nothin in yo whole life yuh kin keep from em! They take yo lan! They take yo freedom! They take yo women! N then they take yo life!"

He turned to her, screaming. "N then Ah gits stabbed in the back by mah own blood! When mah eyes is on the white folks to keep em from killin me, mah own blood trips me up!" He knelt in the dust again and sobbed; after a bit he looked to the sky, his face wet with tears. "Ahm gonna be hard like they is! So hep me, Gawd, Ahm gonna be *hard!* When they come fer me Ahm gonna *be here!* N when they git me outta here theys gonna *know* Ahm gone! Ef Gawd lets me live Ahm gonna make em *feel* it!" He stopped and tried to get his breath. "But, Lawd, Ah don wanna be this way! I don mean nothin! Yuh die ef yuh fight! Yuh die ef yuh don fight! Either way yuh die n it don mean nothin . . ."

He was lying flat on the ground, the side of his face deep in dust. Sarah stood nursing the baby with eyes black and stony. Silas pulled up slowly and stood again on the porch.

"Git on t An Peels, Sarah!"

A dull roar came from the south. They both turned. A long streak of brown dust was weaving down the hillside.

"Silas!"

"Go on cross the fiels, Sarah!"

"We kin *both* go! Git the hosses!"

He pushed her off the porch, grabbed her hand, and led her to the rear of the house, past the well, to where a path led up a slope to the elm tree.

"Silas!"

"Yuh git on fo they ketch yuh too!"

Blind from tears, she went across the swaying fields, stumbling over blurred grass. It ain no use! She knew it was now too late to make him change his mind. The calves of her legs knotted. Suddenly her throat tightened, aching. She stopped, closed her eyes and tried to stem a flood of sorrow that drenched her. Yes, killing of white men by black men and killing of black men by white men went on in spite of the hope of white bright days and the desire of dark black nights and the long gladness of green cornfields in summer and the deep dream of sleepy grey skies in winter. And when killing started it went on, like a river flowing. Oh, she felt sorry for Silas! Silas. . . . He was following that long river of blood. Lawd, how come he wans t stay there like tha? And he did not want to die; she knew he hated dying by the way he talked of it. Yet he followed the old river of blood, knowing that it meant nothing. He followed it, cursing and whimpering. But he followed it. She stared before her at the dry, dusty grass. Somehow, men, black men and white men, land and houses, green cornfields and grey skies, gladness and dreams, were all a part of that which made life good. Yes, somehow, they were linked, like the spokes in a spinning wheel. She felt they were. She knew they were. She felt it when she breathed and knew it when she looked. But she could not say how; she could not put her finger on it and when she thought hard about it it became all mixed up, like milk spilling suddenly. Or else it knotted in her throat and chest in a hard aching lump, like the one she felt now. She touched her face to the baby's face and cried again.

There was a loud blare of auto horns. The growing roar made her turn round. Silas was standing, seemingly unafraid, leaning against a post of the porch. The long line of cars came speeding in clouds of dust. Silas moved toward the door and went in. Sarah ran down the slope a piece, coming again to the elm tree. Her breath was slow and hard. The cars stopped in front of the house. There was a steady drone of motors and drifting clouds of dust. For a moment she could not see what was happening. Then on all sides white men with pistols and rifles swarmed over the fields. She dropped to her knees, unable to take her eyes away, unable it seemed to breathe. A shot rang out. A white man fell, rolling over, face downward.

"Hes gotta gun!"

"Git back!"

"Lay down!"

The white men ran back and crouched behind cars. Three more shots came from the house. She looked, her head and eyes aching. She rested the baby in her lap and shut her eyes. Her knees sank into the dust. More shots came, but it was no use looking now. She knew it all by heart. She could feel it happening even before it happened. There were men killing and being killed. Then she jerked up, being compelled to look.

"Burn the bastard out!"

"Set the sonofabitch on fire!"

"Cook the coon!"

"Smoke im out!"

She saw two white men on all fours creeping past the well. One carried a gun and the other a red tin can. When they reached the back steps the one with the tin can crept under the house and crept out again. Then both rose and ran. Shots. One fell. A yell went up. A yellow tongue of fire licked out from under the back steps.

"Burn the nigger!"

"C mon out, nigger, n git yos!"

She watched from the hill-slope; the back steps blazed. The white men fired a steady stream of bullets. Black smoke spiraled upward in the sunshine. Shots came from the house. The white men crouched out of sight, behind their cars.

"Make up your mind, nigger!"

"C mon out er burn, yuh black bastard!"

"Yuh think yuhre white now, nigger?"

The shack blazed, flanked on all sides by whirling smoke filled with flying sparks. She heard the distant hiss of flames. White men were crawling on their stomachs. Now and then they stopped, aimed, and fired into the bulging smoke. She looked with a tense numbness; she looked, waiting for Silas to scream, or run out. But the house crackled and blazed, spouting yellow plumes to the blue sky. The white men shot again, sending a hail of bullets into the furious pillars of smoke. And still she could not see Silas running out, or hear his voice calling. Then she jumped, standing. There was a loud crash; the roof caved in. A black chimney loomed amid crumbling wood. Flames roared and black smoke billowed, hiding the house. The white men stood up, no longer afraid. Again she waited for Silas, waited to see him fight his way out, waited to hear his call. Then she breathed a long, slow breath, emptying her lungs. She knew now. Silas had killed as many as he could and stayed on to burn, had stayed without a murmur. She filled her lungs with a quick gasp as the walls fell in; the house was hidden by eager plumes of red. She turned and ran with the baby in her arms, ran blindly across the fields, crying "Naw, Gawd!"

afterword

Hatred for the Southern system of white supremacy is the major motivating force for Silas' violence in "Long Black Song." After having dedicated himself all his life to hard work in an effort to win a measure of success and dignity for himself despite all the barriers placed in his way by whites, Silas returns from selling his cotton to find his home violated and his self-image destroyed by the white man who crudely seduced Sarah. This precipitates Silas' angry response, an attempt to gain revenge upon a race from whom he has endured too much pain. Consequently, his action, though brutal, does have some compelling extenuating circumstances, and his death, though unnecessary, is presented by Wright as something of a triumph as it attests to the desire of the black man for dignity and respect.

Richard Wright was born in 1908 on a plantation near Natchez, Mississippi, and spent his youth in Memphis, Tennessee. His father was a farm and mill worker; his mother a country school teacher. When Wright was five, the father deserted the family, and the mother supported her children as best she could. Part of the time she was obliged to put Richard in an orphan asylum. Before he was ten, she was totally paralyzed, and he was shipped from one poor relative to another. Finally, under an aunt's tutelage in a Seventh Day Adventist school in Jackson, Mississippi, he found an outlet for his energy in reading. In his later teens, he journeyed to Chicago where he worked at odd jobs while writing his first book, *Uncle Tom's Children* (1938). In 1940, his novel *Native Son* became a best seller, enabling the writer to purchase his mother a home in Chicago and move to Mexico to write full time. He made his home in Paris for more than a decade before his death in 1960. Wright's other works include *Twelve Million Black Voices* (1941), *Black Boy* (1945), *The Outsider* (1953), *The Long Dream* (1958), *Eight Men* (1961), *White Man, Listen* (1957), and *Lawd Today* (1963).

questions for general discussion

1. Why is the word "Lawd" used so often in this story? In what senses is it used?

2. What are your reactions to the scene in which the baby is "banging, banging, banging" on the old clock, and Sarah thinks, "How come they wanna make blood? Killing was not what men ought to do"?

3. What human attitude is reflected by the last two words of the story?

4. Why is Sarah's memory of Tom mentioned?

5. Are there any symbols or symbolic acts in the story?

6. Comment on the story's violent resolution. Could it be "improved"?

suggestions for writing

1. Write an essay in which you compare and contrast the final scenes and actions in this story with those in Diane Oliver's story, "Neighbors."

2. Analyze the scene which strikes you as the most powerful or affecting one. Explore some reasons for its effect.

3. Comment on the story's structure, giving attention to scene changes, balance of description with dialogue, and shifting pace.

the man who was almost a man

Dave struck out across the fields, looking homeward through paling light. Whut's the usa talkin wid em niggers in the field? Anyhow, his mother was putting supper on the table. Them niggers can't understan nothing. One of these days he was going to get a gun and practice shooting, then they can't talk to him as though he were a little boy. He slowed, looking at the ground. Shucks, Ah ain scareda them even ef they are biggern me! Aw, Ah know whut Ahma do. . . . Ahm going by ol Joe's sto n git that Sears Roebuck catlog n look at them guns. Mabbe Ma will lemme buy one when she gits mah pay from ol man Hawkins. Ahma beg her t gimme some money. Ahm ol ernough to hava gun. Ahm seventeen. Almos a man. He strode, feeling his long, loose-jointed limbs. Shucks, a man oughta hava little gun aftah he done worked hard all day. . . .

He came in sight of Joe's store. A yellow lantern glowed on the front porch. He mounted steps and went through the screen door, hearing it bang behind him. There was a strong smell of coal oil and mackerel fish. He felt very confident until he saw fat Joe walk in through the rear door, then his courage began to ooze.

"Howdy, Dave! Whutcha want?"

"How yuh, Mistah Joe? Aw. Ah don wanna buy nothing. Ah jus wanted t see ef yuhd lemme look at tha ol catlog erwhile."

"Sure! You wanna see it here?"

"Nawsuh. Ah wans t take it home wid me. Ahll bring it back termorrow when Ah come in from the fiels."

"You plannin on buyin something?"

"Yessuh."

"Your ma letting you have your own money now?"

"Shucks. Mistah Joe, Ahm gittin t be a man like anybody else!"

Joe laughed and wiped his greasy white face with a red bandanna.

"Whut you plannin on buyin?"

Dave looked at the floor, scratched his head, scratched his thigh, and smiled. Then he looked up shyly.

"Ahll tell yuh, Mistah Joe, ef yuh promise yuh won't tell."

"I promise."

"Waal, Ahma buy a gun."

"A gun? Whut you want with a gun?"

"Ah wanna keep it."

"You ain't nothing but a boy. You don't need a gun."

"Aw, lemme have the catlog, Mistah Joe. Ahll bring it back."

Joe walked through the rear door. Dave was elated. He looked around at barrels of sugar and flour. He heard Joe coming back. He craned his neck to see if he were bringing the book. Yeah, he's got it! Gawddog, he's got it!

"Here, but be sure you bring it back. It's the only one I got."

"Sho, Mistah Joe."

"Say, if you wanna buy a gun, why don't you buy one from me? I gotta gun to sell."

"Will it shoot?"

"Sure it'll shoot."

"Whut kind is it?"

"Oh, it's kinda old. . . . A lefthand Wheeler. A pistol. A big one."

"Is it got bullets in it?"

"It's loaded."

"Kin Ah see it?"

"Where's your money?"

"Whut yuh wan fer it?"

"I'll let you have it for two dollars."

"Just two dollahs? Shucks, Ah could buy tha when Ah git mah pay."

"I'll have it here when you want it."

"Awright, suh. Ah be in fer it."

He went through the door, hearing it slam again behind him. Ahma git some money from Ma n buy me a gun! Only two dollahs! He tucked the thick catalogue under his arm and hurried.

"Where yuh been, boy?" His mother held a steaming dish of black-eyed peas.

"Aw, Ma, Ah just stopped down the road t talk wid th boys."

"Yuh know bettah than t keep suppah waitin."

He sat down, resting the catalogue on the edge of the table.

"Yuh git up from there and git to the well n wash yosef! Ah ain feedin no hogs in mah house!"

She grabbed his shoulder and pushed him. He stumbled out of the room, then came back to get the catalogue.

"Whut this?"

"Aw, Ma, it's jusa catlog."

"Who yuh git it from?"

"From Joe, down at the sto."

"Waal, thas good. We kin use it around the house."

"Naw, Ma." He grabbed for it. "Gimme mah catlog, Ma."

She held onto it and glared at him.

"Quit hollerin at me! Whut's wrong wid yuh? Yuh crazy?"

"But Ma, please. It ain mine! It's Joe's! He tol me t bring it back t im termorrow."

She gave up the book. He stumbled down the back steps, hugging the thick book under his arm. When he had splashed water on his face and hands, he groped back to the kitchen and fumbled in a corner for the towel. He bumped into a chair; it clattered to the floor. The catalogue sprawled at his feet. When he had dried his eyes, he snatched up the book and held it again under his arm. His mother stood watching him.

"Now, ef yuh gonna acka fool over that ol book, Ahll take it n burn it up."

"Naw, Ma, please."

"Waal, set down n be still!"

He sat down and drew the oil lamp close. He thumbed page after page, unaware of the food his mother set on the table. His father came in. Then his small brother.

"Whutcha got there, Dave?" his father asked.

"Jusa catlog," he answered, not looking up.

"Yawh, here they is!" His eyes glowed at blue and black revolvers. He glanced up, feeling sudden guilt. His father was watching him. He eased the book under the table and rested it on his knees. After the blessing was asked, he ate. He scooped up peas and swallowed fat meat without chewing. Buttermilk helped to wash it down. He did not want to mention money before his father. He would do much better by cornering his mother when she was alone. He looked at his father uneasily out of the edge of his eye.

"Boy, how come yuh don quit foolin wid tha book n eat yo suppah."

"Yessuh."

"How yuh n ol man Hawkins gittin erlong?"

"Shuh?"

"Can't yuh hear. Why don yuh listen? Ah ast yuh how wuz yuh n ol man Hawkins gittin erlong?"

"Oh, swell, Pa. Ah plows mo lan than anybody over there."

"Waal, yuh oughta keep yo min on whut yuh doin."

"Yessuh."

He poured his plate full of molasses and sopped at it slowly with a dunk of cornbread. When all but his mother had left the kitchen he still sat and looked again at the guns in the catalogue. Lawd, ef Ah only had the pretty one! He could almost feel the slickness of the weapon with his fingers. If he had a gun like that he would polish it and keep it shining so it would never rust. N Ahd keep it loaded, by Gawd!

"Ma?"

"Hunh?"

"Ol man Hawkins give yuh mah money yit?"

"Yeah, but ain no usa yuh thinin bout thowin nona it erway. Ahm keepin tha money sos yuh kin have cloes t go to school this winter."

He rose and went to her side with the open catalogue in his palms. She was washing dishes, her head bent low over a pan. Shyly he raised the open book. When he spoke his voice was husky, faint.

"Ma, Gawd knows Ah wans one of these."

"One of whut?" she asked, not raising her eyes.

"One of these," he said again, not daring even to point. She glanced up at the page, then at him with wide eyes.

"Nigger, is yuh gone plum crazy?"

"Aw, Ma—"

"Git outta here! Don't yuh talk t me bout no gun! Yuh a fool!"

"Ma, Ah kin buy one fer two dollahs."

"Not ef Ah knows it yuh ain!"

"But yuh promised one more—"

"Ah don care whut Ah promised! Yuh ain nothing but a boy yit!"

"Ma, ef yuh lemme buy one Ahll never ast yuh fer nothing no mo."

"Ah tol yuh t git outta here! Yuh ain gonna toucha penny of tha money fer no gun! Thas how come Ah has Mistah Hawkins pay yo wages t me, cause Ah knows yuh ain got no sense."

"But Ma, we needa gun. Pa ain got no gun. We needa gun in the house. Yuh kin never tell whut might happen."

"Now don yuh try to maka fool outta me, boy! Ef we did hava gun yuh wouldn't have it!"

He laid the catalogue down and slipped his arm around her waist. "Aw, Ma, Ah done worked hard alls summer n ain ast yuh fer nothing, is Ah, now?"

"Thas whut yuh spose t do!"

"But Ma. Ah wants a gun. Yuh kin lemme have two dollah outa mah money. Please Ma. I kin give it to Pa. . . . Please, Ma! Ah loves yuh, Ma."

When she spoke her voice came soft and low.

"What yuh wan wida gun, Dave? Yuh don need no gun. Yuhll git in trouble. N ef yo Pa jus thought Ah letyuh have money t buy a gun he'd hava fit."

"Ahll hide it, Ma. It ain but two dollahs."

"Lawd, chil, whuts wrong wid yuh?"

"Ain nothing wrong, Ma. Ahm almos a man now. Ah wants a gun."

"Who gonna sell yuh a gun?"

"Ol Joe at the sto."

"N it don cos but two dollahs?"

"Thas all, Ma. Just two dollahs. Please, Ma."

She was stacking the plates away; her hands moved slowly, reflectively. Dave kept an anxious silence. Finally she turned to him.

"Ahll let yuh git the gun ef yuh promise me one thing."

"Whuts tha, Ma?"

"Yuh bring it straight back t me, yuh hear? It'll be fer Pa."

"Yessum! Lemme go now, Ma."

She stooped, turned slightly to one side, raised the hem of her dress, rolled down the top of her stocking, and came up with a slender wad of bills.

"Here," she said. "Lawd knows yuh don need no gun. But yer Pa does. Yuh bring it right back t me, yuh hear. Ahma put it up. Now ef yuh don, Ahma have yuh Pa lick yuh so hard yuh won ferget it."

"Yessum."

He took the money, ran down the steps, and across the yard.

"Dave, Yuuuuuuh Daaaaaave!"

He heard, but he was not going to stop now. "Naw, Lawd!"

The first movement he made the following morning was to reach under his pillow for the gun. In the gray light of dawn he held it loosely, feeling a sense of power. Could killa man wida gun like this. Kill anybody, black or white. And if he were holding this gun in his hand nobody could run over him; they would have to respect him. It was a big gun, with a long barrel and a heavy handle. He raised and lowered it in his hand, marveling at its weight.

He had not come straight home with it as his mother had asked; instead he had stayed out in the fields, holding the weapon in his hand, aiming it now and then at some imaginary foe. But he had not fired it; he had been afraid that his father might hear. Also he was not sure he knew how to fire it.

To avoid surrendering the pistol he had not come into the house until he knew that all were asleep. When his mother had tiptoed to his bedside late that night and demanded the gun, he had first played 'possum; then he had told her that the gun was hidden outdoors, that he would bring it to her in the morning. Now he lay turning it slowly in his hands. He broke it, took out the cartridges, felt them, and put them back.

He slid out of bed, got a long strip of old flannel from a trunk, wrapped the gun in it, and tied it to his naked thigh while it was still loaded. He did not go in to breakfast. Even though it was not yet daylight, he started for Jim Hawkins's plantation. Just as the sun was rising he reached the barns where the mules and plows were kept.

"Hey! That you, Dave?"

He turned. Jim Hawkins stood eyeing him suspiciously.

"What're yuh doing here so early?"

"Ah didn't know Ah wuz gittin up so early, Mistah Hawkins. Ah wuz fixing hitch up of Jenny n take her t the fiels."

"Good. Since you're here so early, how about plowing that stretch down by the woods?"

"Suits me, Mistah Hawkins."

"O.K. Go to it!"

He hitched Jenny to a plow and started across the fields. Hot dog! This was just what he wanted. If he could get down by the woods, he could shoot his gun and nobody would hear. He walked behind the plow, hearing the traces creaking, feeling the gun tied tight to his thigh.

When he reached the woods, he plowed two whole rows before he decided to take out the gun. Finally he stopped, looked in all directions, then untied the gun and held it in his hand. He turned to the mule and smiled.

"Know whut this is, Jenny? Naw, yuh wouldn't know! Yuhs just ol mule! Anyhow, this is a gun, n it kin shoot, by Gawd!"

He held the gun at arm's length. Whut t hell, Ahma shoot this thing! He looked at Jenny again.

"Lissen here, Jenny! When Ah pull this ol trigger Ah don wan yuh t run n acka fool now."

Jenny stood with head down, her short ears pricked straight. Dave walked off about twenty feet, held the gun far out from him, at arm's length, and turned his head. Hell, he told himself, Ah ain afraid. The gun felt loose in his fingers; he waved it wildly for a moment. Then he shut his eyes and tightened his forefinger. Bloom! The report half-deafened him and he thought his right hand was torn from his arm. He heard Jenny whinnying and galloping over the field, and he found himself on his knees squeezing his fingers hard between his legs. His hand was numb; he jammed it into his mouth, trying to warm it, trying to stop the pain. The gun lay at his feet. He did not quite know what had happened. He stood up and stared at the gun as though it were a living thing. He gritted his teeth and kicked the gun. Yuh almos broke mah arm! He turned to look for Jenny; she was far over the fields, tossing her head and kicking wildly.

"Hol on there, ol mule!"

When he caught up with her she stood trembling, walling her big white eyes at him. The plow was far away; the traces had broken. Then Dave stopped short, looking, not believing. Jenny was bleeding. Her left side was red and wet with blood. He went closer. Lawd, have mercy! Wondah did Ah shoot this mule? He grabbed for Jenny's mane. She flinched, snorted, whirled, tossing her head.

"Hol on now! Hol on."

Then he saw the hole in Jenny's side, right between the ribs. It was round, wet, red. A crimson stream streaked down the front leg, flowing fast. Good Gawd! Ah wuzn't shootin at tha mule. He felt panic. He knew he had to stop that blood, or Jenny would bleed to death. He had never seen so much blood in all his life. He chased the mule for half a mile, trying to catch her. Finally she stopped, breathing hard, stumpy tail half arched. He caught her mane and led her back to where the plow and gun lay. Then he stooped and grabbed handfuls of damp black earth and tried to plug the bullet hole. Jenny shuddered, whinnied, and broke from him.

"Hol on! Hol on now!"

He tried to plug it again, but blood came anyhow. His fingers were hot and sticky. He rubbed dirt into his palms, trying to dry them. Then again he attempted to plug the bullet hole, but Jenny shied away, kicking her heels high. He stood helpless. He had to do something. He ran at Jenny; she dodged him. He watched a red stream of blood flow down Jenny's leg and form a bright pool at her feet.

"Jenny . . . Jenny . . ." he called weakly.

His lips trembled! She's bleeding t death! He looked in the direction of home, wanting to go back, wanting to get help. But he saw the pistol lying in the damp black clay. He had a queer feeling that if he only did something, this would not be; Jenny would not be there bleeding to death.

When he went to her this time, she did not move. She stood with sleepy, dreamy eyes; and when he touched her she gave a low-pitched whinny and knelt to the ground, her front knees slopping in blood.

"Jenny . . . Jenny . . ." he whispered.

For a long time she held her neck erect; then her head sank, slowly. Her ribs swelled with a mighty heave and she went over.

Dave's stomach felt empty, very empty. He picked up the gun and held it gingerly between his thumb and forefinger. He buried it at the foot of a tree. He took a stick and tried to cover the pool of blood with dirt—but what was the use? There was Jenny lying with her mouth open and her eyes walled and glassy. He could not tell Jim Hawkins he had shot his mule. But he had to tell him something. Yeah, Ahll tell em Jenny started gittin wil n fell on the point of the plow. . . . But that would hardly happen to a mule. He walked across the field slowly, head down.

It was sunset. Two of Jim Hawkins's men were over near the edge of the woods digging a hole in which to bury Jenny. Dave was surrounded by a knot of people; all of them were looking down at the dead mule.

"I don't see how in the world it happened," said Jim Hawkins for the tenth time.

The crowd parted and Dave's mother, father, and small brother pushed into the center.

"Where Dave?" his mother called.

"There he is," said Jim Hawkins.

His mother grabbed him.

"Whut happened, Dave? Whut yuh done?"

"Nothing."

"C'mon, boy, talk," his father said.

Dave took a deep breath and told the story he knew nobody believed.

"Waal," he drawled. "Ah brung ol Jenny down here sos Ah could do mah plowin. Ah plowed bout two rows, just like yuh see." He stopped and pointed at the long rows of upturned earth. "Then something musta been wrong wid ol Jenny. She wouldn't ack right a-tall. She started snortin n kickin her heels. Ah tried to hol her, but she pulled erway, rearin n goin on. Then when the point of the plow was stickin up in the air, she swung erroun n twisted herself back on it. . . . She stuck herself n started t bleed. N fo Ah could do anything, she wuz dead."

"Did you ever hear of anything like that in all your life?" asked Jim Hawkins.

There were white and black standing in the crowd. They murmured. Dave's mother came close to him and looked hard into his face.

"Tell the truth, Dave," she said.

"Looks like a bullet hole ter me," said one man.

"Dave, whut yuh do wid tha gun?" his mother asked.

The crowd surged in, looking at him. He jammed his hands into his pockets, shook his head slowly from left to right, and backed away. His eyes were wide and painful.

"Did he hava gun?" asked Jim Hawkins.

"By Gawd, Ah tol yuh tha wuz a gunwound," said a man, slapping his thigh.

His father caught his shoulders and shook him till his teeth rattled.

"Tell whut happened, yuh rascal! Tell whut . . ."

Dave looked at Jenny's stiff legs and began to cry.

"Whut yuh do wid tha gun?" his mother asked.

"Come on and tell the truth," said Hawkins. "Ain't nobody going to hurt you. . . ."

His mother crowded close to him.

"Did yuh shoot tha mule, Dave?"

Dave cried, seeing blurred white and black faces.

"Ahh ddinnt gggo tt sshoooot hher. . . . Ah ssswear off Gawd Ahh ddint. . . . Ah wuz a-tryin t sssee ef the ol gggun would sshoot—"

"Where yuh git the gun from?" his father asked.

"Ah got it from Joe, at the sto."

"Where yuh git the money?"

"Ma give it t me."

"He kept worryin me, Bob. . . . Ah had t. . . . Ah tol im t bring the gun right back t me. . . . It was fer yuh, the gun."

"Ah wuznt shootin at the mule, Mistah Hawkins. The gun jumped when Ah pulled the trigger . . . N for Ah knowed anything Jenny wuz there a-bleedin."

Somebody in the crowd laughed. Jim Hawkins walked close to Dave and looked into his face.

"Well, looks like you have bought you a mule, Dave."

"Ah swear for Gawd, Ah didn't go t kill the mule, Mistah Hawkins!"

"But you killed her!"

All the crowd was laughing now. They stood on tiptoe and poked heads over one another's shoulders.

"Well, boy, looks like yuh done bought a dead mule! Hahaha."

"Ain tha ershame."

"Hohohohoho."

Dave stood, head down, twisting his feet in the dirt.

"Well, you needn't worry about it, Bob," said Jim Hawkins to Dave's father. "Just let the boy keep on working and pay me two dollars a month."

"Whut yuh wan fer yo mule, Mistah Hawkins?"

Jim Hawkins screwed up his eyes.

"Fifty dollars."

"Whut yuh do wid tha gun?" Dave's father demanded.

Dave said nothing.

"Yuh wan me t take a tree lim n beat yuh till yuh talk!"

"Nawsuh!"

"Whut yuh do wid it?"

"Ah thowed it erway."

"Where?"

"Ah . . . Ah thowed it in the creek."

"Waal, c mon home. N firs thing in the mawnin git to tha creek n fin tha gun."

"Yessuh."

"Whut yuh pay fer it?"

"Two dollahs."

"Take tha gun n git yo money back n carry it t Mistah Hawkins, yuh hear? N don fergit Ahma lam you black bottom good fer this! Now march yosef on home, suh!"

Dave turned and walked slowly. He heard people laughing. Dave glared, his eyes welling with tears. Hot anger bubbled in him. Then he swallowed and stumbled on.

That night Dave did not sleep. He was glad that he had gotten out of killing the mule so easily, but he was hurt. Something hot seemed to turn over inside him each time he remembered how they had laughed. He tossed on his bed, feeling his hard pillow. N Pa says he's gonna beat me. . . . He remembered other beatings, and his back quivered. Naw, naw, Ah sho don wan im t beat me tha way no mo. . . . Dam em all! Nobody ever gave him anything. All he did was work. They treat me lika mule. . . . N then they beat me. . . . He gritted his teeth. N Ma had t tell on me.

Well, if he had to, he would take old man Hawkins that two dollars. But that meant selling the gun. And he wanted to keep that gun. Fifty dollahs fer a dead mule.

He turned over, thinking how he had fired the gun. He had an itch to fire it again. Ef other men kin shoota gun, by Gawd, Ah kin! He was still listening. Mebbe they all sleepin now. . . . The house was still. He heard the soft breathing of his brother. Yes, now! He would go down an get that gun and see if he could fire it! He eased out of bed and slipped into overalls.

The moon was bright. He ran almost all the way to the edge of the woods. He stumbled over the ground, looking for the spot where he had buried the gun. Yeah, here it is. Like a hungry dog scratching for a bone he pawed it up. He puffed his black cheeks and blew dirt from the trigger and barrel. He broke it and found four cartridges unshot. He looked around; the fields were filled with silence and moonlight. He clutched the gun stiff and hard in his fingers. But as soon as he wanted to pull the trigger, he shut his eyes and turned his head. Naw, Ah can't shoot wid mah eyes closed n mah head turned. With effort he held his eyes open; then he squeezed. Blooooom! He was stiff, not breathing. The gun was still in his hands. Dammit, he'd done it! He fired again. Bloooom! He smiled. Blooooom! Blooooom! Click, click. There! It was empty. If anybody could shoot a gun, he could. He put the gun into his hip pocket and started across the fields.

When he reached the top of a ridge he stood straight and proud in the moonlight, looking at Jim Hawkins's big white house, feeling the gun sagging in his pocket. Lawd, ef Ah had jus one mo bullet Ahd taka shot at tha house. Ahd like t scare ol man Hawkins jussa little. . . . Jussa enough t let im know Dave Sanders is a man.

To his left the road curved, running to the tracks of the Illinois Central. He jerked his head, listening. From far off came a faint hoooof-hoooof; hoooof-hoooof; hoooof-hoooof. . . . That's number eight. He took a swift look at Jim Hawkins's white house; he thought of Pa, of Ma, of his little brother, and the boys. He thought of the dead mule and heard hoooof-hoooof; hoooof-hoooof; hoooof-hoooof. . . . He stood rigid. Two dollahs a mont. Les see now . . . Tha means itll take bout two years. Shucks! Ahll be dam! He started down the road, toward the tracks. Yeah, here she comes! He stood beside the track and held himself stiffly. Here she comes, erroun the ben. . . . C mon, yuh slow poke! C mon! He had his hand on his gun; something quivered in his stomach. Then the train thundered past, the gray and brown boxcars rumbling and clinking. He gripped the gun tightly; then he jerked his hand out of his pocket. Ah betcha Bill wouldn't do it! Ah betcha. . . . The cars slid past, steel grinding upon steel. Ahm riding yuh ternight so hep me Gawd! He was hot all over. He hesitated just a moment; then he grabbed, pulled atop of a car, and lay flat. He felt his pocket; the gun was still there. Ahead the long rails were glinting in moonlight, stretching away, away to somewhere, somewhere where he could be a man. . . .

afterword

Although Richard Wright spent most of his adult years away from the South, the experiences of his childhood in Natchez and Memphis retained an immediate significance for him, for he knew from first-hand observation that too many Southern Negro youngsters were, like Dave in this angry story, headed for self-destruction in their attempts to gain adulthood. Poorly educated members of a white-supremacist society, frustrated by their inevitable poverty and subordination, many young Negroes turned to violence as a means of self-assertion. Thus, Dave's pathetic dependence on a tough-guy image of himself as a means of attaining a sense of dignity is less a result of his own shortcomings than of a society which allows him so few options.

questions for general discussion

1. Does Wright spend more time describing the death of the mule than seems necessary? Support your answer.

2. What does the gun represent to Dave?

3. How does Wright vary the tone of "The Man Who Was Almost a Man"?

4. How does Wright effectively criticize the Southern racial situation without making an explicit statement of criticism?

suggestions for writing

1. Write a theme describing Wright's use of irony in this story.

2. Write a theme comparing Dave with the narrator of Ellison's story, "Battle Royal." How does each react to adversity, for instance? What are the goals of each?

3. Write a theme in which you show how Dave is distinctly a product of his environment.

4. Comment on the story's title as a statement of theme. Support your paper with at least one specific reference from each of the four sections.

FLANNERY O'CONNOR
a late encounter with the enemy

General Sash was a hundred and four years old. He lived with his grand-daughter, Sally Poker Sash, who was sixty-two years old and who prayed every night on her knees that he would live until her graduation from college. The General didn't give two slaps for her graduation but he never doubted he would live for it. Living had got to be such a habit with him that he couldn't conceive of any other condition. A graduation exercise was not exactly his idea of a good time, even if, as she said, he would be expected to sit on the stage in his uniform. She said there would be a long procession of teachers and students in their robes but that there wouldn't be anything to equal *him* in his uniform. He knew this well enough without her telling him, and as for the damm procession, it could march to hell and back and not cause him a quiver. He liked parades with floats full of Miss Americas and Miss Daytona Beaches and Miss Queen Cotton Products. He didn't have any use for processions and a procession full of schoolteachers was about as deadly as the River Styx to his way of thinking. However, he was willing to sit on the stage in his uniform so that they could see him.

Sally Poker was not as sure as he was that he would live until her graduation. There had not been any perceptible change in him for the last five years, but she had the sense that she might be cheated out of her triumph because she so often was. She had been going to summer school every year for the past twenty because when she started teaching, there were no such things as degrees. In those times, she said, everything was normal but nothing had been normal since she was sixteen, and for the past twenty summers, when she should have been resting, she had had to take a trunk in the burning heat to the state teacher's college; and though when she returned in the fall, she always taught in the exact way she had been taught not to teach, this was a mild revenge that didn't satisfy her sense of justice. She wanted the General at her graduation because she wanted to show what she stood for, or, as she said, "what all was behind her," and was not behind them. This *them* was not anybody in particular. It was just all the upstarts who had turned the world on its head and unsettled the ways of decent living.

She meant to stand on that platform in August with the General sitting in his wheel chair on the stage behind her and she meant to hold her head very high as if she were saying, "See him! See him! My kin, all you upstarts! Glorious upright old man standing for the old traditions! Dignity! Honor! Courage! See him!" One night in her sleep she screamed, "See him! See him!" and turned her head and found him sitting in his wheel chair behind her with a terrible expression on his face and with all his clothes off except the general's hat and she had waked up and had not dared to go back to sleep again that night.

For his part, the General would not have consented even to attend her graduation if she had not promised to see to it that he sit on the stage. He liked to sit on any stage. He considered that he was still a very handsome man. When he had been able to stand up, he had measured five feet four inches of pure game cock. He had white hair that reached to his shoulders behind and he would not wear teeth because he thought his profile was more striking without them. When he put on his full-dress general's uniform, he knew well enough that there was nothing to match him anywhere.

This was not the same uniform he had worn in the War between the States. He had not actually been a general in that war. He had probably been a foot soldier; he didn't remember what he had been; in fact, he didn't remember that war at all. It was like his feet, which hung down now shriveled at the very end of him, without feeling, covered with a blue-gray afghan that Sally Poker had crocheted when she was a little girl. He didn't remember the Spanish-American War in which he had lost a son; he didn't even remember the son. He didn't have any use for history because he never expected to meet it again. To his mind, history was connected with processions and life with parades and he liked parades. People were always asking him if he remembered this or that—a dreary black procession of questions about the past. There was only one event in the past that had any significance for him and that he cared to talk about: that was twelve years ago when he had received the general's uniform and had been in the premiere.

"I was in that preemy they had in Atlanta," he would tell visitors sitting on his front porch. "Surrounded by beautiful guls. It wasn't a thing local about it. It was nothing local about it. Listen here. It was a nashnul event and they had me in it—up onto the stage. There was no bob-tails at it. Ever person at it had paid ten dollars to get in and had to wear his tuxseeder. I was in this uniform. A beautiful gul presented me with it that afternoon in a hotel room."

"It was in a suite in the hotel and I was in it too, Papa," Sally Poker would say, winking at the visitors. "You weren't alone with any young lady in a hotel room."

"Was, I'd a known what to do," the old General would say with a sharp look and the visitors would scream with laughter. "This was a Hollywood, California, gul," he'd continue. "She was from Hollywood, California, and didn't have any part in the pitcher. Out there they have so many beautiful guls that they don't need that they call them a extra and they don't use them for nothing but presenting people with things and having their pitchers taken.

They took my pitcher with her. No, it was two of them. One on either side and me in the middle with my arms around each of them's waist and their waist ain't any bigger than a half a dollar."

Sally Poker would interrupt again. "It was Mr. Govisky that gave you the uniform, Papa, and he gave me the most exquisite corsage. Really, I wish you could have seen it. It was made with gladiola petals taken off and painted gold and put back together to look like a rose. It was exquisite. I wish you could have seen it, it was . . ."

"It was as big as her head," the General would snarl. "I was tellin it. They gimme this uniform and they gimme this soward and they say, 'Now General, we don't want you to start a war on us. All we want you to do is march right up on that stage when you're innerduced tonight and answer a few questions. Think you can do that?' 'Think I can do it!' I say. 'Listen here. I was doing things before you were born,' and they hollered."

"He was the hit of the show," Sally Poker would say, but she didn't much like to remember the premiere on account of what had happened to her feet at it. She had bought a new dress for the occasion—a long black crepe dinner dress with a rhinestone buckle and a bolero—and a pair of silver slippers to wear with it, because she was supposed to go up on the stage with him to keep him from falling. Everything was arranged for them. A real limousine came at ten minutes to eight and took them to the theater. It drew up under the marquee at exactly the right time, after the big stars and the director and the author and the governor and the mayor and some less important stars. The police kept traffic from jamming and there were ropes to keep the people off who couldn't go. All the people who couldn't go watched them step out of the limousine into the lights. Then they walked down the red and gold foyer and an usherette in a Confederate cap and little short skirt conducted them to their special seats. The audience was already there and a group of UDC members began to clap when they saw the General in his uniform and that started everybody to clap. A few more celebrities came after them and then the doors closed and the lights went down.

A young man with blond wavy hair who said he represented the motion-picture industry came out and began to introduce everybody and each one who was introduced walked up on the stage and said how really happy he was to be here for this great event. The General and his granddaughter were introduced sixteenth on the program. He was introduced as General Tennessee Flintrock Sash of the Confederacy, though Sally Poker had told Mr. Govisky that his name was George Poker Sash and that he had only been a major. She helped him up from his seat but her heart was beating so fast she didn't know whether she'd make it herself.

The old man walked up the aisle slowly with his fierce white head high and his hat held over his heart. The orchestra began to play the Confederate Battle Hymn very softly and the UDC members rose as a group and did not sit down again until the General was on the stage. When he reached the center of the stage with Sally Poker just behind him guiding his elbow, the orchestra burst out in a loud rendition of the Battle Hymn and the old man, with real stage presence, gave a vigorous trembling salute and stood at attention until the last blast had died away. Two of the usherettes in Confederate caps and short skirts held a Confederate and a Union flag crossed behind them.

The General stood in the exact center of the spotlight and it caught a weird moon-shaped slice of Sally Poker—the corsage, the rhinestone buckle and one hand clenched around a white glove and handkerchief. The young man with the blond wavy hair inserted himself into the circle of light and said he was *really* happy to have here tonight for this great event, one, he said, who had fought and bled in the battles they would soon see daringly re-acted on the screen, and "Tell me, General," he asked, "how old are you?"

"Niiiiiinnttty-two!" the General screamed.

The young man looked as if this were just about the most impressive thing that had been said all evening. "Ladies and gentlemen," he said, "let's give the General the biggest hand we've got!" and there was applause immediately and the young man indicated to Sally Poker with a motion of his thumb that she could take the old man back to his seat now so that the next person could be introduced; but the General had not finished. He stood immovable in the exact center of the spotlight, his neck thrust forward, his mouth slightly open, and his voracious gray eyes drinking in the glare and the applause. He elbowed his granddaughter roughly away. "How I keep so young," he screeched, "I kiss all the pretty guls!"

This was met with a great din of spontaneous applause and it was at just that instant that Sally Poker looked down at her feet and discovered that in the excitement of getting ready she had forgotten to change her shoes: two brown Girl Scout oxfords protruded from the bottom of her dress. She gave the General a yank and almost ran with him off the stage. He was very angry that he had not got to say how glad he was to be here for this event and on the way back to his seat, he kept saying as loud as he could, "I'm glad to be here at this preemy with all these beautiful guls!" but there was another celebrity going up the other aisle and nobody paid any attention to him. He slept through the picture, muttering fiercely every now and then in his sleep.

Since then, his life had not been very interesting. His feet were completely dead now, his knees worked like old hinges, his kidneys functioned when they would, but his heart persisted doggedly to beat. The past and the future were the same thing to him, one forgotten and the other not remembered; he had no more notion of dying than a cat. Every year on Confederate Memorial Day, he was bundled up and lent to the Capitol City Museum where he was displayed from one to four in a musty room full of old photographs, old uniforms, old artillery, and historic documents. All these were carefully preserved in glass cases so that children would not put their hands on them. He wore his general's uniform from the premiere and sat, with a fixed scowl, inside a small roped area. There was nothing about him to indicate that he was alive except an occasional movement in his milky gray eyes, but once when a bold child touched his sword, his arm shot forward and slapped the hand off in an instant. In the spring when the old homes were opened for pilgrimages, he was invited to wear his uniform and sit in some conspicuous spot and lend atmosphere to the scene. Some of these times he only snarled at the visitors but sometimes he told about the premiere and the beautiful girls.

If he had died before Sally Poker's graduation, she thought she would have died herself. At the beginning of the summer term, even before she knew if she would pass, she told the Dean that her grandfather, General Tennessee Flintrock Sash of the Confederacy, would attend her graduation and that he was a hundred and four years old and that his mind was still clear as a bell. Distinguished visitors were always welcome and could sit on the stage and be introduced. She made arrangements with her nephew, John Wesley Poker Sash, a Boy Scout, to come wheel the General's chair. She thought how sweet it would be to see the old man in his courageous gray and the young boy in his clean khaki—the old and the new, she thought appropriately—they would be behind her on the stage when she received her degree.

Everything went almost exactly as she had planned. In the summer while she was away at school, the General stayed with other relatives and they brought him and John Wesley, the Boy Scout, down to the graduation. A reporter came to the hotel where they stayed and took the General's picture with Sally Poker on one side of him and John Wesley on the other. The General, who had had his picture taken with beautiful girls, didn't think much of this. He had forgotten precisely what kind of event this was he was going to attend but he remembered that he was to wear his uniform and carry the sword.

On the morning of the graduation, Sally Poker had to line up in the academic procession with the B.S.'s in Elementary Education and she couldn't see to getting him on the stage herself—but John Wesley, a fat blond boy of ten with an executive expression, guaranteed to take care of everything. She came in her academic gown to the hotel and dressed the old man in his uniform. He was as frail as a dried spider. "Aren't you just thrilled, Papa?" she asked. "I'm just thrilled to death!"

"Put the soward acrost my lap, damm you," the old man said, "where it'll shine."

She put it there and then stood back looking at him. "You look just grand," she said.

"God damm it," the old man said in a slow monotonous certain tone as if he were saying it to the beating of his heart. "God damm every goddam thing to hell."

"Now, now," she said and left happily to join the procession.

The graduates were lined up behind the Science building and she found her place just as the line started to move. She had not slept much the night before and when she had, she had dreamed of the exercises, murmuring, "See him, see him?" in her sleep but waking up every time just before she turned her head to look at him behind her. The graduates had to walk three blocks in the hot sun in their black wool robes and as she plodded stolidly along she thought that if anyone considered this academic procession something impressive to behold, they need only wait until they saw that old General in his courageous gray and that clean young Boy Scout stoutly wheeling his chair across the stage with the sunlight catching the sword. She imagined that John Wesley had the old man ready now behind the stage.

The black procession wound its way up the two blocks and started on the main walk leading to the auditorium. The visitors stood on the grass, picking out their graduates. Men were pushing back their hats and wiping their foreheads and women were lifting their dresses slightly from the shoulders to keep them from sticking to their backs. The graduates in their heavy robes looked as if the last beads of ignorance were being sweated out of them. The sun blazed off the fenders of automobiles and beat from the columns of the buildings and pulled the eye from one spot of glare to another. It pulled Sally Poker's toward the big red Coca-Cola machine that had been set up by the side of the auditorium. Here she saw the General parked, scowling and hatless in his chair in the blazing sun while John Wesley, his blouse loose behind, his hip and cheek pressed to the red machine, was drinking a Coca-Cola. She broke from the line and galloped to them and snatched the bottle away. She shook the boy and thrust in his blouse and put the hat on the old man's head. "Now get him in there!" she said, pointing one rigid finger to the side door of the building.

For his part the General felt as if there were a little hole beginning to widen in the top of his head. The boy wheeled him rapidly down a walk and up a ramp and into a building and bumped him over the stage entrance and into position where he had been told and the General glared in front of him at heads that all seemed to flow together and eyes that moved from one face to another. Several figures in black robes came and picked up his hand and shook it. A black procession was flowing up each aisle and forming to stately music in a pool in front of him. The music seemed to be entering his head through the little hole and he thought for a second that the procession would try to enter it too.

He didn't know what procession this was but there was something familiar about it. It must be familiar to him since it had come to meet him, but he didn't like a black procession. Any procession that came to meet him, he thought irritably, ought to have floats with beautiful guls on them like the floats before the preemy. It must be something connected with history like they were always having. He had no use for any of it. What happened then wasn't anything to a man living now and he was living now.

When all the procession had flowed into the black pool, a black figure began orating in front of it. The figure was telling something about history and the General made up his mind he wouldn't listen, but the words kept seeping in through the little hole in his head. He heard his own name mentioned and his chair was shuttled forward roughly and the Boy Scout took a big bow. They called his name and the fat brat bowed. Goddam you, the old man tried to say, get out of my way, I can stand up!—but he was jerked back again before he could get up and take the bow. He supposed the noise they made was for him. If he was over, he didn't intend to listen to any more of it. If it hadn't been for the little hole in the top of his head, none of the words would have got to him. He thought of putting his finger up there into the hole to block them but the hole was a little wider than his finger and it felt as if it were getting deeper.

Another black robe had taken the place of the first one and was talking now and he heard his name mentioned again but they were not talking about him, they were still talking about history. "If we forget our past," the speaker was saying, "we won't remember our future and it will be as well for we won't have one." The General heard some of these words gradually. He had forgotten history and he didn't intend to remember it again. He had forgotten the name and face of his wife and the names and faces of his children or even if he had a wife and children, and he had forgotten the names of places and the places themselves and what had happened at them.

He was considerably irked by the hole in his head. He had not expected to have a hole in his head at this event. It was the slow black music that had put it there and though most of the music had stopped outside, there was still a little of it in the hole, going deeper and moving around in his thoughts, letting the words he heard into the dark places of his brain. He heard the words, Chickamauga, Shiloh, Johnston, Lee, and he knew he was inspiring all these words that meant nothing to him. He wondered if he had been a general at Chickamauga or at Lee. Then he tried to see himself and the horse mounted in the middle of a float full of beautiful girls, being driven slowly through downtown Atlanta. Instead, the old words began to stir in his head as if they were trying to wrench themselves out of place and come to life.

The speaker was through with that war and had gone on to the next one and now he was approaching another and all his words, like the black procession, were vaguely familiar and irritating. There was a long finger of music in the General's head, probing various spots that were words, letting in a little light on the words and helping them to live. The words began to come toward him and he said, Dammit! I ain't going to have it! and he started edging backwards to get out of the way. Then he saw the figure in the black robe sit down and there was a noise and the black pool in front of him began to rumble and to flow toward him from either side to the black slow music, and he said, Stop dammit! I can't do but one thing at a time! He couldn't protect himself from the words and attend to the procession too and the words were coming at him fast. He felt that he was running backwards and the words were coming at him like musket fire, just escaping him but getting nearer and nearer. He turned around and began to run as fast as he could but he found himself running toward the words. He was running into a regular volley of them and meeting them with quick curses. As the music swelled toward him, the entire past opened up on him out of nowhere and he felt his body riddled in a hundred places with sharp stabs of pain and he fell down, returning a curse for every hit. He saw his wife's narrow face looking at him critically through her round gold-rimmed glasses; he saw one of his squinting bald-headed sons; and his mother ran toward him with an anxious look; then a succession of places—Chicamauga, Shiloh, Marthasville—rushed at him as if the past were the only future now and he had to endure it. Then suddenly he saw that the black procession was almost on him. He recognized it, for it had been dogging all his days. He made such a desperate effort to see over it and find out what comes after the past that his hand clenched the sword until the blade touched the bone.

The graduates were crossing the stage in a long file to receive their scrolls and shake the president's hand. As Sally Poker, who was near the end, crossed, she glanced at the General and saw him sitting fixed and fierce, his eyes wide open, and she turned her head forward again and held it a perceptible degree higher and received her scroll. Once it was all over and she was out of the auditorium in the sun again, she located her kin and they waited together on a bench in the shade for John Wesley to wheel the old man out. That crafty scout had bumped him out the back way and rolled him at high speed down a flagstone path and was waiting now, with the corpse, in the long line at the Coca-Cola machine.

afterword

"A Late Encounter with the Enemy" concerns itself with one of Flannery O'Connor's major themes—the refusal of many white Southerners to face reality because of their psychological dependence on the past. As Miss O'Connor sees it, many Southerners distort Southern history, romanticizing it by ignoring its evils and emphasizing its legendary heroics. With this predilection for romance and for an evasion of unpleasant facts, too many Southerners find themselves, in the mid-twentieth century, unable to resolve or even understand current problems. Thus, their inability to acknowledge the failures of the past renders them incapable of coping with problems of the present.

In this story, Sally Poker Sash's attempt to justify her wasted life, by telling herself and showing those around her that she is, after all, the granddaughter of a Civil War hero, typifies this Southern failure to accept reality. Her failure to face reality leads Sally into committing another error, one which the author conceives to be a major shortcoming of the Southern experience, that of cutting oneself off from one's fellows. The characters in Miss O'Connor's stories rarely communicate with each other except by the most bizarre means. Their constant talking, their droning voices which never truly reveal basic emotions, contribute to a grotesque spiritual and psychological isolation which O'Connor suggests is the common state for all too many Southerners.

Flannery O'Connor probes these and other themes of the Southern experience in a forceful, deceptively simple style. Through startling juxtapositions and through striking pictures of both the banal and the macabre, she prompts in her readers a kind of humor-within-horror response which makes them peculiarly receptive to her views of Southern life.

Born in Savannah, Georgia, in 1925, Miss O'Connor lived most of her creative years on a farm near the industrial and agricultural town of Milledgeville, Georgia. There, in 1964, she died at the age of thirty-nine, having never enjoyed truly good health. She began to write during her years at the Woman's College of Georgia, and by the time she received her Master of Fine Arts from the State University of Iowa she was being published regularly. Subsequently encouraged by such grants as the O. Henry Award in 1957 and a Ford Foundation Grant in 1959, she struggled valiantly against her steadily advancing affliction of Lupus while producing such novels as *Wise Blood* (1952) and *The Violent Bear It Away* (1960). Her volumes of short stories are *A Good Man Is Hard to Find* (1955) and *Everything That Rises Must Converge* (1965).

questions for general discussion

1. Why does the story not end with the discovery of the General's death?

2. What is the significance of the word "displayed" in the statement, "he was displayed from one to four"?

3. Are there any obvious symbols in the story?

4. What does the General's presence at her graduation really mean to Sally?

5. What is the significance of the sentence, "He wondered if he had been a general at Chickamauga or at Lee"?

6. At the graduation ceremony, why are the words coming at the General "like musket fire"?

7. Why is the last scene, in which we see the General's corpse in the "long line at the Coca-Cola machine," particularly powerful?

suggestions for writing

1. Write a theme in which you discuss the significance of the recurring phrase, "See him! See him!"

2. Comment on O'Connor's use of bizarre or shocking details. Suggest some possible reasons for the use of such details.

3. Comment briefly on the senses of reality revealed by either Sally, the

General, or John Wesley. What does each of them think of as being "real"?

4. What is the significance of the forms of dress in this story?

5. What is the author's attitude toward the movie premiere?

the river

The child stood glum and limp in the middle of the dark living room while his father pulled him into a plaid coat. His right arm was hung in the sleeve but the father buttoned the coat anyway and pushed him forward toward a pale spotted hand that stuck through the half-open door.

"He ain't fixed right," a loud voice said from the hall.

"Well then for Christ's sake fix him," the father muttered. "It's six o'clock in the morning." He was in his bathrobe and barefooted. When he got the child to the door and tried to shut it, he found her looming in it, a speckled skeleton in a long pea-green coat and felt helmet.

"And his and my carfare," she said. "It'll be twict we have to ride the car."

He went in the bedroom again to get the money and when he came back, she and the boy were both standing in the middle of the room. She was taking stock. "I couldn't smell those dead cigarette butts long if I was ever to come sit with you," she said, shaking him down in his coat.

"Here's the change," the father said. He went to the door and opened it wide and waited.

After she had counted the money she slipped it somewhere inside her coat and walked over to a watercolor hanging near the phonograph. "I know what time it is," she said, peering closely at the black lines crossing into broken planes of violent color. "I ought to. My shift goes on at 10 P.M. and don't get off till 5 and it takes me one hour to ride the Vine Street car."

"Oh, I see," he said; "well, we'll expect him back tonight, about eight or nine?"

"Maybe later," she said. "We're going to the river to a healing. This particular preacher don't get around this way often. I wouldn't have paid for that," she said, nodding at the painting, "I would have drew it myself."

"All right, Mrs. Connin, we'll see you then," he said, drumming on the door.

A toneless voice called from the bedroom, "Bring me an icepack."

"Too bad his mamma's sick," Mrs. Connin said. "What's her trouble?"

"We don't know," he muttered.

"We'll ask the preacher to pray for her. He's healed a lot of folks. The Reverend Bevel Summers. Maybe she ought to see him sometime."

"Maybe so," he said. "We'll see you tonight," and he disappeared into the bedroom and left them to go.

The little boy stared at her silently his nose and eyes running. He was four or five. He had a long face and bulging chin and half-shut eyes set far apart. He seemed mute and patient, like an old sheep waiting to be let out.

"You'll like this preacher," she said. "The Reverend Bevel Summers. You ought to hear him sing."

The bedroom door opened suddenly and the father stuck his head out and said, "Good-by, old man. Have a good time."

"Good-by," the little boy said and jumped as if he had been shot.

Mrs. Connin gave the watercolor another look. Then they went out into the hall and rang for the elevator. "I wouldn't have drew it," she said.

Outside the gray morning was blocked off on either side by the unlit empty buildings. "It's going to fair up later," she said, "but this is the last time we'll be able to have any preaching at the river this year. Wipe your nose, Sugar Boy."

He began rubbing his sleeve across it but she stopped him. "That ain't nice," she said. "Where's your handkerchief?"

He put his hands in his pockets and pretended to look for it while she waited. "Some people don't care how they send one off," she murmured to her reflection in the coffee shop window. "You pervide." She took a red and blue flowered handkerchief out of her pocket and stooped down and began to work on his nose. "Now blow," she said and he blew. "You can borry it. Put it in your pocket."

He folded it up and put it in his pocket carefully and they walked on to the corner and leaned against the side of a closed drugstore to wait for the car. Mrs. Connin turned up her coat collar so that it met her hat in the back. Her eyelids began to droop and she looked as if she might go to sleep against the wall. The little boy put a slight pressure on her hand.

"What's your name?" she asked in a drowsy voice. "I don't know but only your last name. I should have found out your first name."

His name was Harry Ashfield and he had never thought at any time before of changing it. "Bevel," he said.

Mrs. Connin raised herself from the wall. "Why ain't that a coincident!" she said. "I told you that's the name of this preacher!"

"Bevel," he repeated.

She stood looking down at him as if he had become a marvel to her. "I'll have to see you meet him today," she said. "He's no ordinary preacher. He's a healer. He couldn't do nothing for Mr. Connin though. Mr. Connin didn't have the faith but he said he would try anything once. He had this griping in his gut."

The trolley appeared as a yellow spot at the end of the deserted street.

"He's gone to the government hospital now," she said, "and they taken one-third of his stomach. I tell him he better thank Jesus for what he's got left but he says he ain't thanking nobody. Well I declare," she murmured, "Bevel!"

They walked out to the tracks to wait. "Will he heal me?" Bevel asked.

"What you got?"

"I'm hungry," he decided finally.

"Didn't you have your breakfast?"

"I didn't have time to be hungry yet then," he said.

"Well when we get home we'll both have us something," she said. "I'm ready myself."

They got on the car and sat down a few seats behind the driver and Mrs. Connin took Bevel on her knees. "Now you be a good boy," she said, "and let me get some sleep. Just don't get off my lap." She lay her head back and as he watched, gradually her eyes closed and her mouth fell open to show a few long scattered teeth, some gold and some darker than her face; she began to whistle and blow like a musical skeleton. There was no one in the car but themselves and the driver and when he saw she was asleep, he took out the flowered handkerchief and unfolded it and examined it carefully. Then he folded it up again and unzipped a place in the innerlining of his coat and hid it in there and shortly he went to sleep himself.

Her house was a half-mile from the end of the car line, set back a little from the road. It was tan paper brick with a porch across the front of it and a tin top. On the porch there were three little boys of different sizes with identical speckled faces and one tall girl who had her hair up in so many aluminum curlers that it glared like the roof. The three boys followed them inside and closed in on Bevel. They looked at him silently, not smiling.

"That's Bevel," Mrs. Connin said, taking off her coat. "It's a coincident he's named the same as the preacher. These boys are J. C., Spivey, and Sinclair, and that's Sarah Mildred on the porch. Take off that coat and hang it on the bed post, Bevel."

The three boys watched him while he unbuttoned the coat and took it off. Then they watched him hang it on the bed post and then they stood, watching the coat. They turned abruptly and went out the door and had a conference on the porch.

Bevel stood looking around him at the room. It was part kitchen and part bedroom. The entire house was two rooms and two porches. Close to his foot the tail of a light-colored dog moved up and down between two floor boards as he scratched his back on the underside of the house. Bevel jumped on it but the hound was experienced and had already withdrawn when his feet hit the spot.

The walls were filled with pictures and calendars. There were two round photographs of an old man and woman with collapsed mouths and another picture of a man whose eyebrows dashed out of two bushes of hair and clashed in a heap on the bridge of his nose; the rest of his face stuck out like a bare cliff to fall from. "That's Mr. Connin," Mrs. Connin said, standing back from the stove for a second to admire the face with him, "but it don't favor him any more." Bevel turned from Mr. Connin to a colored picture over the bed of a man wearing a white sheet. He had long hair and a gold circle around his head and he was sawing on a board while some children stood watching him. He was going to ask who that was when the three boys came in again and motioned for him to follow them. He thought of crawling under the bed and hanging onto one of the legs but the three boys only stood there, speckled and silent, waiting, and after a second he followed them at a little distance out on the porch and around the corner of the house. They started off through a field of rough yellow weeds to the hog pen, a five-foot boarded square full of shoats, which they intended to ease him over into. When they reached it, they turned and waited silently, leaning against the side.

He was coming very slowly, deliberately bumping his feet together as if he had trouble walking. Once he had been beaten up in the park by some strange boys when his sitter forgot him, but he hadn't known anything was going to happen that time until it was over. He began to smell a strong odor of garbage and to hear the noises of a wild animal. He stopped a few feet from the pen and waited, pale but dogged.

. The three boys didn't move. Something seemed to have happened to them. They stared over his head as if they saw something coming behind him but he was afraid to turn his own head and look. Their speckles were pale and their eyes were still and gray as glass. Only their ears twitched slightly. Nothing happened. Finally, the one in the middle said, "She'd kill us," and turned, dejected and hacked, and climbed up on the pen and hung over, staring in.

Bevel sat down on the ground, dazed with relief, and grinned up at them.

The one sitting on the pen glanced at him severely. "Hey you," he said after a second, "if you can't climb up and see these pigs you can lift that bottom board off and look in thataway." He appeared to offer this as a kindness.

Bevel had never seen a real pig but he had seen a pig in a book and knew they were small fat pink animals with curly tails and round grinning faces and bow ties. He leaned forward and pulled eagerly at the board.

"Pull harder," the littlest boy said. "It's nice and rotten. Just life out thet nail."

He eased a long reddish nail out of the soft wood.

"Now you can lift up the board and put your face to the . . ." a quiet voice began.

He had already done it and another face, gray, wet and sour, was pushing into his, knocking him down and back as it scraped out under the plank. Something snorted over him and charged back again, rolling him over and pushing him up from behind and then sending him forward, screaming through the yellow field, while it bounded behind.

The three Connins watched from where they were. The one sitting on the pen held the loose board back with his dangling foot. Their stern faces didn't brighten any but they seemed to become less taut, as if some great need had been partly satisfied. "Maw ain't going to like him lettin out thet hawg," the smallest one said.

Mrs. Connin was on the back porch and caught Bevel up as he reached the steps. The hog ran under the house and subsided, panting, but the child screamed for five minutes. When she had finally calmed him down, she gave him his breakfast and let him sit on her lap while he ate it. The shoat climbed the two steps onto the back porch and stood outside the screen door, looking in with his head lowered sullenly. He was long-legged and hump-backed and part of one of his ears had been bitten off.

"Git away!" Mrs. Connin shouted. "That one yonder favors Mr. Paradise that has the gas station," she said. "You'll see him today at the healing. He's got the cancer over his ear. He always comes to show he ain't been healed."

The shoat stood squinting a few seconds longer and then moved off slowly. "I don't want to see him," Bevel said.

They walked to the river, Mrs. Connin in front with him and the three boys strung out behind and Sarah Mildred, the tall girl, at the end to holler if one of them ran out on the road. They looked like the skeleton of an old boat with two pointed ends, sailing slowly on the edge of the highway. The white Sunday sun followed at a little distance, climbing fast through a scum of gray cloud as if it mean to overtake them. Bevel walked on the outside edge, holding Mrs. Connin's hand and looking down into the orange and purple gulley that dropped off from the concrete.

It occurred to him that he was lucky this time that they had found Mrs. Connin who would take you away for the day instead of an ordinary sitter who only sat where you lived or went to the park. You found out more when you left where you lived. He had found out already this morning that he had been made by a carpenter named Jesus Christ. Before he had thought it had been a doctor named Sladewall, a fat man with a yellow mustache who gave him shots and thought his name was Herbert, but this must have been a joke. They joked a lot where he lived. If he had thought about it before, he would have thought Jesus Christ was a word like "oh" or "damm" or "God," or maybe somebody who had cheated them out of something sometime. When he had asked Mrs. Connin who the man in the sheet in the picture over her bed was, she had looked at him a while with her mouth open. Then she had said, "That's Jesus," and she had kept on looking at him.

In a few minutes she had got up and got a book out of the other room. "See here," she said, turning over the cover, "this belonged to my great grand-mamma. I wouldn't part with it for nothing on earth." She ran her finger under some brown writing on a spotted page. "Emma Stevens Oakley, 1832," she said. "Ain't that something to have? And every word of it the gospel truth." She turned the next page and read him the name: "The Life of Jesus Christ for Readers Under Twelve." Then she read him the book.

It was a small book, pale brown on the outside with gold edges and a smell like old putty. It was full of pictures, one of the carpenter driving a crowd of pigs out of a man. They were real pigs, gray and sour-looking, and Mrs. Connin said Jesus had driven them all out of this one man. When she finished reading, she let him sit on the floor and look at the pictures again.

Just before they left for the healing, he had managed to get the book inside his innerlining without her seeing him. Now it made his coat hang down a little farther on one side than the other. His mind was dreamy and serene as they walked along and when they turned off the highway onto a long red clay road winding between banks of honeysuckle, he began to make wild leaps and pull forward on her hand as if he wanted to dash off and snatch the sun which was rolling away ahead of them now.

They walked on the dirt road for a while and then they crossed a field stippled with purple weeds and entered the shadows of a wood where the ground was covered with thick pine needles. He had never been in woods before and he walked carefully, looking from side to side as if he were entering a strange country. They moved along a bridle path that twisted downhill through crackling red leaves, and once, catching at a branch to keep himself from slipping, he looked into two frozen green-gold eyes enclosed in the darkness of a tree hole. At the bottom of the hill, the woods opened suddenly onto a pasture dotted here and there with black and white cows and sloping down, tier after tier, to a broad orange stream where the reflection of the sun was set like a diamond.

There were people standing on the near bank in a group, singing. Long tables were set up behind them and a few cars and trucks were parked in a road that came up by the river. They crossed the pasture, hurrying, because Mrs. Connin, using her hand for a shed over her eyes, saw the preacher already standing out in the water. She dropped her basket on one of the tables and pushed the three boys in front of her into the knot of people so that they wouldn't linger by the food. She kept Bevel by the hand and eased her way up to the front.

The preacher was standing about ten feet out in the stream where the water came up to his knees. He was a tall youth in khaki trousers that he had rolled up higher than the water. He had on a blue shirt and a red scarf around his neck but no hat and his light-colored hair was cut in sideburns that curved into the hollows of his cheeks. His face was all bone and red light reflected from the river. He looked as if he might have been nineteen years old. He was singing in a high twangy voice, above the singing on the bank, and he kept his hands behind him and his head tilted back.

He ended the hymn on a high note and stood silent, looking down at the water and shifting his feet in it. Then he looked up at the people on the bank. They stood close together, waiting; their faces were solemn but expectant and every eye was on him. He shifted his feet again.

"Maybe I know why you come," he said in the twangy voice, "maybe I don't."

"If you ain't come for Jesus, you ain't come for me. If you just come to see can you leave your pain in the river, you ain't come for Jesus. You can't leave your pain in the river," he said. "I never told nobody that." He stopped and looked down at his knees.

"I seen you cure a woman oncet!" a sudden high voice shouted from the hump of people. "Seen that woman git up and walk out straight where she had limped in!"

The preacher lifted one foot and then the other. He seemed almost but not quite to smile. "You might as well go home if that's what you come for," he said.

Then he lifted his head and arms and shouted, "Listen to what I got to say, you people! There ain't but one river and that's the River of Life, made out of Jesus' Blood. That's the river you have to lay your pain in, in the River of Faith, in the River of Life, in the River of Love, in the rich red river of Jesus' Blood, you people!"

His voice grew soft and musical. "All the rivers come from that one River and go back to it like it was the ocean sea and if you believe, you can lay your pain in that River and get rid of it because that's the River that was made to carry sin. It's a River full of pain itself, pain itself, moving toward the Kingdom of Christ, to be washed away, slow, you people, slow as this here old red water river round my feet.

"Listen," he sang, "I read in Mark about an unclean man, I read in Luke about a blind man, I read in John about a dead man! Oh you people hear! The same blood that makes this River red, made that leper clean, made that blind man stare, made that dead man leap! You people with trouble," he cried, "lay it in that River of Blood, lay it in that River of Pain, and watch it move away toward the Kingdom of Christ."

While he preached, Bevel's eyes followed drowsily the slow circles of two silent birds revolving high in the air. Across the river there was a low red and gold grove of sassafras with hills of dark blue trees behind it and an occasional pine jutting over the skyline. Behind, in the distance, the city rose like a cluster of warts on the side of the mountain. The birds revolved downward and dropped lightly in the top of the highest pine and sat hunch-shouldered as if they were supporting the sky.

"If it's this River of Life you want to lay you pain in, then come up," the preacher said, "and lay your sorrow here. But don't be thinking this is the last of it because this old red river don't end here. This old red suffering stream goes on, you people, slow to the Kingdom of Christ. This old red river is good to Baptize in, good to lay your faith in, good to lay your pain in, but it ain't this muddy water here that saves you. I been all up and down this river this week," he said. "Tuesday I was in Fortune Lake, next day in Ideal, Friday me and my wife drove to Lulawillow to see a sick man there. Them people didn't see no healing," he said and his face burned redder for a second. "I never said they would."

While he was talking a fluttering figure had begun to move forward with a kind of butterfly movement—an old woman with flapping arms whose head wobbled as if it might fall off any second. She managed to lower herself at the edge of the bank and let her arms churn in the water. Then she bent farther and pushed her face down in it and raised herself up finally, streaming wet; and still flapping, she turned a time or two in a blind circle until someone reached out and pulled her back into the group.

"She's been that way for thirteen years," a rough voice shouted. "Pass the hat and give this kid his money. That's what he's here for." The shout, directed out to the boy in the river, came from a huge old man who sat like a humped stone on the bumper of a long ancient gray automobile. He had on a gray hat that was turned down over one ear and up over the other to expose a purple bulge on his left temple. He sat bent forward with his hands hanging between his knees and his small eyes half closed.

Bevel stared at him once and then moved into the folds of Mrs. Connin's coat and hid himself.

The boy in the river glanced at the old man quickly and raised his fist. "Believe Jesus or the devil!" he cried. "Testify to one or the other!"

"I know from my own self-experience," a woman's mysterious voice called from the knot of people, "I know from it that this preacher can heal. My eyes have been opened! I testify to Jesus!"

The preacher lifted his arms quickly and began to repeat all that he had said before about the River and the Kingdom of Christ and the old man sat on the bumper, fixing him with a narrow squint. From time to time Bevel stared at him again from around Mrs. Connin.

A man in overalls and a brown coat leaned forward and dipped his hand in the water quickly and shook it and leaned back, and a woman held a baby over the edge of the bank and splashed its feet with water. One man moved a little distance away and sat down on the bank and took off his shoes and waded out into the stream; he stood there for a few minutes with his face tilted as far back as it would go, then he waded back and put on his shoes. All this time, the preacher sang and did not appear to watch what went on.

As soon as he stopped singing, Mrs. Connin lifted Bevel up and said, "Listen here, preacher, I got a boy from town today that I'm keeping. His mamma's sick and he wants you to pray for her. And this is a coincident—his name is Bevel! Bevel," she said, turning to look at the people behind her, "same as his. Ain't that a coincident, though?"

There were some murmurs and Bevel turned and grinned over her shoulder at the faces looking at him. "Bevel," he said in a loud jaunty voice.

"Listen," Mrs. Connin said, "have you ever been Baptized, Bevel?"

He only grinned.

"I suspect he ain't ever been Baptized," Mrs. Connin said, raising her eyebrows at the preacher.

"Swang him over here," the preacher said and took a stride forward and caught him.

He held him in the crook of his arm and looked at the grinning face. Bevel rolled his eyes in a comical way and thrust his face forward, close to the preacher's. "My name is Bevvvuuuuul," he said in a loud deep voice and let the tip of his tongue slide across his mouth.

The preacher didn't smile. His bony face was rigid and his narrow gray eyes reflected the almost colorless sky. There was a loud laugh from the old man sitting on the car bumper and Bevel grasped the back of the preacher's collar and held it tightly. The grin had already disappeared from his face. He had the sudden feeling that this was not a joke. Where he lived everything was a joke. From the preacher's face, he knew immediately that nothing the preacher said or did was a joke. "My mother named me that," he said quickly.

"Have you ever been Baptized?" the preacher asked.

"What's that?" he murmured.

"If I Baptize you," the preacher said, "you'll be able to go to the Kingdom of Christ. You'll be washed in the river of suffering, son, and you'll go by the deep river of life. Do you want that?"

"Yes," the child said, and thought, I won't go back to the apartment then, I'll go under the river.

"You won't be the same again," the preacher said. "You'll count." Then he turned his face to the people and began to preach and Bevel looked over his shoulder at the pieces of the white sun scattered in the river. Suddenly the preacher said, "All right, I'm going to Baptize you now," and without more warning, he tightened his hold and swung him upside down and plunged his head into the water. He held him under while he said the words of Baptism and then he jerked him up again and looked sternly at the gasping child. Bevel's eyes were dark and dilated. "You count now," the preacher said. "You didn't even count before."

The little boy was too shocked to cry. He spit out the muddy water and rubbed his wet sleeve into his eyes and over his face.

"Don't forget his mamma," Mrs. Connin called. "He wants you to pray for his mamma. She's sick."

"Lord," the preacher said, "we pray for somebody in affliction who isn't here to testify. Is your mother sick in the hospital?" he asked. "Is she in pain?"

The child stared at him. "She hasn't got up yet," he said in a high dazed voice. "She has a hangover." The air was so quiet he could hear the broken pieces of the sun knocking in the water.

The preacher looked angry and startled. The red drained out of his face and the sky appeared to darken in his eyes. There was a loud guffaw from the bank and Mr. Paradise shouted, "Haw! Cure the afflicted woman with the hangover!" and began to beat his knee with his fist.

"He's had a long day," Mrs. Connin said, standing with him in the door of the apartment and looking sharply into the room where the party was going on. "I reckon it's past his regular bedtime." One of Bevel's eyes was closed and the other half closed; his nose was running and he kept his mouth open and breathed through it. The damp plaid coat dragged down on one side.

That would be her, Mrs. Connin decided, in the black britches—long black satin britches and barefoot sandals and red toenails. She was lying on half the sofa, with her knees crossed in the air and her head propped on the arm. She didn't get up.

"Hello Harry," she said. "Did you have a big day?" She had a long pale face, smooth and blank, and straight sweet-potato-colored hair, pulled back.

The father went off to get the money. There were two other couples. One of the men, blond with little violet-blue eyes, leaned out of his chair and said, "Well Harry, old man, have a big day?"

"His name ain't Harry. It's Bevel," Mrs. Connin said.

"His name is Harry," *she* said from the sofa. "Whoever heard of anybody named Bevel?"

The little boy had seemed to be going to sleep on his feet, his head drooping farther and farther forward; he pulled it back suddenly and opened one eye; the other was stuck.

"He told me this morning his name was Bevel," Mrs. Connin said in a shocked voice. "The same as our preacher. We been all day at a preaching and healing at the river. He said his name was Bevel, the same as the preacher's. That's what he told me."

"Bevel!" his mother said. "My God! what a name."

"This preacher is name Bevel and there's no better preacher around," Mrs. Connin said. "And furthermore," she added in a defiant tone, "he Baptized this child this morning!"

His mother sat straight up. "Well the nerve!" she muttered.

"Furthermore," Mrs. Connin said, "he's a healer and he prayed for you to be healed."

"Healed!" she almost shouted. "Healed of what for Christ's sake?"

"Of your affliction," Mrs. Connin said icily.

The father had returned with the money and was standing near Mrs. Connin waiting to give it to her. His eyes were lined with red threads. "Go on, go on," he said, "I want to hear more about her affliction. The exact nature of it has escaped . . ." He waved the bill and his voice trailed off. "Healing by prayer is mighty inexpensive," he murmured.

Mrs. Connin stood a second, staring into the room, with a skeleton's appearance of seeing everything. Then, without taking the money, she turned and shut the door behind her. The father swung around, smiling vaguely, and shrugged. The rest of them were looking at Harry. The little boy began to shamble toward the bedroom.

"Come here, Harry," his mother said. He automatically shifted his direction toward her without opening his eye any farther. "Tell me what happened today," she said when he reached her. She began to pull off his coat.

"I don't know," he muttered.

"Yes you do know," she said, feeling the coat heavier on one side. She unzipped the innerlining and caught the book and a dirty handkerchief as they fell out. "Where did you get these?"

"I don't know," he said and grabbed for them. "They're mine. She gave them to me."

She threw the handkerchief down and held the book too high for him to reach and began to read it, her face after a second assuming an exaggerated comical expression. The others moved around and looked at it over her shoulder. "My God," somebody said.

One of the men peered at it sharply from behind a thick pair of glasses. "That's valuable," he said. "That's a collector's item," and he took it away from the rest of them and retired to another chair.

"Don't let George go off with that," his girl said.

"I tell you it's valuable," George said. "1832."

Bevel shifted his direction again toward the room where he slept. He shut the door behind him and moved slowly in the darkness to the bed and sat down and took off his shoes and got under the cover. After a minute a shaft of light let in the tall silhouette of his mother. She tiptoed lightly across the room and sat down on the edge of his bed. "What did that dolt of a preacher say about me?" she whispered. "What lies have you been telling today, honey?"

He shut his eye and heard her voice from a long way away, as if he were under the river and she on top of it. She shook his shoulder. "Harry," she said, leaning down and putting her mouth to his ear, "tell me what he said." She pulled him into a sitting position and he felt as if he had been drawn up from under the river. "Tell me," she whispered and her bitter breath covered his face.

He saw the pale oval close to him in the dark. "He said I'm not the same now," he muttered. "I count."

After a second, she lowered him by his shirt front onto the pillow. She hung over him an instant and brushed her lips against his forehead. Then she got up and moved away, swaying her hips lightly through the shaft of light.

He didn't wake up early but the apartment was still dark and close when he did. For a while he lay there, picking his nose and eyes. Then he sat up in bed and looked out the window. The sun came in palely, stained gray by the glass. Across the street at the Empire Hotel, a colored cleaning woman was looking down from an upper window, resting her face on her folded arms. He got up and put on his shoes and went to the bathroom and then into the front room. He ate two crackers spread with anchovy paste, that he found on the coffee table, and drank some ginger ale left in a bottle and looked around for his book but it was not there.

The apartment was silent except for the faint humming of the refrigerator. He went into the kitchen and found some raisin bread heels and spread a half jar of peanut butter between them and climbed up on the tall kitchen stool and sat chewing the sandwich slowly, wiping his nose every now and then on his shoulder. When he finished he found some chocolate milk and drank that. He would rather have had the ginger ale he saw but they left the bottle openers where he couldn't reach them. He studied what was left in the refrigerator for a while—some shriveled vegetables that she had forgot were there and a lot of brown oranges that she bought and didn't squeeze; there were three or four kinds of cheese and something fishy in a paper bag; the rest was a pork bone. He left the refrigerator door open and wandered back into the dark living room and sat down on the sofa.

He decided they would be out cold until one o'clock and that they would all have to go to a restaurant for lunch. He wasn't high enough for the table yet and the waiter would bring a highchair and he was too big for a highchair. He sat in the middle of the sofa, kicking it with his heels. Then he got up and wandered around the room, looking into the ashtrays at the butts as if this might be a habit. In his own room he had picture books and blocks but they were for the most part torn up; he found the way to get new ones was to tear up the ones he had. There was very little to do at any time but eat; however, he was not a fat boy.

He decided he would empty a few of the ashtrays on the floor. If he only emptied a few, she would think they had fallen. He emptied two, rubbing the ashes carefully into the rug with his finger. Then he lay on the floor for a while, studying his feet which he held up in the air. His shoes were still damp and he began to think about the river.

Very slowly, his expression changed as if he were gradually seeing appear what he didn't know he'd been looking for. Then all of a sudden he knew what he wanted to do.

He got up and tiptoed into their bedroom and stood in the dim light there, looking for her pocketbook. His glance passed her long pale arm hanging off the edge of the bed down to the floor, and across the white mound his father made, and past the crowded bureau, until it rested on the pocketbook hung on the back of a chair. He took a car-token out of it and half a package of Life Savers. Then he left the apartment and caught the car at the corner. He hadn't taken a suitcase because there was nothing from there he wanted to keep.

He got off the car at the end of the line and started down the road he and Mrs. Connin had taken the day before. He knew there wouldn't be anybody at her house because the three boys and the girl went to school and Mrs. Connin had told him she went out to clean. He passed her yard and walked on the way they had gone to the river. The paper brick houses were far apart and after a while the dirt place to walk on ended and he had to walk on the edge of the highway. The sun was pale yellow and high and hot.

He passed a shack with an orange gas pump in front of it but he didn't see the old man looking out at nothing in particular from the doorway. Mr. Paradise was having an orange drink. He finished it slowly, squinting over the bottle at the small plaid-coated figure disappearing down the road. Then he set the empty bottle on a bench and, still squinting, wiped his sleeve over his mouth. He went in the shack and picked out a peppermint stick, a foot long and two inches thick, from the candy shelf, and stuck it in his hip pocket. Then he got in his car and drove slowly down the highway after the boy.

By the time Bevel came to the field speckled with purple weeds, he was dusty and sweating and he crossed it at a trot to get into the woods as fast as he could. Once inside, he wandered from tree to tree, trying to find the path they had taken yesterday. Finally he found a line worn in the pine needles and followed it until he saw the steep trail twisting down through the trees.

Mr. Paradise had left his automobile back some way on the road and had walked to the place where he was accustomed to sit almost every day, holding an unbaited fishline in the water while he stared at the river passing in front of him. Anyone looking at him from a distance would have seen an old boulder half hidden in the bushes.

Bevel didn't see him at all. He only saw the river, shimmering reddish yellow, and bounded into it with his shoes and his coat on and took a gulp. He swallowed some and spit the rest out and then he stood there in water up to his chest and looked around him. The sky was a clear pale blue, all in one piece —except for the hole the sun made—and fringed around the bottom with treetops. His coat floated to the surface and surrounded him like a strange gay lily pad and he stood grinning in the sun. He intended not to fool with preachers any more but to Baptize himself and to keep on going this time until he found the Kingdom of Christ in the river. He didn't mean to waste any more time. He put his head under the water at once and pushed forward.

In a second he began to gasp and sputter and his head reappeared on the surface; he started under again and the same thing happened. The river wouldn't have him. He tried again and came up, choking. This was the way it had been when the preacher held him under—he had had to fight with something that pushed him back in the face. He stopped and thought suddenly: it's another joke, it's just another joke! He thought how far he had come for nothing and he began to hit and splash and kick the filthy river. His feet were already treading on nothing. He gave one low cry of pain and indignation. Then he heard a shout and turned his head and saw something like a giant pig bounding after him, shaking a red and white club and shouting. He plunged under once and this time, the waiting current caught him like a long gentle hand and pulled him swiftly forward and down. For an instant he was overcome with surprise; then since he was moving quickly and knew that he was getting somewhere, all his fury and his fear left him.

Mr. Paradise's head appeared from time to time on the surface of the water. Finally, far downstream, the old man rose like some ancient water monster and stood empty-handed, staring with his dull eyes as far down the river line as he could see.

afterword

In "The River," a young boy, ignored by his super-sophisticated parents, who care more about cocktail parties than they do about him, finds fulfillment in the fundamentalist religion into which he has been initiated by his babysitter and the faith-healing minister in whom she believes. Baptized at the river, the boy experiences a longing for heaven familiar to many Southern fundamentalists, but completely alien to the milieu in which he has been brought up. Not really understanding the ceremony at the river, the boy returns there and drowns himself seeking the heaven about which the minister has spoken.

One might suppose that O'Connor's tone here as she describes this forlorn child's seemingly futile search for happiness is one of unrelieved bitterness and despair. However, this is not the case, for it is O'Connor's belief that God saves people in spite of themselves. Thus, in her terms, even though the boy is operating upon his own imperfect comprehension of an imperfect religion and destroys himself in the process, ultimately he is not lost, for God's grace is all-encompassing. Indeed, this story is one of affirmation. Miss O'Connor once stated that one of her major themes was "the conflict between an attraction to the Holy and the disbelief in it that we breathe in with the times," and in this story little Bevel attains a belief in the Holy which enables him to escape the ugliness and skepticism of a world which hurts him.

questions for general discussion

1. Why does the little boy assume the preacher's name?

2. What is the effect of the scene describing little Bevel's introduction to real hogs?

3. How is the story's title affected by preacher Bevel Summers' shouted words: "Listen to what I got to say, you people! There ain't but one river and that's the River of Life. . . . That's the river you have to lay your pain in. . . ."?

4. Comment on the devices, such as similes and metaphors, which Miss O'Connor uses in describing her characters.

5. What is the theme of this story?

suggestions for writing

1. Comment on the contrasts of two ways of living reflected in little Bevel's thinking that "Where he lived everything was a joke. From the preacher's face, he knew immediately that nothing the preacher said or did was a joke."

2. Develop a theme concerning the resolution of little Bevel's conflict with his home life. What, for instance, are the real implications of his declaration to his mother, "I'm not the same now. . . . I count"?

3. Comment on symbolic characters, actions, or situations in the story.

PETER TAYLOR
venus, cupid, folly and time

Their house alone would not have made you think there was anything so awfully wrong with Mr. Dorset or his old maid sister. But certain things about the way both of them dressed had, for a long time, annoyed and disturbed everyone. We used to see them together at the grocery store, for instance, or even in one of the big department stores downtown, wearing their bedroom slippers. Looking more closely we would sometimes see the cuff of a pajama top or the hem of a hitched up nightgown showing from underneath their ordinary daytime clothes. Such slovenliness in one's neighbors is so unpleasant that even husbands and wives in West Vesey Place, which was the street where the Dorsets lived, had got so they didn't like to joke about it with each other. Were the Dorsets, poor old things, losing their minds? If so, what was to be done about it? Some neighbors got so they would not even admit to themselves what they saw. And a child coming home with an ugly report on the Dorsets was apt to be told that it was time he learned to curb his imagination.

Mr. Dorset wore tweed caps and sleeveless sweaters. Usually he had his sweater stuffed down inside his trousers with his shirt tails. To the women and young girls in West Vesey Place this was extremely distasteful. It made them feel as though Mr. Dorset had just come from the bathroom and had got his sweater inside his trousers by mistake. There was, in fact, nothing about Mr. Dorset that was not offensive to the women. Even the old touring car he drove was regarded by most of them as a disgrace to the neighborhood. Parked out in front of his house, as it usually was, it seemed a worse violation of West Vesey's zoning than the house itself. And worst of all was seeing Mr. Dorset wash the car.

Mr. Dorset washed his own car! He washed it not back in the alley or in his driveway but out there in the street of West Vesey Place. This would usually be on the day of one of the parties which he and his sister liked to give for young people or on a day when they were going to make deliveries of the paper flowers or the home-grown figs which they sold to their friends. Mr. Dorset would appear in the street carrying two buckets of warm water and wearing a pair of skin-tight coveralls. The skin-tight coveralls, of khaki material but faded almost to flesh color, were still more offensive to the women and young girls than his way of wearing his sweaters. With sponges and chamois cloths and a large scrub brush (for use on the canvas top) the old fellow would fall to and scrub away, gently at first on the canvas top and more vigorously as he progressed to the hood and body, just as though the car were something alive. Neighbor children felt that he went after the headlights exactly as if he were scrubbing the poor car's ears. There was an element of brutality in the way he did it and yet an element of tenderness too. An old lady visiting in the neighborhood once said that it was like the cleansing of a sacrificial animal. I suppose it was some such feeling as this that made all women want to turn away their eyes whenever the spectacle of Mr. Dorset washing his car presented itself.

As for Mr. Dorset's sister, her behavior was in its way just as offensive as his. To the men and boys in the neighborhood it was she who seemed quite beyond the pale. She would come out on her front terrace at mid-day clad in a faded flannel bathrobe and with her dyed black hair all undone and hanging down her back like the hair of an Indian squaw. To us whose wives and mothers did not even come downstairs in their negligees, this was very unsettling. It was hard to excuse it even on the grounds that the Dorsets were too old and lonely and hard-pressed to care about appearances any more.

Moreover, there was a boy who had gone to Miss Dorset's house one morning in the early fall to collect for his paper route and saw this very Miss Louisa Dorset pushing a carpet sweeper about one of the downstairs rooms without a stitch of clothes on. He saw her through one of the little lancet windows that opened on the front loggia of the house, and he watched her for quite a long while. She was cleaning the house in preparation for a party they were giving for young people that night, and the boy said that when she finally got hot and tired she dropped down in an easy chair and crossed her spindly, blue veined, old legs and sat there completely naked, with her legs crossed and shaking one scrawny little foot, just as unconcerned as if she didn't care that somebody was likely to walk in on her at any moment. After a little bit the boy saw her get up again and go and lean across a table to arrange some paper flowers in a vase. Fortunately he was a nice boy, though he lived only on the edge of the West Vesey Place neighborhood, and he went away without ringing the doorbell or collecting for his paper that week. But he could not resist telling his friends about what he had seen. He said it was a sight he would never forget! And she an old lady more than sixty years old who, had she not been so foolish and self-willed, might have had a house full of servants to push that carpet sweeper for her!

This foolish pair of old people had given up almost everything in life for each other's sake. And it was not at all necessary. When they were young they could have come into a decent inheritance, or now that they were old they might have been provided for by a host of rich relatives. It was only a matter of their being a little tolerant—or even civil—toward their kinspeople. But this was something that old Mr. Dorset and his sister could never consent to do. Almost all their lives they had spoken of their father's kin as "Mama's in-laws" and of their mother's kin as "Papa's in-laws." Their family name was

Dorset, not on one side but on both sides. Their parents had been distant cousins. As a matter of fact, the Dorset family in the city of Chatham had once been so large and was so long established there that it would have been hard to estimate how distant the kinship might be. But still it was something that the old couple never liked to have mentioned. Most of their mother's close kin had, by the time I am speaking of, moved off to California, and most of their father's people lived somewhere up east. But Miss Dorset and her old bachelor brother found any contact, correspondence, even an exchange of Christmas cards with these in-laws intolerable. It was a case, so they said, of the in-laws respecting the value of the dollar above all else, whereas they, Miss Louisa and Mr. Alfred Dorset, placed importance on other things.

They lived in a dilapidated and curiously mutilated house on a street which, except for their own house, was the most splendid street in the entire city. Their house was one that you or I would have been ashamed to live in—even in the lean years of the early thirties. In order to reduce taxes the Dorsets had had the third story of the house torn away, leaving an ugly, flat-topped effect without any trim or ornamentation. Also they had had the south wing pulled down and had sealed the scars not with matching brick but with a speckled stucco that looked raw and naked. All this the old couple did in violation of the strict zoning laws of West Vesey Place, and for doing so they would most certainly have been prosecuted except that they were the Dorsets and except that this was during the depression when zoning laws weren't easy to enforce in a city like Chatham.

To the young people whom she and her brother entertained at their house once each year Miss Louisa Dorset liked to say: "We have given up everything for each other. Our only income is from our paper flowers and our figs." The old lady, though without showing any great skill or talent for it, made paper flowers. During the winter months her brother took her in that fifteen-year-old touring car of theirs, with its steering wheel on the wrong side and with isinglass side-curtains that were never taken down, to deliver these flowers to her customers. The flowers looked more like sprays of tinted potato chips than like any real flowers. Nobody could possibly have wanted to buy them except that she charged next to nothing for them and except that to people with children it seemed important to be on the Dorsets' list of worthwhile people. Nobody could really have wanted Mr. Dorset's figs either. He cultivated a dozen little bushes along the back wall of their house, covering them in the wintertime with some odd looking boxes which he had had constructed for the purpose. The bushes were very productive, but the figs they produced were dried up little things without much taste. During the summer months he and his sister went about in their car, with the side-curtains still up, delivering the figs to the same customers who bought the paper flowers. The money they made could hardly have paid for the gas it took to run the car. It was a great waste and it was very foolish of them.

And yet, despite everything, this foolish pair of old people, this same Miss Louisa and Mr. Alfred Dorset, had become social arbiters of a kind in our city. They had attained this position entirely through their fondness for giving an annual dancing party for young people. To *young* people—to *very* young people—the Dorsets' hearts went out. I don't mean to suggest that their hearts went out to orphans or to the children of the poor, for they were not foolish in that way. The guests at their little dancing parties were the thirteen and fourteen year-olds from families like the one they had long ago set themselves against, young people from the very houses to which, in season, they delivered their figs and their paper flowers. And when the night of one of their parties came round, it was in fact the custom for Mr. Alfred to go in the same old car and fetch all the invited guests to his house. His sister might explain to reluctant parents that this saved the children the embarrassment of being taken to their first dance by mommy or daddy. But the parents knew well enough that for twenty years the Dorsets had permitted no adult person, besides themselves, to put foot inside their house.

At those little dancing parties which the Dorsets gave, peculiar things went on—unsettling things to the boys and girls who had been fetched round in the old car. Sensible parents wished to keep their children away. Yet what could they do? For a Chatham girl to have to explain, a few years later, why she never went to a party at the Dorsets' was like having to explain why she had never been a debutante. For a boy it was like having to explain why he had not gone up east to school or even why his father hadn't belonged to the Chatham Racquet Club. If when you were thirteen or fourteen you got invited to the Dorsets' house, you went; it was the way of letting people know from the outset who you were. In a busy, modern city like Chatham you cannot afford to let people forget who you are—not for a moment, not at any age. Even the Dorsets knew that.

Many a little girl, after one of those evenings at the Dorsets', was heard to cry out in her sleep. When waked, or half waked, her only explanation might be: "It was just the fragrance from the paper flowers." Or: "I dreamed I could really smell the paper flowers." Many a boy was observed by his parents to seem "different" afterward. He became "secretive." The parents of the generation that had to attend those parties never pretended to understand what went on at the Dorsets' house. And even to those of us who were in that unlucky generation it seemed we were half a lifetime learning what really took place during our one evening under the Dorsets' roof. Before our turn to go ever came round we had for years been hearing about what it was like from older boys and girls. Afterward, we continued to hear about it from those who followed us. And, looking back on it, nothing about the one evening when you were actually there ever seemed quite so real as the glimpses and snatches which you got from those people before and after you—the second-hand impressions of the Dorsets' behavior, of things they said, of looks that passed between them.

Since Miss Dorset kept no servants she always opened her own door. I suspect that for the guests at her parties the sight of her opening her door, in her astonishing attire, came as the most violent shock of the whole evening. On these occasions she and her brother got themselves up as we had never seen them before and never would again. The old lady invariably wore a modish white evening gown, a garment perfectly fitted to her spare and scrawny figure and cut in such high fashion that it must necessarily have been new that year. And never to be worn but that one night! Her hair, long and thick and newly dyed for the occasion, would be swept upward and forward in a billowy mass which was topped by a corsage of yellow and coral paper flowers. Her cheeks and lips would be darkly rouged. On her long bony arms and her bare shoulders she would have applied some kind of suntan powder. Whatever else you had been led to expect of the evening, no one had ever warned you sufficiently about the radical change to be noted in her appearance—or in that of her brother, either. By the end of the party Miss Louisa might look as dowdy as ever, and Mr. Alfred a little worse than usual. But at the outset, when the party was assembling in their drawing room, even Mr. Alfred appeared resplendent in a nattily tailored tuxedo, with exactly the shirt, the collar, and the tie which fashion prescribed that year. His gray hair was nicely trimmed, his puffy old face freshly shaven. He was powdered with the same dark powder that his sister used. One felt even that his cheeks had been lightly touched with rouge.

A strange perfume pervaded the atmosphere of the house. The moment you set foot inside, this awful fragrance engulfed you. It was like a mixture of spicy incense and sweet attar of roses. And always, too, there was the profusion of paper flowers. The flowers were everywhere—on every cabinet and console, every inlaid table and carved chest, on every high, marble mantel piece, on the book shelves. In the entrance hall special tiers must have been set up to hold the flowers, because they were there in overpowering masses. They were in such abundance that it seemed hardly possible that Miss Dorset could have made them all. She must have spent weeks and weeks preparing them, even months, perhaps even the whole year between parties. When she went about delivering them to her customers, in the months following, they were apt to be somewhat faded and dusty; but on the night of the party the colors of the flowers seemed even more impressive and more unlikely than their number. They were fuchsia, they were chartreuse, they were coral, aquamarine, brown, they were even black.

Everywhere in the Dorsets' house too were certain curious illuminations and lighting effects. The source of the light was usually hidden and its purpose was never obvious at once. The lighting was a subtler element than either the perfume or the paper flowers, and ultimately it was more disconcerting. A shaft of lavender light would catch a young visitor's eye and lead it, seemingly without purpose, in among the flowers. Then just beyond the point where the strength of the light would begin to diminish, the eye would discover something. In a small aperture in the mass of flowers, or sometimes in a larger grotto-like opening, there would be a piece of sculpture—in the hall a plaster replica of Rodin's *The Kiss,* in the library an antique plaque of Leda and the Swan. Or just above the flowers would be hung a picture, usually a black and white print but sometimes a reproduction in color. On the landing of the stairway leading down to the basement ballroom was the only picture that one was likely to learn the title of at the time. It was a tiny color print of Bronzino's *Venus, Cupid, Folly and Time.* This picture was not even framed. It was simply tacked on the wall, and it had obviously been torn—rather carelessly, perhaps hurriedly—from a book or magazine. The title and the name of the painter were printed in the white margin underneath.

About these works of art most of us had been warned by older boys and girls; and we stood in painful dread of that moment when Miss Dorset or her brother might catch us staring at any one of their pictures or sculptures. We had been warned, time and again, that during the course of the evening moments would come when she or he would reach out and touch the other's elbow and indicate, with a nod or just the trace of a smile, some guest whose glance had strayed among the flowers.

To some extent the dread which all of us felt that evening at the Dorsets' cast a shadow over the whole of our childhood. Yet for nearly twenty years the Dorsets continued to give their annual party. And even the most sensible of parents were not willing to keep their children away.

But a thing happened finally which could almost have been predicted. Young people, even in West Vesey Place, will not submit forever to the prudent counsel of their parents. Or some of them won't. There was a boy named Ned Meriwether and his sister Emily Meriwether, who lived with their parents in West Vesey Place just one block away from the Dorsets' house. In November Ned and Emily were invited to the Dorsets' party, and because they dreaded it they decided to play a trick on everyone concerned—even on themselves, as it turned out. . . . They got up a plan for smuggling an uninvited guest into the Dorsets' party.

The parents of this Emily and Ned sensed that their children were concealing something from them and suspected that the two were up to mischief of some kind. But they managed to deceive themselves with the thought that it was only natural for young people—"mere children"—to be nervous about going to the Dorsets' house. And so instead of questioning them during the last hour before they left for the party, these sensible parents tried to do everything in their power to calm their two children. The boy and the girl, seeing that this was the case, took advantage of it.

"You must not go down to the front door with us when we leave," the daughter insisted to her mother. And she persuaded both Mr. and Mrs. Meriwether that after she and her brother were dressed for the party they should all wait together in the upstairs sitting room until Mr. Dorset came to fetch the two young people in his car.

When, at eight o'clock, the lights of the automobile appeared in the street below, the brother and sister were still upstairs—watching from the bay window of the family sitting room. They kissed Mother and Daddy goodbye and then they flew down the stairs and across the wide, carpeted entrance hall to a certain dark recess where a boy named Tom Bascomb was hidden. This boy was the uninvited guest whom Ned and Emily were going to smuggle into the party. They had left the front door unlatched for Tom, and from the upstairs window just a few minutes ago they had watched him come across their front lawn. Now in the little recess of the hall there was a quick exchange of overcoats and hats between Ned Meriwether and Tom Bascomb; for it was a feature of the plan that Tom should attend the party as Ned and that Ned should go as the uninvited guest.

In the darkness of the recess Ned fidgeted and dropped Tom Bascomb's coat on the floor. But the boy, Tom Bascomb, did not fidget. He stepped out into the light of the hall and began methodically getting into the overcoat which he would wear tonight. He was not a boy who lived in the West Vesey Place neighborhood (he was in fact the very boy who had once watched Miss Dorset cleaning house without any clothes on), and he did not share Emily's and Ned's nervous excitement about the evening. The sound of Mr. Dorset's footsteps outside did not disturb him. When both Ned and Emily stood frozen by that sound, he continued buttoning the unfamiliar coat and even amused himself by stretching forth one arm to observe how high the sleeve came on his wrist.

The doorbell rang, and from his dark corner Ned Meriwether whispered to his sister and to Tom: "Don't worry. I'll be at the Dorsets' in plenty of time."

Tom Bascomb only shrugged his shoulders at this reassurance. Presently when he looked at Emily's flushed face and saw her batting her eyes like a nervous monkey, a crooked smile played upon his lips. Then, at a sign from Emily, Tom followed her to the entrance door and permitted her to introduce him to old Mr. Dorset as her brother.

From the window of the upstairs sitting room the Meriwether parents watched Mr. Dorset and this boy and this girl walking across the lawn toward Mr. Dorset's peculiar-looking car. A light shone bravely and protectively from above the entrance of the house, and in its rays the parents were able to detect the strange angle at which Brother was carrying his head tonight and how his new fedora already seemed too small for him. They even noticed that he seemed a bit taller tonight.

"I hope it's all right," said the mother.

"What do you mean 'all right'?" the father asked petulantly.

"I mean—," the mother began, and then she hesitated. She did not want to mention that the boy out there did not look like their own Ned. It would have seemed to give away her feelings too much. "I mean that I wonder if I should have put Sister in that long dress at this age and let her wear my cape. I'm afraid the cape is really inappropriate. She's still young for that sort of thing."

"Oh," said the father, "I thought you meant something else."

"Whatever else did you think I meant, Edwin?" the mother said, suddenly breathless.

"I thought you meant the business we've discussed before," he said although this was of course not what he had thought she meant. He had thought she meant that the boy out there did not look like their Ned. To him it had seemed even that the boy's step was different from Ned's. "The Dorsets' parties," he said, "are not very nice affairs to be sending your children to, Muriel. That's all I thought you meant."

Taylor / Venus, Cupid, Folly and Time 99

"But we *can't* keep them away," the mother said defensively.

"Oh, it's just that they are growing up faster than we realize," said the father, glancing at his wife out of the corner of his eye.

By this time Mr. Dorset's car had pulled out of sight, and from downstairs Muriel Meriwether thought she heard another door closing. "What was that?" she said, putting one hand on her husband's.

"Don't be so jumpy," her husband said irritably, snatching away his hand. "It's the servants closing up in the kitchen."

Both of them knew that the servants had closed up in the kitchen long before this. Both of them had heard quite distinctly the sound of the side door closing as Ned went out. But they went on talking and deceiving themselves in this fashion during most of the evening.

Even before she opened the door to Mr. Dorset, little Emily Meriwether had known that there would be no difficulty about passing Tom Bascomb off as her brother. In the first place, she knew that without his spectacles Mr. Dorset could hardly see his hand before his face and knew that due to some silly pride he had he never put on his spectacles except when he was behind the wheel of his automobile. This much was common knowledge. In the second place, Emily knew from experience that neither he nor his sister ever made any real pretense of knowing one child in their general acquaintance from another. And so, standing in the doorway and speaking almost in a whisper, Emily had merely to introduce first herself and then her pretended brother to Mr. Dorset. After that the three of them walked in silence from her father's house to the waiting car.

Emily was wearing her mother's second best evening wrap, a white lapin cape which, on Emily, swept the ground. As she walked between the boy and the man, the touch of the cape's soft silk lining on her bare arms and on her shoulders spoke to her silently of a strange girl she had seen in her looking-glass upstairs tonight. And with her every step toward the car the skirt of her long taffeta gown whispered her own name to her: *Emily . . . Emily.* She heard it distinctly, and yet the name sounded unfamiliar. Once during this unreal walk from house to car she glanced at the mysterious boy, Tom Bascomb, longing to ask him—if only with her eyes—for some reassurance that she was really she. But Tom Bascomb was absorbed in his own irrelevant observations. With his head tilted back he was gazing upward at the nondescript winter sky where, among drifting clouds, a few pale stars were shedding their dull light alike on West Vesey Place and on the rest of the world. Emily drew her wrap tightly about her, and when presently Mr. Dorset held open the door to the back seat of his car she shut her eyes and plunged into the pitch-blackness of the car's interior.

Tom Bascomb was a year older than Ned Meriwether and he was nearly two years older than Emily. He had been Ned's friend first. He and Ned had played baseball together on Saturdays before Emily ever set eyes on him. Yet according to Tom Bascomb himself, with whom several of us older boys talked just a few weeks after the night he went to the Dorsets', Emily always insisted that it was she who had known him first. On what she based this false claim Tom could not say. And on the two or three other occasions when we got Tom to talk about that night, he kept saying that he didn't understand what it was that had made Emily and Ned quarrel over which of them knew him first and knew him better.

We could have told him what it was, I think. But we didn't. It would have been too hard to say to him that at one time or another all of us in West Vesey had had our Tom Bascombs. Tom lived with his parents in an apartment house on a wide thoroughfare known as Division Boulevard, and his only real connection with West Vesey Place was that that street was included in his paper route. During the early morning hours he rode his bicycle along West Vesey and along other quiet streets like it, carefully aiming a neatly rolled paper at the dark loggia, at the colonnaded porch, or at the ornamented doorway of each of the palazzos and chateaux and manor houses that glowered at him in the dawn. He was well thought of as a paper boy. If by mistake one of his papers went astray and lit on an upstairs balcony or on the roof of a porch, Tom would always take more careful aim and throw another. Even if the paper only went into the shrubbery, Tom got off his bicycle and fished it out. He wasn't the kind of boy to whom it would have occurred that the old fogies and the rich kids in West Vesey could very well get out and scramble for their own papers.

Actually, a party at the Dorsets' house was more a grand tour of the house than a real party. There was a half hour spent over very light refreshments (fruit jello, English tea biscuits, lime punch). There was another half hour ostensibly given to general dancing in the basement ballroom (to the accompaniment of victrola music). But mainly there was the tour. As the party passed through the house, stopping sometimes to sit down in the principal rooms, the host and hostess provided entertainment in the form of an almost continuous dialogue between themselves. This dialogue was famous and was full of interest, being all about how much the Dorsets had given up for each other's sake and about how much higher the tone of Chatham society used to be than it was nowadays. They would invariably speak of their parents, who had died within a year of each other when Miss Louisa and Mr. Alfred were still in their teens; they even spoke of their wicked in-laws. When their parents died, the wicked in-laws had first tried to make them sell the house, then had tried to separate them and send them away to boarding schools, and had ended by trying to marry them off to "just anyone." Their two grandfathers had still been alive in those days and each had had a hand in the machinations, after the failure of which each grandfather had disinherited them. Mr. Alfred and Miss Louisa spoke also of how, a few years later, a procession of "young nobodies" had come of their own accord trying to steal the two of them away from each other. Both he and she would scowl at the very recollection of those "just anybodies" and those "nobodies," those "would-be suitors" who always turned out to be misguided fortune-hunters and had to be driven away.

The Dorsets' **dialogue** usually began in the living room the moment Mr. Dorset returned with his last collection of guests. (He sometimes had to make five or six trips in the car.) There, as in other rooms afterward, they were likely to begin with a reference to the room itself or perhaps to some piece of furniture in the room. For instance, the extraordinary length of the drawing room—or reception room, as the Dorsets called it—would lead them to speak of an even longer room which they had had torn away from the house. "It grieved us, we wept," Miss Dorset would say, "to have Mama's French drawing room torn away from us."

"But we tore it away from ourselves," her brother would add, "as we tore away our in-laws—because we could not afford them." Both of them spoke in a fine declamatory style, but they frequently interrupted themselves with a sad little laugh which expressed something quite different from what they were saying and which seemed to serve them as an aside not meant for our ears.

"That was one of our greatest sacrifices," Miss Dorset would say, referring still to her mother's French drawing room.

And her brother would say: "But we knew the day had passed in Chatham for entertainments worthy of that room."

"It was the room which Mama and Papa loved best, but we gave it up because we knew, from our upbringing, which things to give up."

From this they might go on to anecdotes about their childhood. Sometimes their parents had left them for months or even a whole year at a time with only the housekeeper or with trusted servants to see after them. "You could trust servants then," they explained. And: "In those days parents could do that sort of thing, because in those days there was a responsible body of people within which your young people could always find proper companionship."

In the library, to which the party always moved from the drawing room, Mr. Dorset was fond of exhibiting snapshots of the house taken before the south wing was pulled down. As the pictures were passed around, the dialogue continued. It was often there that they told the story of how the in-laws had tried to force them to sell the house. "For the sake of economy!" Mr. Dorset would exclaim, adding an ironic "Ha ha!"

"As though money—" he would begin.

"As though money ever took the place," his sister would come in, "of living with your own kind."

"Or of being well born," said Mr. Dorset.

After the billiard room, where everyone who wanted it was permitted one turn with the only cue that there seemed to be in the house, and after the dining room, where it was promised refreshments would be served later, the guests would be taken down to the ballroom—purportedly for dancing. Instead of everyone's being urged to dance, however, once they were assembled in the ballroom, Miss Dorset would announce that she and her brother understood the timidity which young people felt about dancing and that all that she and he intended to do was to set the party a good example. . . . It was only Miss Louisa and Mr. Alfred who danced. For perhaps thirty minutes, in a room without light excepting that from a few weak bulbs concealed among the flowers, the old couple danced; and they danced with such grace and there was such perfect harmony in all their movements that the guests stood about in stunned silence, as if hypnotized. The Dorsets waltzed, they two-stepped, they even fox-trotted, stopping only long enough between dances for Mr. Dorset, amid general applause, to change the victrola record.

But it was when their dance was ended that all the effects of the Dorsets' careful grooming that night would have vanished. And, alas, they made no effort to restore themselves. During the remainder of the evening Mr. Dorset went about with his bow tie hanging limply on his damp shirtfront, a gold collar button shining above it. A strand of gray hair, which normally covered his bald spot on top, now would have fallen on the wrong side of his part and hung like fringe about his ear. On his face and neck the thick layer of powder was streaked with perspiration. Miss Dorset was usually in an even more dishevelled state, depending somewhat upon the fashion of her dress that year. But always her powder was streaked, her lipstick entirely gone, her hair falling down on all sides, and her corsage dangling somewhere about the nape of her neck. In this condition they led the party upstairs again, not stopping until they had reached the second floor of the house.

On the second floor we—the guests—were shown the rooms which the Dorsets' parents had once occupied (The Dorsets' own rooms were never shown). We saw, in glass museum cases along the hallway, the dresses and suits and hats and even the shoes which Miss Louisa and Mr. Alfred had worn to parties when they were very young. And now the dialogue, which had been left off while the Dorsets danced, was resumed. "Ah, the happy time," one of them would say, "was when we were *your* age!" And then, exhorting us to be happy and gay while we were still safe in the bosom of our own kind and before the world came crowding in on us with its ugly demands, the Dorsets would recall the happiness they had known when they were very young. This was their *pièce de résistance*. With many a wink and blush and giggle and shake of the forefinger—and of course standing before the whole party—they each would remind the other of his or her naughty behavior in some old-fashioned parlor game or of certain silly little flirtations which they had long ago caught each other in.

They were on their way downstairs again now, and by the time they had finished with this favorite subject they would be downstairs. They would be in the dark, flower-bedecked downstairs hall and just before entering the dining room for the promised refreshments: the fruit jello, the English tea biscuits, the lime punch.

And now for a moment Mr. Dorset bars the way to the dining room and prevents his sister from opening the closed door. "Now, my good friends," he says, "let us eat, drink, and be merry!"

"For the night is yet young," says his sister.

"Tonight you must be gay and carefree," Mr. Dorset enjoins.

"Because in this house we are all friends," Miss Dorset says. "We are all young, we all love one another."

"And love can make us all young forever," her brother says.

"Remember!"

"Remember this evening always, sweet young people!"

"Remember!"

"Remember what our life is like here!"

And now Miss Dorset, with one hand on the knob of the great door which she is about to throw open, leans a little toward the guests and whispers hoarsely: "This is what it is like to be young forever!"

Ned Meriwether was waiting behind a big japonica shrub near the sidewalk when, about twenty minutes after he had last seen Emily, the queer old touring car drew up in front of the Dorsets' house. During the interval, the car had gone from the Meriwether house to gather a number of other guests, and so it was not only Emily and Tom who alighted on the sidewalk before the Dorsets' house. The group was just large enough to make it easy for Ned to slip out from his dark hiding place and join them without being noticed by Mr. Dorset. And now the group was escorted rather unceremoniously up to the door of the house, and Mr. Dorset departed to fetch more guests.

They were received at the door by Miss Dorset. Her eyesight was no doubt better than her brother's, but still there was really no danger of her detecting an uninvited guest. Those of us who had gone to that house in the years just before Ned and Emily came along, could remember that during a whole evening, when their house was full of young people, the Dorsets made no introductions and made no effort to distinguish which of their guests was which. They did not even make a count of heads. Perhaps they did vaguely recognize some of the faces, because sometimes when they had come delivering figs or paper flowers to a house they had of necessity encountered a young child there, and always they smiled sweetly at it, asked its age, and calculated on their old fingers how many years must pass before the child would be eligible for an invitation. Yet at those moments something in the way they had held up their fingers and in the way they had gazed *at* the little face instead of into it had revealed their lack of interest in the individual child. And later when the child was finally old enough to receive their invitation he found it was still no different with the Dorsets. Even in their own house it was evidently to the young people as a group that the Dorsets' hearts went out; while they had the boys and girls under their roof they herded them about like so many little thoroughbred calves. Even when Miss Dorset opened the front door she did so exactly as though she were opening a gate. She pulled it open very slowly, standing half behind it to keep out of harm's way. And the children, all huddled together, surged in.

How meticulously this Ned and Emily Meriwether must have laid their plans for that evening! And the whole business might have come out all right if only they could have foreseen the effect which one part of their plan— rather a last minute embellishment of it—would produce upon Ned himself. Barely ten minutes after they entered the house Ned was watching Tom as he took his seat on the piano bench beside Emily. Ned probably watched Tom closely, because certainly he knew what the next move was going to be. The moment Miss Louisa Dorset's back was turned Tom Bascomb slipped his arm gently about Emily's little waist and commenced kissing her all over her pretty face. It was almost as if he were kissing away tears.

This spectacle on the piano bench, and others like it which followed, had been an inspiration of the last day or so before the party. Or so Ned and Emily maintained afterward when defending themselves to their parents. But no matter when it was conceived, a part of their plan it was, and Ned must have believed himself fully prepared for it. Probably he expected to join in the round of giggling which it produced from the other guests. But now that the time had come—it is easy to imagine—the boy Ned Meriwether found himself not quite able to join in the fun. He watched with the others, but he was not quite infected by their laughter. He stood a little apart, and possibly he was hoping that Emily and Tom would not notice his failure to appreciate the success of their comedy. He was no doubt baffled by his own feelings, by the failure of his own enthusiasm, and by a growing desire to withdraw himself from the plot and from the party itself.

It is easy to imagine Ned's uneasiness and confusion that night. And I believe the account which I have given of Emily's impressions and her delicate little sensations while on the way to the party has the ring of truth about it, though actually the account was supplied by girls who knew her only slightly, who were not at the party, who could not possibly have seen her afterward. It may, after all, represent only what other girls imagined she would have felt. As for the account of how Mr. and Mrs. Meriwether spent the evening, it is their very own. And they did not hesitate to give it to anyone who would listen.

It was a long time, though, before many of us had a clear picture of the main events of the evening. We heard very soon that the parties for young people were to be no more, that there had been a wild scramble and chase through the Dorsets' house, and that it had ended by the Dorsets locking some boy—whether Ned or Tom was not easy to determine at first—in a queer sort of bathroom in which the plumbing had been disconnected, and even the fixtures removed, I believe. (Later I learned that there was nothing literally sinister about the bathroom itself. By having the pipes disconnected to this, and perhaps other bathrooms, the Dorsets had obtained further reductions in their taxes.) But a clear picture of the whole evening wasn't to be had—not without considerable searching. For one thing, the Meriwether parents immediately, within a week after the party, packed their son and daughter off to boarding schools. Accounts from the other children were contradictory and vague—perversely so, it seemed. Parents reported to each other that the little girls had nightmares which were worse even than those which their older sisters had had. And the boys were secretive and elusive, even with us older boys when we questioned them about what had gone on.

One sketchy account of events leading up to the chase, however, did go the rounds almost at once. Ned must have written it back to some older boy in a letter, because it contained information which no one but Ned could have had. The account went like this: When Mr. Dorset returned from his last round-up of guests, he came hurrying into the drawing room where the others were waiting and said in a voice trembling with excitement: "Now, let us all be seated, my young friends, and let us warm ourselves with some good talk."

At that moment everyone who was not already seated made a dash for a place on one of the divans or love seats or even in one of the broad window seats. (There were no individual chairs in the room.) Everyone made a dash, that is, except Ned. Ned did not move. He remained standing beside a little table rubbing his fingers over its polished surface. And from this moment he was clearly an object of suspicion in the eyes of his host and hostess. Soon the party moved from the drawing room to the library, but in whatever room they stopped Ned managed to isolate himself from the rest. He would sit or stand looking down at his hands until once again an explosion of giggles filled the room. Then he would look up just in time to see Tom Bascomb's cheek against Emily's or his arm about her waist.

For nearly two hours Ned didn't speak a word to anyone. He endured the Dorsets' dialogue, the paper flowers, the perfumed air, the works of art. Whenever a burst of giggling forced him to raise his eyes he would look up at Tom and Emily and then turn his eyes away. Before looking down at his hands again he would let his eyes travel slowly about the room until they came to rest on the figures of the two Dorsets. That, it seems, was how he happened to discover that the Dorsets understood, or thought they understood, what the giggles meant. In the great mirror mounted over the library mantel he saw them exchanging half suppressed smiles. Their smiles lasted precisely as long as the giggling continued, and then, in the mirror, Ned saw their faces change and grow solemn when their eyes—their identical, tiny, dull, amber colored eyes—focused upon himself.

From the library the party continued on the regular tour of the house. At last when they had been to the ballroom and watched the Dorsets dance, had been upstairs to gaze upon the faded party clothes in the museum cases, they descended into the downstairs hall and were just before being turned into the dining room. The guests had already heard the Dorsets teasing each other about the silly little flirtations and about their naughtiness in parlor games when they were young and had listened to their exhortations to be gay and happy and carefree. Then just when Miss Dorset leaned toward them and whispered, "This is what it is like to be young forever," there rose a chorus of laughter, breathless and shrill, yet loud and intensely penetrating.

Ned Meriwether, standing on the bottom step of the stairway, lifted his eyes and looked over the heads of the party to see Tom and Emily half hidden in a bower of paper flowers and caught directly in a ray of mauve light. The two had squeezed themselves into a little niche there and stood squarely in front of the Rodin statuary. Tom had one arm placed about Emily's shoulders and he was kissing her lightly first on the lobe of one ear and then on the tip of her nose. Emily stood as rigid and pale as the plaster sculpture behind her and with just the faintest smile on her lips. Ned looked at the two of them and then turned his glance at once on the Dorsets.

He found Miss Louisa and Mr. Alfred gazing quite openly at Tom and Emily and frankly grinning at the spectacle. It was more than Ned could endure. "Don't you *know?*" he wailed, as if in great physical pain. "Can't you *tell?* Can't you see who they *are?* They're *brother* and *sister!*"

From the other guests came one concerted gasp. And then an instant later, mistaking Ned's outcry to be something he had planned all along and probably intended—as they imagined—for the very cream of the jest, the whole company burst once again into laughter—not a chorus of laughter this time but a volley of loud guffaws from the boys, and from the girls a cacophony of separately articulated shrieks and trills.

None of the guests present that night could—or would—give a satisfactory account of what happened next. Everyone insisted that he had not even looked at the Dorsets, that he, or she, didn't know how Miss Louisa and Mr. Alfred reacted at first. Yet this was precisely what those of us who had gone there in the past *had* to know. And when finally we did manage to get an account of it, we knew that it was a very truthful and accurate one. Because we got it, of course, from Tom Bascomb.

Since Ned's outburst came after the dancing exhibition, the Dorsets were in their most dishevelled state. Miss Louisa's hair was fallen half over her face, and that long, limp strand of Mr. Alfred's was dangling about his left ear. Like that, they stood at the doorway to the dining room grinning at Tom Bascomb's antics. And when Tom Bascomb, hearing Ned's wail, whirled about, the grins were still on the Dorsets' faces even though the guffaws and the shrieks of laughter were now silenced. Tom said that for several moments they continued to wear their grins like masks and that you couldn't really tell how they were taking it all until presently Miss Louisa's face, still wearing the grin, began turning all the queer colors of her paper flowers. Then the grin vanished from her lips and her mouth fell open and every bit of color went out of her face. She took a step backward and leaned against the doorjamb with her mouth still open and her eyes closed. If she hadn't been on her feet, Tom said he would have thought she was dead. Her brother didn't look at her, but his own grin had vanished just as hers did, and his face, all drawn and wrinkled, momentarily turned a dull copperish green.

Presently, though, he too went white, not white in faintness but in anger. His little brown eyes now shone like rosin. And he took several steps toward Ned Meriwether. "What we know is that you are not one of us," he croaked. "We have perceived that from the beginning! We don't know how you got here or who you are. But the important question is, What are you doing here among these nice children?"

The question seemed to restore life to Miss Louisa. Her amber eyes popped wide open. She stepped away from the door and began pinning up her hair which had fallen down on her shoulders, and at the same time addressing the guests who were huddled together in the center of the hall. "Who is he, children? He is an intruder, that we know. If you know who he is, you must tell us."

"Who *am* I? Why, I am Tom Bascomb!" shouted Ned, still from the bottom step of the stairway. "I am Tom Bascomb, your paper boy!"

Then he turned and fled up the stairs toward the second floor. In a moment Mr. Dorset was after him.

To the real Tom Bascomb it had seemed that Ned honestly believed what he had been saying; and his own first impulse was to shout a denial. But being a level-headed boy and seeing how bad things were, Tom went instead to Miss Dorset and whispered to her that Tom Bascomb was a pretty tough guy and that she had better let *him* call the police for her. She told him where the telephone was in the side hall, and he started away.

But Miss Dorset changed her mind. She ran after Tom telling him not to call. Some of the guests mistook this for the beginning of another chase. Before the old lady could overtake Tom, however, Ned himself had appeared in the doorway toward which she and Tom were moving. He had come down the back stairway and he was calling out to Emily, "We're going *home,* Sis!"

A cheer went up from the whole party. Maybe it was this that caused Ned to lose his head, or maybe it was simply the sight of Miss Dorset rushing at him that did it. At any rate, the next moment he was running up the front stairs again, this time with Miss Dorset in pursuit.

When Tom returned from the telephone, all was quiet in the hall. The guests—everybody except Emily—had moved to the foot of the stairs and they were looking up and listening. From upstairs Tom could hear Ned saying, "All right. All right. All right." The old couple had him cornered.

Emily was still standing in the little niche among the flowers. And it is the image of Emily Meriwether standing among the paper flowers that tantalizes me whenever I think or hear someone speak of that evening. That, more than anything else, can make me wish that I had been there. I shall never cease to wonder what kind of thoughts were in her head to make her seem so oblivious to all that was going on while she stood there, and, for that matter, what had been in her mind all evening while she endured Tom Bascomb's caresses. When, in years since, I have had reason to wonder what some girl or woman is thinking—some Emily grown older—my mind nearly always returns to the image of that girl among the paper flowers. Tom said that when he returned from the telephone she looked very solemn and pale still but that her mind didn't seem to be on any of the present excitement. Immediately he went to her and said, "Your dad is on his way over, Emily." For it was the Meri-wether parents he had telephoned, of course, and not the police.

It seemed to Tom that so far as he was concerned the party was now over. There was nothing more he could do. Mr. Dorset was upstairs guarding the door to the strange little room in which Ned was locked up. Miss Dorset was serving lime punch to the other guests in the dining room, all the while listening with one ear for the arrival of the police whom Tom pretended he had called. When the doorbell finally rang and Miss Dorset hurried to answer it, Tom slipped quietly out through the pantry and through the kitchen and left the house by the back door as the Meriwether parents entered by the front.

There was no difficulty in getting Edwin and Muriel Meriwether, the children's parents, to talk about what happened after they arrived that night. Both of them were sensible and clear-headed people, and they were not so conservative as some of our other neighbors in West Vesey. Being fond of gossip of any kind and fond of reasonably funny stories on themselves, they told how their children had deceived them earlier in the evening and how they had deceived themselves later. They tended to blame themselves more than the children for what had happened. They tried to protect the children from any harm or embarrassment that might result from it by sending them off to boarding school. In their talk they never referred directly to Tom's reprehensible conduct or to the possible motives that the children might have had for getting up their plan. They tried to spare their children and they tried to spare Tom, but fortunately it didn't occur to them to try to spare the poor old Dorsets.

When Miss Louisa opened the door, Mr. Meriwether said, "I'm Edwin Meriwether, Miss Dorset. I've come for my son, Ned."

"And for your daughter Emily, I hope," his wife whispered to him.

"And for my daughter Emily."

Before Miss Dorset could answer him Edwin Meriwether spied Mr. Dorset descending the stairs. With his wife, Muriel, sticking close to his side Edwin now strode over to the foot of the stairs. "Mr. Dorset," he began, "my son Ned—"

From behind them, Edwin and Muriel now heard Miss Dorset saying, "All the invited guests are gathered in the dining room." From where they were standing the two parents could see into the dining room. Suddenly they turned and hurried in there. Mr. Dorset and his sister of course followed them.

Muriel Meriwether went directly to Emily who was standing in a group of girls. "Emily, where is your brother?"

Emily said nothing, but one of the boys answered: "I think they've got him locked up upstairs somewhere."

"Oh, no!" said Miss Louisa, a hairpin in her mouth—for she was still rather absent-mindedly working at her hair. "It is an intruder that my brother has upstairs."

Mr. Dorset began speaking in a confidential tone to Edwin. "My dear neighbor," he said, "our paper boy saw fit to intrude himself upon our company tonight. But we recognized him as an outsider from the start."

Muriel Meriwether asked: "Where *is* the paper boy? Where is the paper boy, Emily?"

Again one of the boys volunteered: "He went out through the back door, Mrs. Meriwether."

The eyes of Mr. Alfred and Miss Louisa searched the room for Tom. Finally their eyes met and they smiled coyly. "*All* the children are being mischievous tonight," said Miss Louisa, and it was quite as though she had said, "all *we* children." Then, still smiling, she said, "Your tie has come undone, Brother. Mr. and Mrs. Meriwether will hardly know what to think."

Mr. Alfred fumbled for a moment with his tie but soon gave it up. Now with a bashful glance at the Meriwether parents, and giving a nod in the direction of the children, he actually said, "I'm afraid we've all decided to play a trick on Mr. and Mrs. Meriwether."

Miss Louisa said to Emily: "We've hidden our brother somewhere, haven't we?"

Emily's mother said firmly: "Emily, tell me where Ned is."

"He's upstairs, Mother," said Emily in a whisper.

Emily's father said: "I wish you to take me to the boy upstairs, Mr. Dorset."

The coy, bashful expressions vanished from the faces of the two Dorsets. Their eyes were little dark pools of incredulity, growing narrower by the second. And both of them were now trying to put their hair in order. "Why, *we* know nice children when we see them," Miss Louisa said peevishly. There was a pleading quality in her voice, too. "We knew from the beginning that that boy upstairs didn't belong amongst us," she said. "Dear neighbors, it isn't just the money, you know, that makes the difference." All at once she sounded like a little girl about to burst into tears.

"It isn't just the money?" Edwin Meriwether repeated.

"Miss Dorset," said Muriel with new gentleness in her tone, as though she had just recognized that it was a little girl she was talking to, "there has been some kind of mistake—a misunderstanding."

Mr. Alfred Dorset said: "Oh, we wouldn't make a mistake of that kind! People *are* different. It isn't something you can put your finger on, but it isn't the money."

"I don't know what you're talking about," Edwin said, exasperated. "But I'm going upstairs and find that boy." He left the room with Mr. Dorset following him with quick little steps—steps like those of a small boy trying to keep up with a man.

Miss Louisa now sat down in one of the high-backed dining chairs which were lined up along the oak wainscot. She was trembling, and Muriel came and stood beside her. Neither of them spoke, and in almost no time Edwin Meriwether came downstairs again with Ned. Miss Louisa looked at Ned, and tears came into her eyes. "Where is my brother?" she asked accusingly, as though she thought possibly Ned and his father had locked Mr. Dorset in the bathroom.

"I believe he has retired," said Edwin. "He left us and disappeared into one of the rooms upstairs."

"Then I must go up to him," said Miss Louisa. For a moment she seemed unable to rise. At last she pushed herself up from the chair and walked from the room with the slow, steady gait of a somnambulist. Muriel Meriwether followed her into the hall and as she watched the old woman ascending the steps, leaning heavily on the rail, her impulse was to go and offer to assist her. But something made her turn back into the dining room. Perhaps she imagined that her daughter, Emily, might need her now.

The Dorsets did not reappear that night. After Miss Louisa went upstairs,

Muriel promptly got on the telephone and called the parents of some of the other boys and girls. Within a quarter of an hour half a dozen parents had assembled. It was the first time in many years that any adult had set foot inside the Dorset house. It was the first time that any parent had ever inhaled the perfumed air or seen the masses of paper flowers and the illuminations and the statuary. In the guise of holding consultations over whether or not they should put out the lights and lock up the house the parents lingered much longer than was necessary before taking the young people home. Some of them even tasted the lime punch. But in the presence of their children they made no comment on what had happened and gave no indication of what their own impressions were—not even their impressions of the punch. At last it was decided that two of the men should see to putting out the lights everywhere on the first floor and down in the ballroom. They were a long time in finding the switches for the indirect lighting. In most cases they simply resorted to unscrewing the bulbs. Meanwhile the children went to the large cloak closet behind the stairway and got their wraps. When Ned and Emily Meriwether rejoined their parents at the front door to leave the house, Ned was wearing his own overcoat and held his own fedora in his hand.

Miss Louisa and Mr. Alfred Dorset lived on for nearly ten years after that night, but they gave up selling their figs and paper flowers and of course they never entertained young people again. I often wonder if growing up in Chatham can ever have seemed quite the same since. Some of the terror must have gone out of it. Half the dread of coming of age must have vanished with the dread of the Dorsets' parties.

After that night, their old car would sometimes be observed creeping about town, but it was never parked in front of their house any more. It stood usually at the side entrance where the Dorsets could climb in and out of it without being seen. They began keeping a servant too—mainly to run their errands for them, I imagine. Sometimes it would be a man, sometimes a woman, never the same one for more than a few months at a time. Both of the Dorsets died during the Second World War while many of us who had gone to their parties were away from Chatham. But the story went round—and I am inclined to believe it—that after they were dead and the house was sold, Tom Bascomb's coat and hat were found still hanging in the cloak closet behind the stairs.

Tom himself was a pilot in the war and was a considerable hero. He was such a success and made such a name for himself that he never came back to Chatham to live. He found bigger opportunities elsewhere I suppose, and I don't suppose he ever felt the ties to Chatham that people with Ned's kind of upbringing do. Ned was in the war too, of course. He was in the navy and after the war he did return to Chatham to live, though actually it was not until then that he had spent much time here since his parents bundled him off to boarding school. Emily came home and made her début just two or three years before the war, but she was already engaged to some boy in the East; she never comes back any more except to bring her children to see their grandparents for a few days during Christmas or at Easter.

I understand that Emily and Ned are pretty indifferent to each other's existence nowadays. I have been told this by Ned Meriwether's own wife. Ned's wife maintains that the night Ned and Emily went to the Dorsets' party marked the beginning of this indifference, that it marked the end of their childhood intimacy and the beginning of a shyness, a reserve, even an animosity between them that was destined to be a sorrow forever to the two sensible parents who had sat in the upstairs sitting room that night waiting until the telephone call came from Tom Bascomb.

Ned's wife is a girl he met while he was in the navy. She was a Wave, and her background isn't the same as his. Apparently she isn't too happy with life in what she refers to as "Chatham proper." She and Ned have recently moved out into a suburban development, which she doesn't like either and which she refers to as "greater Chatham." She asked me at a party one night how Chatham got its name (She was just making conversation and appealing to my interest in such things) and when I told her that it was named for the Earl of Chatham and pointed out that the city is located in Pitt County she burst out laughing. "How very elegant," she said. "Why has nobody ever told me that before?" But what interests me most about Ned's wife is that after a few drinks she likes to talk about Ned and Emily and Tom Bascomb and the Dorsets. Tom Bascomb has become a kind of hero—and I don't mean a wartime hero—in her eyes, though of course not having grown up in Chatham she has never seen him in her life. But she is a clever girl, and there are times when she will say to me, "Tell me about Chatham. Tell me about the Dorsets." And I try to tell her. I tell her to remember that Chatham looks upon itself as a rather old city. I tell her to remember that it was one of the first English-speaking settlements west of the Alleghenies and that by the end of the American Revolution, when veterans began pouring westward over the Wilderness Road or down the Ohio River, Chatham was often referred to as a thriving village. Then she tells me that I am being dull, because it is hard for her to concentrate on any aspect of the story that doesn't center around Tom Bascomb and that night at the Dorsets'.

But I make her listen. Or at least one time I did. The Dorset family, I insisted on saying, was in Chatham even in those earliest times right after the Revolution, but they had come here under somewhat different circumstances from those of the other early settlers. How could that really matter, Ned's wife asked, after a hundred and fifty years? How could distinctions between the first settlers matter after the Irish had come to Chatham, after the Germans, after the Italians? Well, in West Vesey Place it could matter. It had to. If the distinction was false, it mattered all the more and it was all the more necessary to make it.

But let me interject here that Chatham is located in a state about whose history most Chatham citizens—not newcomers like Ned's wife, but old timers —have little interest and less knowledge. Most of us, for instance, are never even quite sure whether during the 1860's our state did secede or didn't secede. As for the city itself, some of us hold that it is geographically Northern and culturally Southern. Others say the reverse is true. We are all apt to want to feel misplaced in Chatham, and so we are not content merely to say that it is a border city. How you stand on this important question is apt to depend entirely on whether your family is one of those with a good Southern name or one that had its origin in New England, because those are the two main categories of old society families in Chatham.

But truly—I told Ned's wife—the Dorset family was never in either of those categories. The first Dorset had come, with his family and his possessions and even a little capital, direct from a city in the English Midlands to Chatham. The Dorsets came not as pioneers, but paying their way all the way. They had not bothered to stop for a generation or two to put down roots in Pennsylvania or Virginia or Massachusetts. And this was the distinction which some people wished always to make. Apparently those early Dorsets had cared no more for putting down roots in the soil of the New World than they had cared for whatever they had left behind in the Old. They were an obscure mercantile family who came to invest in a new western city. Within two generations the business—no, the industry!—which they established made them rich beyond any dreams they could have had in the beginning. For half a century they were looked upon, if any family ever was, as our first family.

And then the Dorsets left Chatham—practically all of them except the one old bachelor and the one old maid—left it just as they had come, not caring much about what they were leaving or where they were going. They were city people, and they were Americans. They knew that what they had in Chatham they could buy more of in other places. For them Chatham was an investment that had paid off. They went to live in Santa Barbara and Laguna Beach, in Newport and on Long Island. And the truth which it was so hard for the rest of us to admit was that, despite our families of Massachusetts and Virginia, we were all more like the Dorsets—those Dorsets who left Chatham—than we were *unlike* them. Their spirit was just a little closer to being the very essence of Chatham than ours was. The obvious difference was that we had to stay on here and pretend that our life had a meaning which it did not. And if it was only by a sort of chance that Miss Louisa and Mr. Alfred played the role of social arbiters among the young people for a number of years, still no one could honestly question their divine right to do so.

"It may have been their right," Ned's wife said at this point, "but just think what might have happened."

"It's not a matter of what might have happened," I said. "It is a matter of what did happen. Otherwise, what have you and I been talking about?"

"Otherwise," she said with an irrepressible shudder, "I would not be forever getting you off in a corner at these parties to talk about my husband and my husband's sister and how it is they care so little for each other's company nowadays?"

And I could think of nothing to say to that except that probably we had now pretty well covered our subject.

afterword

Peter Taylor, who frequently deals with the dark underside of apparently normal human relationships, writes in "Venus, Cupid, Folly and Time" of family situations and indeed citywide social situations which have gone awry. In this story we see at first glance an old, harmlessly eccentric couple, brother and sister, who pride themselves first on their devotion to each other and second on their innate ability as aristocrats to perceive and maintain social quality in others. However, a closer look reveals that their love for each other verges on the abnormal and that as social arbiters they are woefully deficient. Moreover, it reveals the hypocrisy of a town which on the one hand mocks the old couple, yet on the other lets the couple tyrannize them and their children for one strange night a year. The unfortunate emotions awakened in Ned and Emily as a result of their practical joke on the old couple are both an ironic parallel to the emotions long felt by the Dorsets and a lasting remembrance of their society's folly.

Peter Taylor was born in Tennessee in 1917 and attended schools in Memphis, Nashville, and St. Louis. He graduated from Kenyon College in 1940. During that year and the next he began writing seriously, publishing poems and short stories in the *Kenyon Review, Sewanee Review, Southern Review,* and *New Yorker.* After service in World War II, Taylor taught several years at the University of North Carolina at Greensboro. In 1950 he was awarded a Guggenheim fellowship. He now teaches at Kenyon College. His principal works include one novel, *A Woman of Means* (1950), and three collections of short stories, *A Long Fourth and Other Stories* (1948), *The Widows of Thornton* (1954), and *The Collected Stories of Peter Taylor* (1969).

questions for general discussion

1. An obsolete meaning for the word "Folly" is "wickedness or wantonness." Apply this meaning to the story's title and events.

2. What are some of the effects brought about by Peter Taylor's description of the Dorsets' strangely slovenly manners of dressing?

3. Do you view this story as a horror tale? Why?

4. Do you view the story as a comic tale? Why?

5. What purpose is served by the references to Rodin's sculpture, Bronzino's painting, and the plaque of Leda and the Swan?

6. Why do the Dorsets sell flowers and figs?

7. What is the effect of the phrase, "All of us in West Vesey had had our Tom Bascombs"?

8. What is the source of the influence which the Dorsets exert over the parents of 13 and 14 year old boys and girls in West Vesey?

suggestions for writing

1. Comment on the symbols in the story, exploring their meanings.

2. Citing specific examples which cause you to feel as you do about the story, comment on the story's atmosphere as being one of horror or comedy.

3. Comment on specific methods and devices which Peter Taylor uses in order to create characters.

4. Comment on the significance of various specific possessions or traits of the Dorsets.

5. Write an essay on what you feel to be the basic conflicts in the story.

6. Comment on the story's theme, pointing out those scenes or passages which support your idea.

JESSE HILL FORD
to the open water

When the teal leaped from the grass it flew up so swiftly that it was already out of range by the time he fired. At the sound of the shotgun a few blackjacks put up. They rose reluctantly in the cold air and circled a moment before flying straight up channel towards the neck of the bottoms.

He quickly climbed the embankment to the road and ran to the bridge to watch the ducks. Slicing through the sky like arrows, they flew almost out of sight before they veered left, folded suddenly into a soft spiral, and went down beyond the trees.

The open water would be there, where they went down. He knew the place, a logjam island. It would be, perhaps, the only open water to be found on such a day when even the coves along the Tennessee River were frozen solid. Ice was skimming the main channel itself in places.

Even where the pale afternoon sun had shone on the windless side of the levee the air was pinching cold. Since early morning he had scouted the banks about the bottoms without venturing on the ice. Until he saw the teal he had seen only two snipe. He had killed one of them and missed the other.

He left the bridge and walked about seventy yards up the levee, then down the embankment through dead briers and dormant honeysuckle vines. The johnboat lay where he had left it, bottom upward on the bank. He stepped out on the ice.

He stamped his foot. The ice held, solid as concrete, hard as glass it seemed, too thick to break a way through it for the boat. Besides, the boat was small and light-gauge aluminum, not meant to take the punishment of jagged, broken ice. It was made to be sculled through the bottoms on warmer days, to be ghosted along like a feather by the merest dip and twitch of the paddle, to go more quietly than man could walk or duck could fly.

He looked up. By hauling the little boat up the levee to the road he could carry it on his shoulders to the channel and put in at the bridge. He was a stout man of two hundred pounds, well used to work. Had it been morning he wouldn't have hesitated. Time, however, was against him now. Walk fast though he might, carrying the boat, and once in the channel with it, paddle swiftly though he would, there was small chance he could reach the logjam island before sundown. By that time it would be too late to shoot, and he would have labored for nothing.

His only chance was to slide the little johnboat over the ice straight out towards the logjam island, to sled along swiftly directly to his destination, pushing the little craft ahead of him and, for safety, leaning forward over the stern as he went. In that way, should he run upon rotten ice, he would fall in the boat as it cracked through.

He had gone over the ice this way many times before, but never this late in the afternoon, never with the bottoms so silent. The freeze kept other hunters close at home or sitting beside stoves in crossroads country stores. None but the most determined, not even professional guides, would try to find open water in weather such as this, even though once it was found and reached, the shooting was beyond compare. With no other place to land, the ducks would leave when jumped, only to return again and again.

The desire to be where they were this very instant made his throat ache. Once before as he slid over the ice he had cracked through in a bad place several hundred yards out and had been forced to stay where he was until after midnight, when the bottoms froze sufficiently solid for him to walk out and drag the little boat after him. Every other time, though, he had made it to the open water. There was a line of trees marking the grave of an old road buried by the winter flood. By leaping into the boat just there it was possible to coast off the edge of the ice into the water. He had done it with never an accident, a dozen times perhaps, all before he married. Since his marriage six years ago, he had never attempted the trick.

From the time he was ten until the day of his marriage, he had hunted every day of every duck season, every day after school, even Sundays after church, though Sunday hunting was frowned upon. He had hunted them because he loved them then with the same passionate ache in his throat that he felt now for those creatures settled there on the open water by the thousands, their wild hearts calling his own, it seemed.

Marriage had pinched him down. His wife had ambitions for the farm. It wasn't enough to spend spring, summer, and fall riding a tractor, driving a cotton picker, loading and unloading his truck, working at times until long after nightfall, waiting five hours to get his cotton trailer under the suck at the gin. A wife had to have chickens and geese and cattle. Coonhounds and mules weren't creatures enough to care for, not in a wife's estimation. There must be winter duties too—even, finally, a dairy barn. God help him if he once failed to be home in time to milk.

He hadn't gone over the ice in six long years because there had been too many creatures dependent on him, nearly all of them female. First a wife, then infant daughters, and finally the wife's gentle-eyed Jerseys with their slender hips and heavy udders.

A mallard susie quacked in the distance. He turned the johnboat right side up and laid his heavy parka in it next to his gun. Besides two extra boxes of shells in the pockets of the parka, he carried twenty-three magnum loads in a shooting vest which he wore buttoned snugly about his chest for warmth. He opened his half-pint and took a drink of white moonshine whiskey. Over the bottoms the air was still.

With a practiced heave he pushed the boat out ahead of him on the ice, keeping his weight forward, ready to leap in the boat if the ice failed. As he gathered speed, his legs moving in a regular rhythm, running easily, the boat set up a screeching, thundering racket, scraping past trees and cracking through thickets. Mallards rose from the red oak thickets and flew towards the channel. Now in an open space he paused and watched them a moment. Then he pushed on, going even faster now as the open spaces between thickets got wider and wider. He began sweating a little and slowed down.

Farther out, he stopped to rest. He sat on the stern of the little boat, boots on the ice, elbows on knees, looking down at the hard, slick, olive-drab surface. He looked up at the levee, about six hundred yards away now, a long, straight elevated outline. The road was desolate in both directions. Only hunters, trappers, fishermen, or an occasional logger used it. Far down to the left, he saw the black outline of his pickup truck. He had parked it that morning before starting along the north edge of the bottoms where he had killed the snipe.

He leaned back and got the bird from the game pocket of his parka. The little body was frozen. Strangest of all were the eyes; black with life's memory, they seemed, in the instant after death, before the cold seeped into them and did its work. Frozen now, the eyes were white.

He stood up and tossed the snipe into the front of the boat, turning at the same time and leaning forward. The ice cracked. The crack ran under him and on ahead of the boat through the dark-green ice. Though a crack it most surely was, it didn't seem to be a very serious one. He held the sides of the boat, leaning forward to distribute his weight, braced like an athlete preparing to do pushups. He waited. The ice held.

Fifty yards to the right stood a duck blind. The decoys in front of it were frozen solid into the ice and glazed with white frost. Red oak saplings shaded the ice in their direction. There the ice looked pale, almost white. It would be thicker. He could turn back now in that direction and reach the levee.

Far away to his left over the long open stretches he saw the line of trees marking the lost road. Beyond the flat glare he saw the logjam island, and around it the still blue gulf of the open water, reflecting the sky. In ten minutes he could reach the trees for the final, sliding rush.

He skidded the boat left and made straight for the trees, getting up speed first and then making only so much effort with his legs as would keep the boat sliding. Now and again the ice cracked, but the boat outran the cracks, one after the other as he pushed on, keeping his weight carefully distributed forward, over the boat.

Suddenly, with no warning the ice gave under him, and he fell into the boat just in time, just before it cracked through, and not an instant too soon, for the icy water had bitten him almost to mid-thigh, wetting him well above his insulated rubber knee boots. It had happened this way before. It was like being burned, like the sting of flames licking about his legs. He lay face down and still, waiting for his trousers to freeze. It needed only a little patience. When he sat up at last, remembering to wiggle his toes and flex his calf muscles to keep the circulation going, even the splashes had frozen. They looked like drops of candle wax.

Flared by the commotion of his fall, the ducks had flown up. Now they flocked and circled low around the edge of the open water. He slipped a magnum shell into the magazine of the automatic to replace the one fired at the teal. Then he put the parka over his head and shoulders and sat very still. He quacked with his mouth. A susie answered. He quacked again. He patted his lips, making the intimate, stuttering feed call. He tried the raucous call of the wise old susie. It all proved a false hope. The entire drove splashed in beside the island with a brisk rush of sound that set his heart beating faster.

When he put the gun down and took off the parka, his toes were numb. He moved them and rubbed his legs and finally admitted it to himself. He had cracked through; maybe the ice *was* rotten. Very well, but he had broken through only one time in several hundred yards of running, after all. He *had* managed to fall very neatly into the johnboat, hadn't he?

Though it was a ticklish sort of job, there was still a chance that he could get the boat back up on the ice. He moved back cautiously and sat on the stern, balancing his weight until the bow rose high out of the water and less than four inches of freeboard remained beneath him. Then he dipped the paddle and drove the boat hard against the edge, and moving at once, fast, before it could slide off again, he went quickly forward on all fours. The ice cracked, the long, brittle sound of a marble rolling over a glass tabletop. Crouched in the bow, he waited, holding his breath, a dull pain beating in his throat just under the Adam's apple. The ice held. Cautiously, slowly, he leaned far out over the prow and caught a willow limb in his gloved hand and pulled. The boat eased forward with him. He caught another limb and then another, getting farther and farther up on firm ice, hauling the boat painfully hand over hand until at last his arms gave out and he turned carefully and lay on his back breathing the cold, clean air through his mouth, cupping his hands and breathing into them. Lying thus, looking straight up, the depth of the clear sky was blue and magnificent. When he held his breath there was not a stir of sound anywhere to be heard. He might have been the last creature left alive on earth. A feeling of independence entered him like the slow onset of sleep.

When it was time to move again he found he was tired. He moved awkwardly, stiff in his joints, his shoulders aching in the sockets, his toes numb because he had neglected to keep moving them. He took the flat, half-pint bottle from his parka and drank it empty in three long swigs and flung the bottle away. It smashed. The clear little shards of glass slid on for several yards before they finally stopped, gleaming at rest in the waning sunlight like white jewels.

The levee had never before seemed so far away. The slanting sun perhaps added to the illusion. When he stood up he could not see the truck. Willow thickets blocked the way. In the other direction, just ahead, the island loomed from the open water, a tangled mass of roots and black tree trunks. Low in the water all around it the ducks rested, very still, as though waiting for him.

Although they were out of range, he was tempted to fire at them anyway, to put them up for the joy of seeing them fly, for the satisfaction, knowing that though they might circle the whole bottoms, they would come back. The cold air would drive them down again, here, in the last of the open water, perhaps the last open water to be found anywhere about, except in the mid-river channel.

The liquor's warmth caught hold. He hadn't eaten since before daylight. It didn't matter. He had taught himself not to want food. He had taught himself not to want anything but the beautiful joy of killing. He had always hunted this way.

Now he took the bow line, and without hesitating, stepped out on the ice and put it over his shoulder and towed the boat after him. Once started, it seemed to follow him willingly, coming after him across the patch of firm, white ice like a docile beast. When the ice shaded into olive green again, he stopped and fended his way around to the stern to rest a moment before making the final dash for trees at the edge of the open water.

Once the boat slid free he would be in range. The ducks would come up and circle, dipping their dark wings to his call, and he would lovingly kill them. He would scull coaxingly after the cripples one by one, coming so slowly on them that they would hardly know the boat was moving at all. While they flirted in that final, zigzag hesitation, he would suddenly raise the gun and shoot their heads off clean. Their blood would boil below them like a cloud into the dark, clear water.

A whistling flight of teal drove in, wings already set, and pitched in beyond the island. A susie quacked. He drew a deep breath and shoved. The boat groaned against the willows and slid forward. Faster and faster, he pushed on. Exhilaration shook him like a sudden wind among dead leaves. With less than fifty yards to go, speed was in his favor. Instinctively, at the right instant, he would leap lightly forward.

As though struck suddenly blind, however, he was groping, wet to the armpits, his breath coming so fast that his chest seemed about to burst. He saw the johnboat beside him. It had cracked through. He caught its side. Water spilled in, so he pushed back, trying to swim, his hands already so numb he could hardly feel them.

"Still, be still!" he commanded aloud, using words he spoke to the restless cows at milking. The cold drove in from every direction like nails, driving and driving in, searching his vitals.

He must think! Of course, only keep a clear head! Make every move carefully! Sound judgment, no wasted time or motion. "Easy, careful," he said, speaking to the fiery grip of the cold, which now became more powerful than anything he had ever before imagined, for it was taking him over.

In the place of the strong, obedient body he had so long been accustomed to command, he felt a strange and foolish despair at this heaving, disquieted thing that would no longer obey.

In spite of every caution to the contrary, his body suddenly fought like a cat snared on a string. Thrashing and fighting like a dying fish, he fended himself clumsily around to the prow and threw himself hard upon it. Short of seeing it, he could never have believed such an utterly foolish panic to be possible. Already almost in the wink of an eye, he had destroyed his best hope. The incredible, the *impossible* thing happened. The boat filled almost as quickly as he had moved, and rolled down from under him.

Water covered his face. When he had fought to the surface and taken breath, he felt his hair and his eyebrows freezing.

Bottom up now and barely afloat, the boat was another creature entirely, as though it too, the docile beast of a moment before, had now lost all notion of what it was logically supposed to be, and do.

When he touched it, it rolled. When he caught at it, the weird creature shook him off; it threw him a second time, and he gentled cautiously against it, the cold biting clean through his shoulders now, like teeth. His body's least twitch made the boat heave and swing. Holding the boat, huddling on it and fighting its strange movements, he realized for the first time that the shooting vest with its cargo of magnum shells was his enemy now, the perfect weight to sink a man and kill him. Propping a hand and both knees against the boat, he tried the vest's buttons. Briefly his fingers stung back to life, but they were useless against buttons.

He tried to balance himself on the boat and rip the vest apart with both hands, no trick for a strong man in his early prime, yet each time he tried it the other creature, the rebellious animal self, seized him. His arms failed. They disobeyed. His hands groped warily forward like burned stumps, to rest against the boat and balance him.

He remained thus awhile, motionless, not even shivering, such was the marvel of it, his head just above the surface of the freezing water. The thin winter sunlight and the desolate, utter silence of the bottoms, great spanning miles of it, dinned and drummed at him.

He knew he must shout soon. It would be no use, of course. No earthly man would hear. Yet soon he would begin screaming. The body would have that too; the body would have it, though he knew shouting must only exhaust him the sooner and hasten the end. Screams began gathering in his throat like a queer nausea.

If he had only thought to take off the vest before his fingers numbed, to get out of his boots, even kick off his trousers. Then he might have gotten back in the boat. He would have wrung out his clothes and put them back on and huddled under the parka until night froze the bottoms in, and then he would have walked out to the road and gotten in the truck. He would have driven it home and tottered into the house and asked his wife to draw him a hot bath. Once he was warm and rested he would have gotten a friend or two and come back after his boat and the gun.

If they ever found it, anytime within a week or two, the gun would be all right. He kept it oiled, and with the water so cold the oil would stick. The gun wouldn't rust quickly. Perhaps they would find it. He hoped they would.

Finding the gun shouldn't be hard with the boat frozen in the ice right over it. A sudden ruthless pain in his back, above the beltline, jerked his head forward. For the first time he began shuddering. He heard himself shouting, screaming for help, the cries already hoarse though hardly even well begun. The ducks came up and began wheeling and circling above him. Their curved wings were more beautiful than any he had seen before, cupping as gently as a kiss, skimming like a long caress, each pair shaped like the touch of a woman's hands in love.

He stopped yelling and slid peacefully down into the white darkness under the surface.

afterword

In many of his stories, as he does in his novel, *The Liberation of Lord Byron Jones,* Jesse Hill Ford explores the themes of alienation, racial guilt, and divided loyalty which typically command the attentions of other Southern writers. His subjects range from murder to courtship, from tragedy to comedy. In dealing with this material he distinguishes himself by his fusion of contemporary psychological insights with the Southerner's traditional zest for the well-told tale.

The hunter in "To The Open Water" takes pleasure in the danger of hunting in the solitude of the frozen river bottom, pursuing the ducks to the open water where, in celebration of his and their freedoms, "he would lovingly kill them." Intentionally separating himself from the confining atmosphere of his farm, he seeks the freedom and beauty he can see across the treacherous ice; he exults in escaping the "comfort" of wife and home, for "he had taught himself not to want anything but the beautiful joy of killing."

The author of two novels, *Mountains of Gilead* and *The Liberation of Lord Byron Jones,* and one play, *The Conversion of Buster Drumwright,* Jesse Hill Ford lives in Humboldt, Tennessee. His stories have won several literary awards including the *Atlantic* "First" Award and inclusion in the O. Henry Prize Collection. *The Liberation of Lord Byron Jones,* was a candidate for the National Book Award; a movie version was released in 1970.

questions for general discussion

1. What elements of foreshadowing are there in this story? What is their purpose?

2. Why is there so much emphasis on the proper technique of hunting?

3. In the last line of the story, why does Ford describe the water under the surface as a *white* darkness?

4. What is the purpose of Ford's repeated emphasis on the extremely cold weather?

5. Discuss the significance of the hunter's using the same words to calm himself that he uses to soothe restless cattle.

6. Why is it significant that the hunter's boat reacts like a wild beast after the breakthrough in the ice?

suggestions for writing

1. What is the author's attitude toward the hunter, and how is it revealed?

2. Discuss the theme of freedom versus repression in this story.

3. Compare the hunter in this story with Mr. Maury in "Old Red."

4. Discuss the possibility that the hunter may be purposely seeking self-destruction.

5. Discuss the author's control and manipulation of point of view. Suggest some strengths and possible shortcomings of such manipulation.

JOHN WILLIAM CORRINGTON
reunion

All the way up from Milledgeville it had rained off and on. It was early July, and when the rain stopped and the sun came out you could see steam rising from the rutted roads in southern Virginia. But by the time the train crossed into Pennsylvania, there was little sun, and water stood in the roads and there was no steam.

There were just the three of us: grandfather, my brother Bedford, who was nine then, and me. I was almost fifteen. It was the first trip out of Georgia for Bedford and me, and the first time out of the South for anybody in the family for a long time. Grandfather had been north one time before, but it had not been on a train, and he had been only a few years older than me then.

—I don't see how he sleeps like that, Bedford whispered to me.

—When you get old you sleep more, I told him. —It doesn't matter where you are. You could sleep for fifty years, I guess.

Bedford looked out the coach window and squirmed in his seat. He had wanted to come but he had wanted to stay home, too. It was something to take a train trip all the way to Pennsylvania, but at home the fishing was reaching its peak, the woods were full of birds, and the sun had warmed the water until it felt like part of your skin when you were swimming in it.

—How much longer? Bedford asked.

—Not long, my grandfather said from the seat opposite. He did not open his eyes or push his hat back from his face.

—Thought you was still asleep, grampaw, Bedford said.

—I been some. It comes and goes. You sleep more at my age, he said without smiling.

He was sixty-eight years old that summer, and his face was brown and spotted with little discolorations, each one smaller than a dime. His eyebrows were thick and still black, and they made his wrinkled face seem fierce and somehow young under a scattering of pure white hair that was beginning to show some pink scalp through it. The backs of his hands were brown as his face and neck, and tendons showed through the skin almost as if he cupped a powerful light in each palm.

Under his shirt there were three dead-white depressions in his chest. Each one was the size of a quarter, and they were clustered together along his ribs on the right side. In back, there were two white puckered gatherings of flesh, and now we were going back to see the place where he had gotten the marks on his chest and back.

—See those rises, my grandfather said, pointing out the train window. He had opened his eyes. They were large and still bright blue like my father's.
—Over there. Those humps.

—Sure, Bedford said. —If it snowed, you could use a sled on 'em.

—No, grandfather said. —They're too rocky for that. They're called the roundtops, Little Roundtop and Big Roundtop.

—They look like they'd be fun to climb, I said. Then I remembered and bit my lip. But my grandfather smiled.

—They might be. If it was a cool day and nobody minded you climbing.

Then we saw the station up ahead at the end of a long curve of track. All around the edges of the station there was red, white, and blue bunting and there was a United States flag above the station. There was a painted sign that read WELCOME VETERANS with roughly drawn cannon and canteens and bayonetted rifles around the border of it. Underneath the eaves of the station on our side, there was a little wooden plaque hanging down. It said *Gettysburg*.

They registered grandfather and gave him a kind of medal to wear that said he was a veteran who had fought there, and what his rank and regiment had been.

—I expect I'll be a rarity, he said.

—What do you mean, grampaw? Bedford asked him.

—A private soldier. You can't hardly find a private any more. Seems only officers survived.

—That doesn't make any sense, I said. —The officers would have been older to start with.

But he was right. There were all kinds of captains and majors and even a few brigadier generals. My grandfather said the promoting hadn't ended yet, either.

The people in town were nice, mostly. Their voices were funny and harsh, and they moved fast as if they were all after something about to get away from them, and they seemed to be real careful not to say anything that would slight the Southern soldiers. With the Union veterans it was different. They acted as if everybody had been in the same army, fighting for the same thing. We met a man who had been with Sickles' staff.

—It's cooler now, he said to grandfather. —It's a lot cooler.

—The sun's older, grandfather said. —We can use all the warmth we can get.

The Union man laughed. —I thought we'd given each other enough heat those three days to last out all the rest of our lives.

—I expect we feel warmer than the ones who paid to stay home or hid under the chickenhouse when the conscription officer came by.

—That's so, the Union man said lustily. —That's so. Who are these fine boys?

—These are my grandsons. Meet Captain McCleod. Robert and Bedford.

—I expect the Robert is Robert Edward, the captain said, smiling.

—Yes, sir, I said.

—There wasn't a better name on either side. If I had a grandson, I just might have risked it and named him the same.

Bedford kept looking at the captain with an expression on his face like the one you see on a whiteface calf when you come up on it suddenly.

—You're an honest-to-God yankee?

—Bedford, grandfather said mildly, —watch what you say to the gentleman.

—I take that title as an honor, Captain McCleod said, still smiling.

—I expect so, grandfather said. —It's just that I'm not sure the boy intended it that way.

During all that, Bedford was still staring at the captain's rusty blue uniform with its gold shoulder bars and the wide-brimmed black hat. One side of the brim was turned up against the crown and pinned there.

—I never seen a yankee before, Bedford said. —Grammaw said the last ones was run out of Georgia a long time ago after The Drunkard was gone from the White House. Grammaw said . . .

—Hush, boy, grandfather told Bedford. His smile was gone, and I could see the cords in his neck tightening. —Just hush.

Grandfather never raised his voice to either of us, and Bedford was beginning to snuffle because of the tone of voice grandfather had used.

—I'm sorry for that, he said to the Union captain. —My missus never took to the outcome of the war or what followed it. In her latter days, she talked a lot to the boys. She's over it now, I reckon.

The captain didn't say anything. He ruffled Bedford's hair, bowed to me, and shook hands with grandfather. —I know. I suppose it will be a while yet.

—I expect, grandfather said.

After signing up at the encampment office and drinking lemonade, we walked around some. It was hot with the sun standing high above us, and on all sides, as far as we could see, were long rows of army tents set up in orderly streets. In one corner of the tent-city, we found the place reserved for us. It had four cots in it, and Bedford and I put the pallets we had brought to sleep on under one of the cots.

—I expected they'd be here, grandfather said. —They said the second of July for sure.

—Grampaw, Bedford said, —how come you didn't wear no uniform up here like that yankee captain? How come you ain't ever showed us your uniform?

—I had a uniform in 1862, he said, smiling softly. —It was blue. Almost as blue as the captain's.

—Lord, grampaw, you weren't a yankee.

—No. It was a militia uniform. It was all we had, and when they mustered us into the regular army we went on wearing it until it wore out. Then we wore whatever we could get hold of.

—I wouldn't have fought if they didn't give me a uniform, Bedford said.

—Yes you would, grandfather said. —If you had to fight, it wouldn't matter what you had to wear.

—Who are we waiting for? I asked.

—A couple of old friends. They were in Armistead's brigade with me. They were here before.

That afternoon and evening there were speeches welcoming everybody, and a mayor or governor said that the war had been like a great burning sword that had cauterized the soul of America, and from much wrong, much good had come, and that now, North and South, we were united under one flag.

—Huh, Bedford said afterward as we walked in the dark down the torchlit tent-city streets. —That's all he knows. I reckon grammaw could tell him something.

—Your grandmother is dead, grandfather said evenly. —She remembered too much. Sometimes a good memory does you no service.

—How can you help remembering? I asked him. —You've got holes in you to help you remember if you were to start forgetting.

—Holes, grandfather said. —Maybe I fell onto your great-grandfather's picket-fence when I was courting your grandmother.

—Maybe not, too, Bedford said darkly. —Maybe it was some of these bastards . . .

—All right, grandfather said shortly. —Watch your tongue, boy. I remember what your mother told you about coarse talk.

—I don't give a hoot in hell for their flag, Bedford said defiantly.

—Grammaw used to say the red in it was Southern blood. That the union got fat eating its own people when they tried to be free . . .

We reached our tent and went inside. Bedford lighted a kerosene lantern and hung it on the main pole.

—Your grandmother said a lot, grandfather said wearily. —But her text was always the same.

—But . . . , I began.

—Do you want to carry the graves home from here with you? Do you want to carry the graves inside the house and set them up there?

—What're you talking about, grampaw? Bedford asked him.

—This is just a celebration, he said, sitting down heavily on his cot. —It's something for a lot of old men who want to remember that they were once young and brave and maybe held the fate of their nations in their hands. They want to remember that they fought well and did all they could, whether they did or not. The other people just want to look at them like they'd read a history book or look at a painting of Waterloo. It doesn't mean anything any more.

—If it doesn't mean anything any more, why'd you come back up here? Bedford asked cagily.

Grandfather pulled off his trousers and carefully swung his legs up onto the cot. —If it meant anything, he said, —I don't reckon I could have stood to come. It's like a picture in my mind, like photographs in one of those little books Charlie Stokes has—the kind you riffle through and it looks like the pictures move. I see men and horses and cannon, and I see bursts of dark smoke in the air and on the field, and I see men falling. But I can't feel the sun on my back or feel the fear in my belly when we started out. I know my mouth was dry. It was so dry I couldn't move my tongue. And my feet were cut and blistered and wrapped up in pieces of tentcloth.

Grandfather touched the slanting side of the tent with his fingers. —But I can't feel the pain of the grass stubble under foot. All I can feel is sorry for that boy. I feel sorry he had to get himself hurt and had to hurt in his turn. I guess I feel sorry for all of them, but it doesn't mean anything any more. I can't get hold of the heat and the sweat. I can't hope for the Confederacy; I can't hate and respect that goat-whiskered terrible proud Jefferson Davis any more. All of it seems like a picture I saw once. How much can you care about a picture?

—Grammaw cared, Bedford said accusingly.

Grandfather's eyes were closed, and the soft buttery light of the kerosene lantern played across his face in profile. You could see how the flesh of the jaw and around the chin had melted away and left the sharp outline of the bone. The creases around his eyes and on his forehead and cheeks stood out like elevation markings on a map.

—Your grandmother wasn't here, Bedford. Her imagination wasn't limited by having been subjected to the facts. I expect she was making up for not having been here. I think she believed had she been here it might have been different. She had to keep it going until she felt she'd done her duty. But death caught her short.

I almost blushed and I was glad he had his eyes shut. Bedford looked at me, not understanding. But I understood. Because I had felt the way he said grandmother must have felt. I could remember, even when I was younger than Bedford, how I had felt when grandfather took off his shirt to chop firewood or for a bath. I would see how thin and flat his chest was, and the three milky depressions through his ribs and the ugly drawn-up little mouths in his back, and I would feel a funny cold thing move from my tailbone up into my scalp. I knew when he said it that what I had felt was shame just as if I had been alive then, in the brigade, and had run, or been a staff officer or courier, and had stayed behind.

—All I remember, my grandfather was saying, —is a boy just a little older than Robert running across that road filled with fear and thirst and barely aware of his feet being opened again by the stubble. And the smoke and uproar, the artillery and rifle-fire, and then him being hit and falling, but still holding on to his rifle and crawling on until the smoke closed all around him. But even that doesn't mean much because when I remember, it seems he was a boy cut out of paper like a doll, and the minie balls only punched through his paper guts, and the paper boy lay down near a lot of other cutouts under a sun painted on a piece of blue canvas sky with the blue maybe overdone some. How can you care about something like that?

—You were that boy, I said as the fatigue of the long day came over me.

—I expect so, he said, his voice blurring, trailing off. —I expect so.

Then, after a minute: —Youall hang up your clothes, turn down the lantern, and sleep on those cots. They won't be in before morning now. Goodnight, boys.

Before the sun was up, I heard voices just outside the tent. Then I heard somebody fooling with the flap.

—All right, I heard grandfather say without any sign of sleep in his voice. —All right, come on in.

I couldn't get my eyes open right away, but I heard grandfather move toward the lantern, and heard someone else come into the tent.

—I thought maybe he'd caught up with both of you, I heard grandfather say.

—He ain't none too far off, a strange voice answered.

—Specially in the early morning, a third voice said. —Twilight and first light I feel like one of them Greek heroes on the Happy Isles. Like my body was gone, and nothing left but what I look and think with.

—How is it up here?

—All right, I guess, my grandfather said over the sounds of his dressing. —We got here yesterday and they had already started the speeches full-tilt. I think today is the big day.

—I reckon so. Today *was* the big day.

I managed to get up finally and open my eyes. The two of them were sitting on either side of grandfather. The one who had been talking about Greek heroes was short and fleshy without really being fat. His face was red and blotchy, and it showed no feeling at all. He had on a gray uniform with gold braid on the sleeves. The other old man was just under grandfather's six feet in height. His voice was reedy and pleasant. He was narrow all over. From his long head to his narrow hips he looked as if he had spent all his years standing up in a close room, or as if someone had tied him between horses at intervals in order to force his growth.

—Hello, boy, the smaller one said bluffly when he saw I was awake.

—This is Michael Clinton, grandfather said. —We were here together.

—This would be Robert Edward Lee, Michael Clinton said, nodding at me.

—That's him, grandfather said with only a slight smile. —Over there's Nathan Bedford asleep.

—Fine, Michael Clinton said. —Robert, this is John Edgar Turner.

—Sorry, grandfather said. —I was fixing to do the rest of the honors.

—All right, John Edgar Turner said in that soft breathless voice that sounded like a clarinet or a flute. —I been looking him over.

—He's all right, Michael Clinton said. —He's just fine.

I was getting embarrassed, but about then we went outside and found the cook-tent where there were a lot of old men, most of them union veterans, standing in line for coffee and rolls. Up where the food and coffee was, I saw a young man with a fur-collared overcoat on. He was talking to one of the army officers who were trying to make sure everybody was happy and getting to the speeches and fireworks and whatever was going on. The man with the fur collar was gesturing toward the men in line, and the officer, his face set and showing nothing, was listening without seeming to agree or disagree. The young man's face was red, and I thought it was the early morning chill until we got close enough to see all the pimples and scars of old pimples on it. He had a high celluloid collar and kept talking about spectators and the angle, but the officer looked away, and when another officer came by, he excused himself and walked off as if he had something important to do. The young man with pimples didn't look insulted. He pulled a notebook from his pocket and read something, and then started off in the direction opposite from that the officer had taken.

Later we were walking on the east side of the big Pennsylvania memorial. All around us, people looked at tablets and statues and little pillars with bronze plates. Bedford was with us, and we were waiting for the time when President Wilson would speak.

—None of us ever got this far before, John Edgar Turner was saying. I guess we stopped over there a couple hundred yards.

—That's right, my grandfather said. —If you stand on one of these tablets, you can see the wall.

—Do you want to walk over there? John Edgar Turner asked quietly.

—How about some lemonade? Michael Clinton asked us. —Would youall like some lemonade?

—Where did you get your uniform, Mr. Clinton? Bedford asked. —Did you wear it here before?

—Lord no, John Edgar Turner laughed. —We didn't any of us have uniforms.

—My sister . . . , Michael Clinton started to say. He was looking gray, and his hardlipped expressionless face was covered with moisture.

—His sister in Danville had it made for him. We didn't any of us have uniforms that last time.

—I wouldn't have done no fighting if they hadn't given me a uniform. What's the good of joining an army if they don't give you a uniform? Bedford asked.

—I reckon they gave us a kind of uniform, grandfather said. —They gave us one that day.

—That's so, John Edgar Turner said.

Bedford shrugged, and Michael Clinton still looked sick. John Edgar Turner looked at him and frowned.

—Don't be silly, he said to Michael Clinton. —Come on. We'll take a look at the angle. We'll take a look at Cemetery Ridge right after we hear the President talk.

—Maybe the boys would . . .

—Like to see where their country died, John Edgar Turner finished. His long narrow face looked hard and naked in the bright sunlight.

Michael Clinton shrugged, and looked as if he had shrunk some. He followed a few steps behind us.

—You'd think . . . , John Edgar Turner began.

My grandfather cut him off. —Hush, John. Maybe it doesn't seem so long to Mike. I expect he's got something to remember.

—It was the worst way to be hurt. I remember he screamed all the way down through Maryland. I remember . . .

—All right, mind the boys.

—Oh, John Edgar Turner said. —I wasn't going to say anything.

All the President had to say was about how close we all were, and how the Boys in Blue and the Boys in Gray were all heroes and brought glory and unity to the country after all.

—*Whose* country? Bedford snorted right while the President was talking, and some of the old men with Grand Army of the Republic badges stared and frowned at him. My grandfather hushed Bedford hard, but then he stared back at the other men without blushing any at all.

While the President was getting the good old U.S.A. off his chest, Michael Clinton still looked pasty and sick, and after it was over, we started back to see the angle and the fence which we had been started for when it was time to go hear the President.

We went past the little monument they call the High Water Mark, and there right ahead of us was this little square of field, a few trees, and a broken-down snakerail fence running along one side of it. What was left of a broken-down stone wall maybe three and a half or four feet high straggled out perpendicular to the fence. Beyond was a long wide field knee deep in dry summer grass, and down the slope a few hundred yards was a road. That was all there was.

But grandfather and John Edgar Turner and Michael Clinton all walked slowly, as if the place was full of cannon or big statues. Michael Clinton stopped under a tree and mopped his head with a checkered handkerchief.

—Right out there, he said, —I gave 'em my life.

—Sure, John Edgar Turner said, looking over at us kind of nervously. —You gave it all.

—I gave it all, Michael Clinton said after him. —I was only twenty-two. They got as much from me as if I was buried out there. Do youall know what it's like going through life without . . .

—The boys, grandfather cautioned him sternly.

Michael Clinton leaned against the tree. His eyes were damp, but he still had no expression. Just that strange bluff red face with a tortured voice coming out of it, and nothing in the face to match the voice. Like one of those wooden puppets they use in shows.

—Reckon I made it about three-quarters of the way, grandfather said to John Edgar Turner. —I never saw it from this point of view. They say we covered the whole field there as far as you could see.

—I expect we looked like judgment on the way from up here, John Edgar Turner said in his reedy voice.

—I don't see anything, Bedford said. —It's just a pasture. I don't see nothing but a pasture.

—Shut up, I said. —They'll hear you.

— . . . all the way up here to see a pasture and a fence with a couple of trees and a dinky road running through it.

—You want to go back? I said. —I'm going to kick you all the way back to the tent if you don't shut up.

But then a man came walking up and started talking to grandfather and the others. It was the man with the pimples and the celluloid collar. At first I couldn't make out what he wanted.

— . . . in an hour or so. The Pennsylvanian veterans are scheduled to present the Pickett's Division Association folks with an American flag right here.

My grandfather was nodding courteously, and John Edgar Turner was craning his long neck first to one side and then the other like a tall puzzled bird looking down on a hedgehog for the first time. Michael Clinton was still leaning up against the tree and looking out over the field.

— . . . lots of folks from all over, the young man was saying earnestly. —From South and North. Lots of good people to celebrate with you, and we thought . . .

Michael Clinton had stopped rubbing his face with the outsize checkered handkerchief. He stepped over to where the others were talking as if he was drawn by a magnet. His eyes widened as the pimple-faced man went on, but he kept listening as if he couldn't help it and couldn't believe what he was hearing either.

— . . . if you fellas would get together and go on down by the Emmetsburg road there, and then kind of run back up toward this wall here, and maybe give us the old rebel yell . . . you know . . .

My grandfather remained placid and showed nothing of what he was thinking. John Edgar Turner's long gentle face was like rubber, passing from a kind of embarrassed horrified smile to a frown, and back again, like the face of someone confronted with a preposterous and unexpected situation that might turn out funny or dangerous or both.

—Lord, John Edgar Turner said slowly, softly.

—What're they going on about? Bedford whined irritably. —I want to go back. I want to go back. I'm tired.

But now it was coming through to Michael Clinton. —O Jesus Christ, he moaned, looking away from the young man who had not stopped talking even then, but continued to tell how much the good folks would enjoy it, and how much it would add to the celebration.

—O Jesus Christ in heaven, Michael Clinton crooned, and now his rough scarlet face was no longer bland, no longer even a face but a collapsing unsorted collection of wide eyes, a twisted mouth, and fresh streams of sweat flowing into both like the catch of a violent spring rain. —Do you know what they . . .

But the pimple-faced young man only stared at Michael Clinton curiously and drew breath to begin his persuasion again.

—Pickett's charge all over again, he said. —This time the Pennsylvania boys will meet you with open arms. Think of how proud . . .

By then John Edgar Turner and grandfather had turned away from him. They were watching Michael Clinton who had begun staggering back in the direction of the tents. He had gone only a little way when he fell heavily against one of the trees. He held himself up long enough to get turned around. Then he sagged into a sitting position facing us, his back against the tree, his eyes wide and staring past us into that wide grassy field beyond. There was no expression on his face at all.

I started toward him but grandfather caught my arm.

—No. You take Bedford, and go back. If you see one of those boy scouts or army people, send them down here with a stretcher. Tell them to hurry.

As I pulled Bedford along, I could hear the young man with the pimples and high celluloid collar saying to grandfather:

—After you get the old gentleman taken care of, maybe we could go over it with the others . . .

By that time we were too far away to make out words, but I heard grandfather say something in a short vicious tone, and his voice was as strong and deep as a young man's. Then I could hear nothing more.

We had some late lunch, and Bedford fell asleep in the hot stuffy tent afterward. I sat on a campstool outside for a long time, but grandfather didn't come. Old men in blue suits and gray suits moved past quietly talking or, once in a while, laughing in that high womanish shrill of the very old. The sun began slanting downward and when suppertime was near, I began to worry. Bedford woke up covered with sweat. He was sullen and uncomfortable and kept saying he wished he was home, and how all of this didn't mean anything.

—It ain't like all the stories, he said. —All it is, is a lot of old men and ground with the grass all cut and some big places built of marble with iron horses on top. It's not anything.

I sent him on to supper and went to look for grandfather.

I found him my first try. He was sitting on the low stone wall at the place we had been, the place they called the Bloody Angle. All around the green well-trimmed acre or two, there were pieces of paper scattered, some bread crusts, and what looked like a jam-jar. My grandfather was facing west, looking at the long deserted slope that flowed downward to the Emmetsburg road, and then up again to the bulky shadow of Seminary Ridge, where the sun stood low and red like a swollen wound.

—I got worried about you, I said as I climbed up and sat on the stone wall beside him.

He turned and looked at me. It seemed at first he didn't recognize me.

—I'm sorry, he said after a moment. —After we left the hospital, I meant to come back to the tent . . .

—How's Mr. Clinton?

—Mr. Clinton is dead, my grandfather said. —Too much heat. Too much excitement.

—No, it wasn't . . . Did you tell them about that man . . .

—I didn't tell them anything. They told us Michael Clinton was dead. There wasn't anything to tell them. So I came here to take another look before time to go.

He stood up and stretched and when he yawned, with his head thrown back, it seemed all the wrinkles in his cheeks dissolved. It may have been some trick of light in the early summer evening, but he looked for a moment, squinting toward the darkening sun, his mouth open as if to cheer invisible friends forward, no older than myself, and just as strong.

—We should have gone right on, he said quietly. —We never should have stopped.

It was twilight. Then it was dark, and we had put our things in the cardboard suitcase and said goodbye to John Edgar Turner, who held my hand and grandfather's for a long minute, and who embarrassed Bedford by leaning down and kissing him in front of some old men who were shuffling past on their way to a regimental reunion.

—Goodbye, John Edgar Turner called after us. —God bless youall.

—I'll be seeing you, grandfather said, waving.—We'll see you again.

—Sure enough, we heard John Edgar Turner call in his soft reedy voice. —Sure enough.

On the train we split two hotdogs among us, and got the porter to sell us two bags of salted peanuts for a nickel instead of just one. By the time we finished eating, Bedford was beginning to be contrite. He was sorry for letting it show that he wished he had stayed home.

—He was a mighty nice old man, Bedford said. —I'm sorry about it.

—I expect he was ready, grandfather said. —It gets to be that time, and then you get set for it.

He rolled his coat into a ball and set it in the corner of the seat next to the window.

—It's beginning to rain, I said.

—Yes, my grandfather said. —It would.

Outside we could see the raindrops striking our coach window and shattering into long shivering beads that tracked down and across the glass, and then spun off into the night again. There were blurred yellow lights in town windows and on farm porches as we passed. Once there was an empty crossroads with lamps above it on poles. The roadway was slick and shiny with rain and light, and the lamps had halos of swirling mist around them.

My grandfather had pulled his hat down over his eyes, and his arms were folded across his chest.

We rode for a long time in silence, looking out at the rain. I could feel myself going slack inside. It would be easy to sleep in a little while. Bedford took his Ingraham watch out and looked at it.

—It's almost one o'clock. It's the Fourth of July.

—Shut up, I said. —He's trying to sleep.

Bedford leaned over and tried to look up under grandfather's hat.

—You asleep, grampaw? he whispered.

We could see grandfather's mouth twist into a smile under the battered hat.

—Sure now, he said softly. —I reckon I could sleep for fifty years.

afterword

In "Reunion," an old Confederate veteran revisiting Gettysburg fifty years after the battle for a commemorative celebration is awakened anew to the causes which made him fight there. Although he tells his grandsons that the anger and pain he felt that day are gone, that he remembers it only impersonally "like a picture I saw once," it is apparent that the feelings of 1863 are not gone, only dormant. When a young Northerner who wants to stage a vulgar reenactment of the battle so horrifies and enrages the old soldier's friend as to cause his death, the old veteran once again feels what he felt on that day fifty years before and says bitterly, "We should have gone right on. . . . We never should have stopped."

Thus, for the Southerner past events are not gone and forgotten. Frequently they live on, shaping the present, reminding one who he is and where his loyalties lie. It is this sense of "the presentness of the past," as T. S. Eliot calls it, which is reignited in the Grandfather and which will be inevitably impressed upon the boys. As they ride southward through the rain, the battle of Gettysburg is, for them, far less than fifty years old.

Corrington, a professor of English at Loyola University in New Orleans, was born in Memphis, Tennessee, in 1932. In addition to publishing four volumes of poetry, he has written two novels, *And Wait For The Night* (1964) and *The Upper Hand* (1967). His collection of short stories, *The Lonesome Traveller,* appeared in 1969. An editor-at-large of the *New Orleans Review,* he is currently involved in editing a series of anthologies with the title of *Southern Writing In The Sixties.*

questions for general discussion

1. What are some implications of the young narrator's comment, "It was the first trip out of Georgia for Bedford and me, and the first time out of the South for anybody in the family in a long time. Grandfather had been north one time before, but it had not been on a train, and he had been only a few years older than me then"?

2. What is the effect of Corrington's description of weather conditions during the train ride to Gettysburg, during the reunion, and during the return trip to Georgia?

3. Since the story concerns a fiftieth anniversary reunion, what might be significant about the two references—in the story's opening and closing scenes—to sleeping for fifty years?

4. What is ironic about the manner of Michael Clinton's being wounded fifty years earlier and the time and place of his death?

5. What attitudes toward past events are revealed in the Grandfather's answer to Bedford's question about the reunion, "If it doesn't mean anything anymore why'd you come up here"?

6. Is it significant that the narrator describes his grandfather's face as looking like a map?

suggestions for writing

1. Develop a theme suggesting what the Grandfather has learned in the fifty years since Gettysburg.

2. Comment on the different ways in which the Grandfather, Bedford, and the narrator view and talk about the experiences of the past and the present.

3. Discuss some elements of irony in the story.

4. Comment on the concepts of pride and loyalty as they are exemplified by the Grandfather.

the retrievers

SHREVEPORT: 1933

When you come into Shreveport from the southeast, you might end up driving along Fairfield Avenue, which is a long shaded street of big white frame houses and thick with old moss-covered oaks, magnolias, gum trees, and a scattering here and there of tall pines. All the houses were built in the decades just before and just after the Confederate War, and in the days I lived there—all through the late thirties and early forties—the houses themselves had begun to decay a little. One might be needing paint; another would lack some shutters or have a column beginning to sag with the combined weight of long years and close money. Even so, though, it was still a beautiful street, still impressive.

When my father brought us down from Memphis, we used to drive out along Fairfield Avenue on a Sunday afternoon in the Ford. My young brother, Nathan Bedford, my sister, Malissa, and my mother and I would just look. We had lived in a pretty nice house on Poplar in Memphis before my father's business, cotton factoring, had gone to pieces, and we couldn't get used to living in a little three-bedroom place my father had bought in a suburb of town. It was like a sardine tin, and when my mother's father heard we were living in a one-story house, he had taken my father aside during a last visit to Memphis and asked him if this was the way he meant to provide for his family.

So I guess my father was yearning some, too. He'd see a big fine house and point it out to mother. —Looks like our old house, he'd say. —Don't you think?

It really wouldn't, much. At least no more than any big boxy white frame house with a lot of trees and bushes around it looks like any other. But my mother would frown in concentration and then smile. —Yes, she'd answer. —Yes, I believe it does.

Whereupon my father would get glum and forget to stop by the ice cream shop on his way home.

The houses were no mansions. Just great big square places with wide porches and galleries and high ceilings and sometimes some of that ornate cutout wood my mother called gingerbread. They were just comfortable, exuding a kind of lasting hard-won quietude and tranquillity. But they seemed like castles to us. Much later I saw Blenheim and Hampton Court in England, and neither seemed quite so fine as that long procession of houses sitting serene and certain in the shade of Fairfield Avenue.

After we had lived in Shreveport awhile, we came to know something about the people who lived on Fairfield. Some of the houses were owned variously by old families whose eldest male might be called captain or major or colonel—either because he had earned that title in person or because he had received it from a father or grandfather as part of his patrimony and managed to keep the family reputation at least intact enough not to forfeit the title granted by the town and as easily withdrawn by simply letting it lapse. Some of the houses, though, were owned by small merchants who had scrambled for years and managed to get hold of a mortgage or buy it up when the last of a family died off. They would move in and be models of austerity, hoping that enough time would finally pass to give people the impression that they had always lived on Fairfield Avenue. A few of them, anxious to hasten the process, even tried to parlay a captaincy or majority in some World War regiment into a title:— captains of crockery, majors of merchandising, briga-diers of banking. My father would laugh.

Because we didn't much care about being big shots. We just wanted a place on a quiet shady street we could rattle around in without stomping on one another's toes. The only titles we had were three privates and a corporal, my father's great uncles, who had ridden with General Forrest in western Tennessee. My father said our family had been too busy fishing and cutting bait both in the war and after it ever to get hold of a rank. Anyhow, everybody knows that a corporal in Forrest's cavalry was worth any two majors kicking around in a trans-Mississippi commissary company.

But what I want to tell about is how we came to live on Fairfield Avenue without opening a plumbing shop or finding that we were the lost heirs of General Kirby-Smith. We came to be thought of as part of the old folks, one of the families to be consulted, and we got that way overnight. No waiting period. We just overshot the whole gaggle of Heathertons, Priors, Richleys, and Gaineses who had bought in and were busily trying to live down the buying.

It all happened because of my young brother and sister, Nathan and Malissa. They became, you might say, the true founders of the Shreveport branch of the Tennessee Armisteads. It was quite a trick, starting as an embarrassment and ending with a big legal thing complete to U.S. Internal Revenue sneaking around and every trimmer in the parish grinding his teeth and trying to figure a way to cash in on our good luck.

Which is getting ahead. Because it started in the summer of 1933, when we were living out off Highway 20 in a new and nameless suburb a little closer in than Dixie Gardens. There were twenty or thirty houses in the development, and all of them rested on small lots taken from one big tract of land that had once constituted the old Sentell place. I asked a boy I knew at Byrd High School about how it used to be.

—Belonged to the Indians, Joe Hobbs told me. —Then somebody nobody even remembers. Then a man named Sentell who fought in some war. Then his son got it, and that was a shame. 'Cause he went yellow in the war against the Yanks. Come home and stopped fighting, and afterward the Yanks took his place anyhow. Which was good enough for him. Then some colored guy had it till they run him out. And old Cleburne, the storekeeper, got hold of it. Bought up all thousand and five hundred acres. Kept the house and the land that runs where youall live. Broke up the rest and sold it piece by piece. Some Eyetalian truck farmers got 'em a little of it. Where the Cashios live now, and the Firinas. Then Dixie Gardens took up a lot along the river. Then Cleburne died. The rest went for taxes. Till some contractor in Alexandria bought it and parceled it out in lots a few years ago. Which is what youall live in now.

Joe Hobbs' family lived one street behind Fairfield Avenue. His grandfather was still alive, and had seen the soldiers pull down the last Confederate flag. He had watched with a bullet through both legs picked up near Rome, Georgia, while the Yankees marched in. What Joe didn't know wasn't worth knowing. Not because he cared about it, not because he was much interested in family or history or anything, but because he couldn't help himself. It just drifted in. What are you going to do when you live in the middle of a place where things have happened slowly but surely, like a glacier moving, for a century? Joe picked up the pieces, the tags and ends, names and dates as if he were part of the glacier. The only thing he didn't know was when his people had got to Caddo Parish. —I bet we was there to see the Caddo Indians movin' in, Joe Hobbs would say. But it meant nothing to him.

Sometimes Joe would come over to the house and we'd talk. All I had to do was ask the questions. He was like a memory machine. He could tell you *where* and *when* and *how*. Except, being a natural-born engineer (like his older brother at Centenary College), he could not only not tell you *why*, but could not quite understand what you meant when you asked him *why*.

—After Vicksburg, he told me, going on about the Sentells, Major Edward Malcolm Sentell, who had not gone back to fight. —Summer, late summer of 1863. Come home riding and walking all the way across Louisiana with a Yank parole in his pocket.

—How come? I asked. —Was he really yellow?

—Reckon. If you won't fight, you must be yellow.

—Did he fight at Vicksburg?

—Lord, I reckon. They told about this mine he helped plant, and the fighting all along the works. Fought like a tiger. Most of 'em did.

—So why did he stop? You don't fight and then just stop for no reason.

Joe Hobbs shrugged. —He did. And he lost his place. Good enough for him. Lived on right here in town till he died. Folks mostly couldn't stand him. Died just before I was born.

—People said he was yellow?

—Naw. Just said he wouldn't go back.

—Maybe he got religion.

—Naw. They never said nothing except he wouldn't go back.

So he was like some kind of unbelievable parrot, an enchanted one who could tell you everything except what you wanted to know. It made me mad as hell. But I kept pumping him. It was as if I had hold of a human Rosetta stone, and just needed to ask the right question to get a free trip back to the Shreveport that had been almost a hundred years before. I don't know why I wanted to. Maybe it had something to do with the big houses on Fairfield where those old families had lived. Maybe I wanted to know how you managed to get into one of them the right way, what kind of people had lived in them to begin with.

While we talked, Nathan and Malissa would fool around on the porch in their bathing suits. Nathan was building a paper-and-stick model of the *Spirit of St. Louis* with Malissa commenting on every drop of glue he squeezed out.

—Why don't you get your own? he would say finally. —They got a real nice Curtiss *Jenny* down at Wiseman's shop. I'll even give you fifteen cents toward it.

—No, she'd tell him. —It's a waste of time.

—Then why don't you leave me alone?

—You need help. You can't do anything by yourself.

—I'm going to bust your—

—Nathan, my mother would call from the kitchen. —Watch that.

—Yessum.

But neither of them paid any attention to me and my attempts to get something out of Joe Hobbs. Which was a break. Malissa could help you out of your mind.

—They say old Cleburne left a potful of money somewhere, Joe Hobbs said without my even asking. —Say he saved up maybe a million dollars. But nobody ever found a thing. He owned land all over the north part of the parish. Sold a lot of it, but they never found the money. Somebody said he had him a whole bunch of mulatto kids and passed out the money. But most people thought he'd buried it.

—Wow, Nathan put in suddenly, letting the LePage's glue run all over the plans for the *Spirit of St. Louis*. —You mean there's money somewhere around here? Just waiting for somebody to pick up?

—Never said that, Joe Hobbs answered, his voice as smooth as molasses. —Folks say it. Folks say a lot.

I was still interested in Sentell. This buried treasure thing is something you get over after *Treasure Island*. Unless you're a case of arrested development. Spanish galleons. Pieces of eight. Cutlasses. Blood in the scuppers. Wow. But Sentell. And not only him but the Old South. The place we were now in space, but another time. I was kind of hung on it. So I started asking Hobbs what kind of man Sentell was, what did he do.

—Rode good. Shot a pistol like it grew in his hand. Killed a man in Bossier Parish one time.

—Before he went to Vicksburg?

—Naw. Years afterward. Man over to Benton called his wife white trash. Said she wasn't no better than her father. In 1873. Said she was no better than old Murray Taggert, who was sure enough white trash. Said everybody reckoned she'd blowed her old man's head off. Somebody had, back in the summer of 1865. So Sentell called him on it, and this other fella drew down on Sentell, and shot him once in the leg and another time in the side. And Sentell come up with a one-shot derringer and put his shot right between the fella's eyes. They say he walked a mile and a half to a doctor and then stayed outside to get bandaged up so he wouldn't track blood all over the doctor's parlor.

—He did that after the war? And you say he was yellow?

—Must of been. Wouldn't go back after Vicksburg.

I just shook my head, and Nathan started in on the treasure again. So I went to get some iced tea that mother kept already sugared in a big crock out in the kitchen. Then I walked out on the porch again and tried to tune them and their lost million dollars out while I thought of that strange shadowy major, whose face I couldn't make out, but whose heart I would have given that imaginary million just to see into.

The next day it was pretty quiet around the house. I came in so tired from playing ball in ninety-six-degree heat that I just spread out in the bathtub and kind of stared in a trance at the little gas heater which stuck out of the wall like a dormant volcano waiting for winter to start up again. It was fine. The water was only tepid, but cooler than the air, and I lay in it for over an hour before it came to me that I hadn't heard or seen anything of the kids since I woke that morning. No Malissa to yell that she wanted her second bath of the day. No Nathan to barge in and sit on the closed lid of the commode and point out to me in agonizing detail what new struts and spars had been added to the grisly skeleton of the *Spirit of St. Louis* since the last time I had seen it. Nothing but silence. A rustle and an almost indiscernible hum where my mother was weeding a stand of hopeless zinnias out in back. But not another sound. I wondered about that, and then got to thinking about Sentell again. I reckoned I might go up to the public library and see if I could get hold of some old newspapers. Or maybe there were others like Joe Hobbs around. With something going for them besides total recall. There had to be some way to get back there. Nothing that has happened is ever really gone. Nothing can move and have being in time without leaving its traces, going on and spreading, getting fainter and fainter like the ripples that move from the point of a stone's impact in some quiet pool.

I dried off and dressed in a tee shirt. Mother was just coming in with some flowers. —Where are the kids? I asked her.

—"Down by the riverside," she sang, smiling. —Searching the terrain. They caught a huge soft-shell turtle this morning. I expect them to come back with a good-sized leviathan and a pair of small behemoths by suppertime.

I didn't blame them. In the summer, with school out, things got pretty dull. All you could do was swim or stand around in front of Weber's Seabreeze root beer parlor or play baseball like a lunatic seeking sunstroke in one of the parks. All of which I did. With Job Hobbs and Lafayette Gruber and Punch Perkins and some others. Then, in the afternoon, if we could still function after the baseball, we would fish some in Bayou Pierre or down off the river bluffs, half-asleep under a cottonwood tree, waiting for every scrap of breeze that blew up off the water. It was hotter than I can describe, and the heat starting before nine in the morning would go on as late as four or five in the afternoon.

But over the next couple of days, whether I was fishing or swimming, so long as Joe and Lafayette and I were near the river, we kept seeing Malissa and Nathan. They would show up in the sandy stretch back from the river that was choked with second-growth trees and brush and Bermuda grass. We could see them for a moment and then they'd vanish like a pair of foxes or rabbits trying to get across a clearing. I kept wondering if they were just fooling around and not paying any attention to us. Or if they were staying clear of us on purpose. Considering it was the second, I wondered what the purpose might be.

They kept showing up in the vicinity of the old Sentell house. Lafayette or I would wave to them, but Malissa would just look up like a doe and go diving back into the brush or behind the house. Nathan wouldn't even bother looking up. He'd just vanish. Looking back, I can remember that I didn't really pay much attention to this once I got used to not having the carcass of the *Spirit of St. Louis* jammed under my nose every hour and to the quiet around the house without Malissa's loud vocal help stirring up the sweltering afternoon.

Finally, one afternoon, Joe Hobbs and Lafayette Gruber and I were stretched out on the porch like a flock of hounds. We were drinking some of my mother's sugared ice tea, trying to recover from a thirteen-inning game and a bout of seining for river shrimp. Joe and Lafayette were arguing about Sentell. Not because they were interested, but because I had started them off with one of my questions.

—I think you and your grampaw are both missing some marbles, Lafayette was saying. —Major Sentell was a fine man. You better watch your mouth, too. His family is still around. If one of the Sentell boys heard you say his grandfather was yellow or a Yankee lover, he'd deck you for keeps. Them people have family feeling.

—How come he wouldn't fight after Vicksburg?

—He signed one of them papers. Promised not to. Give his word.

—To the Yanks.

—You figure two years in a prison camp somewhere was better? Listen, I never heard of anybody comin' back from one of them camps.

It went on like that till my father came home. Then, while mother was fixing sandwiches, we all got into it. My father told about the time Nathan Bedford Forrest rode his horse into the Gayoso Hotel in Memphis looking for a Yankee general. Who managed to sneak out a window, but had to leave his pants behind. We were laughing and just joshing around when Malissa and Nathan turned up running into the yard from across the street and over the rise that led down to the Sentell place.

—Hey, Malissa called to me. —Look.

She handed me a piece of old and faded paper with some pencil markings on it, while Nathan squatted smirking at everyone on the edge of the porch. —Just look, he echoed.

—It's real. Malissa grinned like an idiot.

—Sure it's real, I said. —Real paper. What are all these squiggly circles?

—Trees, Nathan put in quickly. —In scouts, they showed us how . . . cartographers—

—Whats? Lafayette asked.

—Mapmakers, Malissa translated.

—Show trees like—

I shrugged and tried to signal Joe and Lafayette not to laugh. The kids were asking for it, but you don't have to give people everything they ask for.

—Reckon some pirate captain left it laying around? Lafayette laughed. —Must of been a boy scout. Reckon even a eagle scout pirate captain with fifty merit badges, huh?

Malissa jerked the paper out of my hand and she and Nathan went on into the house. They stayed in there sulking till mother brought out sandwiches and they heard us all laughing and talking. Then they couldn't hold it anymore. They had to come out and tell us how they had been swimming down the river and almost caught a gar barehanded, and how after that they had gone up to the old house to eat lunch. It was while they were looking for a shady place where the noon sun didn't come through the shattered roof that Nathan stepped on a board which came loose and cracked him in the shin, which knocked him into the wall.

—And he went through the wallpaper, and it was so brittle it just fell all to pieces. And his head knocked out another board in the wall and jarred one of the joists loose and—

—My God. My father whistled, interrupting Malissa. —He sounds like a portable wrecking crew. Is there anything left of the house?

Which only brought on another long reign of silence until after mother brought out some homemade peach ice cream. Then Nathan had to let go again. —And behind that joist, next to the clapboards that covered the outside there was this kind of canvas envelope. And inside we found this here map.

Father looked at it. It was a kind of gray-brown like butcher paper or a paper bag. It looked pretty old, but not all that old. Stuck in a wall out at the Sentell house with the weather coming in on it, a month would age it as much as a hundred years.

—It wasn't canvas, Malissa said.

—What? I asked.

—The thing we found it in. It was kind of like oilcloth. Like somebody had tore up a tablecloth and sewed up a little sack of what was left.

—Looks old, my father said. —What are these little irregular circles—

—Trees, I said. —It's a plan for a formal garden somebody forgot to plant.

—Shut up, Malissa said. —It's trees all right. And here's a road. And this is the house.

Everybody was down on the porch floor now. Joe Hobbs, with his eyebrows raised, taking it all in for later recital to whoever asked him. Lafayette, almost strangling to keep from laughing out loud. My father and I caught between curiosity and something in the neighborhood of what Lafayette had called family feeling. Maybe the kids were a little nuts. All kids fourteen and sixteen are a little nuts. Two years before, I had been sixteen and probably a little nuts myself.

—Can't be the old Sentell house, my father said.

Malissa and Nathan turned on him. —Why not? they said together.

—Because this place on the map is at least a quarter of a mile from the water, if the scale means anything. The Sentell place is maybe two hundred yards from the river. And where's this road? There's not even a calf track that looks like this around that old house.

—Maybe the pirate had him a place in the Bahamas. Lafayette sniggered.

—Maybe that thing is the right map in the wrong country.

That took care of the rest of the evening as far as Malissa and Nathan were concerned. In fact, it took care of the next couple of days. They just sat around the house and moped. On Saturday Nathan finished the *Spirit of St. Louis*. That afternoon he and Malissa took it up on the garage, set fire to it, and let it fly off in flames over toward Bayou Pierre. Then they sat on the garage till suppertime. The next day was Sunday, and when my father asked if they wanted to take a ride out Fairfield Avenue, Malissa burst into tears and Nathan said something filthy.

So that Sunday evening, it was a pretty gloomy dump when Joe Hobbs showed up. I poured him a dipper of sugared iced tea and we went out on the porch to watch the moon and slap mosquitoes. He looked worried, and that surprised me. Because Joe Hobbs never looked any way at all. His great-grandfather had been a blacksmith, his grandfather owned an automobile garage, and his father had the biggest hardware and feed-seed store in the parish. And not one of them, so far as I could tell, had ever registered any expression at all. The most dramatic thing that ever happened to a Hobbs face was when a rill of sweat ran down it.

But Joe was troubled, and I thought I'd leave him alone about Sentell and wait to see what he had to say. He finished his tea and kind of picked at his shoe.

—That map, he started.

—Forget it. The kids will be over their sulks in another day or two.

—Naw, that map—

—Some guy stuck it in there. Probably meant to sell it to some fool later on and forgot it.

Naw, Joe said as if I had not even interrupted him, as if he were trying to get it clear in his own head. —I got to talking to my grampaw. He said the river's changed maybe twice along about here in the last fifty years or so. Said it keeps cutting back and forth, but the Corps of Engineers never would come up and—

I felt as if a December wind had just snuck onto the porch and let me have it in the back. Really, as he said it, I could see the whole past laughing at me. What if? Just what if that map?

—The road, I said weakly.

—Used to run up along there till they cut it out when they run Highway Twenty back in the nineteen tens. They just straightened it out on account of the only place that got slighted by the new route was the Sentell place, and there wasn't anybody owned a big enough piece of it to complain. It was there, all right.

So there had been a road. And the river in another place. And I was so hung up in all the history and my circles in a pool that I forgot things do change. That you can concrete or dig up or cover over or build on anything a lot in eighty years. —That doesn't prove the map means anything, I said weakly.

—Naw, Joe said. —It just proves whoever was funning around knew the place he was joking about.

By the next morning, when I woke up and talked to my father about it, I knew that Malissa and Nathan had either heard us or talked to Joe or something. Because they were gone, too. The garage was always a mess, with maybe three or even four hundred old bottles and plenty of newspaper all over. But when one of us really needed money, needed it so bad we were even willing to do something to get it, the garage was always in the way of getting cleaned.

—They woke up before daybreak, my father told me at breakfast. —And took the bottles down to the Youree Drive drugstore and got a dollar and a quarter for cleaning it up. They even took the newspapers to sell.

That afternoon they came tramping in, covered with dust, Malissa's swimming suit wet with sweat, and Nathan almost ready to drop. Nathan got me out in the backyard as if he had murdered somebody and wanted me to help dig the grave.

—That Joe Hobbs is a friend of yours, ain't he?

—Sure.

—He's got a brother out at Centenary College, huh?

—Yep.

—I need a transit.

—You need a kick in the fanny.

—Listen, don't fool with me. You tell him to get me a transit to borrow, and I'll pay him for the loan. I'll pay him so good he won't believe it.

—Sure.

But that misplaced river and that ghost road had made me a little skittish of just shoving Nathan over on the grass and letting it go. So I talked to Joe. Who talked to his big flat-faced identical brother. Who for no reason I could imagine brought a transit over to the house (which was my first chance actually to look through one and get to know what it was really for). He told Nathan that it was borrowed from the college, only nobody knew it had been borrowed since they didn't need it during the summer, and that if anything happened to it, he Buddy Hobbs, would ravel Nathan's spine for him. I asked Joe about it after his brother had left and Nathan and Malissa hit out for their daily rounds.

—Well, I told him about that map.

—So what? It's a joke.

—He said Nathan was old enough to use it.

—But why?

—That map, Joe said, narrowing his eyes, trying to explain. But it wasn't clear in his memory and he couldn't say it. If it had been anybody but Joe, I would have called it a hunch.

—That map, me and Buddy looked at it with Nathan. Looked like somebody knew every tree. Buddy used to hunt squirrel over there in the fall. Said there used to be one old out-of-place cypress which ain't anything but a stump now, and so buried you can't even hardly see the stump. But it was on the map Just like another tree. Even said "Cipres" next to it on there.

Which was the end of that. We talked about Sentell. He told me about a boy Major Sentell and his wife had taken in. Who had lived across the river till a year or so ago when he died. Just talk. The major and his life were fading again. Maybe that goofy map had broken the spell. Some things cancel other things. As if everything were all hooked together in crazy combinations. As if a Chinaman could pull up a rice stalk in his paddy field and make a tree vanish on the Caddo Parish Courthouse Square.

It was almost time for supper when I saw Nathan and Malissa running through the open fields across from us and up into the yard. Malissa held out her hand.

—Spider bit me, she said. —Probably a black widow.

—Probably a giant tarantula, I said.

Nathan set up his transit out on the curb. He aimed it toward the house and beckoned to Malissa. I just sat on the porch and watched them. It was like watching somebody making a movie. Or the way I guessed it would be.

—Thirty-five yards, Nathan said. —Dead that way.

—Through the front door? Malissa asked a little quizzically.

—You want to see that map?

—Okay, she said. —Gimme the tapeline.

Then I saw where their bottle and paper and garage-cleaning money had gone. It was the biggest, shiniest tape measure I ever saw. It must have been a hundred yards long. Malissa took the end of it in her unbitten hand and skipped into the house with it.

—You must be surveying for a railroad, I told him.

—Boy, you're funny, he answered, squinting through the transit. That was the first time my little brother had ever given me the brush-off. But not the last. So I went on inside and washed up. When I came back out of the bathroom, they were in the kitchen. My mother was standing in the breakfast room.

—Look, Nathan was telling Malissa, —you can go all the way back to the last tree if you want. Were we right up to there? I mean, from the house, from that last porch post on out to the tree?

—I reckon.

—Okay. Were we right from there to the curb, even if that road is changed?

—I believe.

—Then we're right now. It's here. Maybe a foot or so off one way or the other. But it's in here. I bet it's right under the stove.

—Will youall—my mother began. But she wasn't in touch with them.

—We've got to get an ax and a couple of shovels, Nathan said. —I forgot that. You reckon we could swap this tapeline for an ax and some shovels?

This time my mother came through a little stronger. —Youall clear out. You've had too much sun. Didn't I tell you they were getting too much sun? she asked me.

—I believe you did, I said.

—And something else. Youall forget that ax and things. You just put it out of mind. If you even look like you mean to go fooling around this kitchen—

—Maybe they could widen it some, I said. —Everybody is always complaining how little it is.

My mother looked at me for a few seconds. —You're funny, she said, and walked out to meet my father who was just putting his car in our clean garage. That did it for me. I guess I sulked till after supper. I guess I sulked longer than that. Because when I went to bed, I never even realized that the kids had been out and were back again and had gone to bed before me. All I remember is hearing my father tell them that the kitchen better stay the way it was, map or no map. If they wanted to stay the way they were.

But it's hard to put the fear of God into a sixteen-year-old, much less into a fourteen-year-old. And I guess it's impossible to hold down a kid of any age who's got a headful of buried treasure. Anyhow, I went to sleep kind of feeling sorry for them. I guess I halfway wanted to see whether there really was anything to that map. But I could see my father's position, too. Who tears up kitchens on a hunch?

About three thirty or four in the morning, I found out who. It seems I was dreaming of this girl I had seen at Centenary College one day when I went over with Job Hobbs. She was tall and tanned dark as walnut, and we were sitting in the student union, and she was looking at me. And somebody was tunneling under our table. Or something.

Then I was awake, and I could still hear it. Like a giant armadillo scratching and scuffling in the dirt. I got up, amazed to find I was as alert as if I had never closed my eyes. Maybe in a way I hadn't. Maybe I knew, not just suspected, but really knew what was going to happen. I passed the door to my parents' room. It was closed. Of course. Then the hall door. Also closed. Of course. So was the door into the dining room. But the door into the kitchen wasn't closed. Just as I reached it, feeling my way in the darkness, I fell into a pile of dirt as tall as I was. I couldn't see anything of the kitchen at all. Except a kind of soft glow coming from up over the dirt as if somebody were using a flashlight with some paper Scotch-taped across it. Which they were.

I managed to scramble up to the top of the pile, and since I'd been asleep, I could see pretty well. The floor in the middle of the kitchen was gone. Just gone. At the back door was a pile of stovewood which I reckoned had once been it. One leg of the stove had fallen into the hole which was already six or six and a half feet deep. And when the stove leg went in, it had pulled the gas connection loose from the wall. They had plugged the fractured pipe with a carrot, though, and the odor of escaping gas wasn't really too bad. Down in the hole there they were, Nathan and Malissa, in underwear, digging like a pair of matched badgers. I was spread out on the rampart of dirt above them, and it was cool beneath me. They had started throwing dirt into the breakfast room, so I didn't even have to worry about a shovelful in the face. I just watched for a while.

—You got maybe an hour to— I began finally.

—Find it, Malissa cut in without even looking up at me. Nathan glanced at me and kept digging.

—Hit oil, I finished. —And it better not be any ten-barrel a day squeaker, either.

—Listen, we'll have—

—Better be a gusher. Even a water gusher would do. That way you can swear you never got out of your bed when it happened, and that the earth's natural forces pushed a waterspout right through the kitchen. Then you could set off the gas and blow the whole kitchen away. Which would probably obscure the evidence. Or if you don't like that, there's a bus for Texarkana leaving every hour, and I'll give you a day's head start before I tell 'em which way you went.

—Don't even talk to him, Malissa told Nathan. —There's no sense in it, Nathan Bedford. He wouldn't believe it if the Lord was to come down and—

—In about an hour that's just what it will take, I told them.

—What? Nathan asked.

—The Lord. And his angels and saints. And you better pray he still knows how to carpenter and brings about a hundred and fifty feet of prime floorboard. But they were both digging again, and so I just slid back down the pile and walked out onto the front porch. I could feel a cynical, kind of superior smile plastered all over my face, and I tried to let it fade. Because they were going to catch nine kinds of particular hell, and it wasn't really their fault. It wasn't even the fault of whoever had stuck that nutty map in the wall of the Sentell place. It was just something in all of us that came out especially strong in them. I stared toward the long low rise of field and sparse trees that rolled down to the Sentell house on the far side, and I thought how all of us are retrievers one way or another. We all want to recapture the past. I had been hung on finding out about a man who was dead before I was born, who had lived and died in a world eighty years and six hundred miles from where I was born. And the kids were caught by it, too. It wasn't just money they were after, not even money for a house. It was the past. They were looking for special money from a special place, and if they missed Cleburne's treasure and found a million dollars worth of nice fresh bills in a bank bag, it would be as much of a letdown in some ways as if they found nothing at all. So over behind the rise the Sentell place was vacant and empty, moldering in the first sickly gray light before dawn. This same kind of summer morning eighty years ago, the Negroes would have been up, listening to Sentell or somebody ringing a bell or a wheel band for breakast. This time of year there would still have been plenty of cotton to chop, and the sun would have been rising at the same moment over Sentell or Cleburne or the anonymous Negro soldier who had owned the land, and they would have been readying themselves for another long burning day, blowing out the coal-oil lamp, finishing a handful of cold corn bread. Ready to throw the dice another time with this land, to see if they could wrench a dollar's worth of cotton out of five dollars' worth of sweat. Somehow that was what I had been trying to touch, to conjure up again. Nathan and Malissa, too. But it was all past, and there are no maps to it at all.

Then, as the sun rose, a great pale-yellow disk in the east, over the distant rise I heard Malissa call. —Hey, come help, will you? Come on.

The cynical smile was gone, and I felt better. Those kids. Those goofy kids. The past dissolved as I turned back into the house, and I found myself wondering if I could hold back the firing squad that would be waking up in a few minutes, not even knowing it had a job of execution to do. Or at least provide some bandage of affection before the first volley went off. I never loved those kids so much. I thought, *They never needed it so much.* Which makes for a good conjunction.

—Okay, I called back to what had once been the kitchen. —You got about ten minutes. Any last words?

—Just one, I heard Malissa say in a muffled tone, as if she were a long way off.

We were just climbing out of the hole when I heard my father coming. He hit the pile of dirt and cursed in a sleepy unexcited voice for a moment. Then it was quiet over there. You could tell when he got his eyes open and oriented and realized what he was up against. —My God, he whispered in awe. —Youall . . . I'm going to—

He was scrambling up that rampart of loose dirt then, and I could feel Nathan shivering up against me as he came over the top. But about then the sun came sliding through the breakfast room windows, and my father could see what Malissa was spreading out on the table.

—I get a hundred and twenty-one thousand dollars, Malissa was saying dryly, still arranging gold coins in the bright morning sunlight, stack after stack after stack. —Not counting those bundles of Confederate bills. Or the silver. And I haven't started on that old carpetbag full of greenbacks yet.

We were all in the dining room a little later. We were eating some doughnuts from down at the Dixie-Maid, and drinking coffee borrowed out of the next-door neighbor's pot. Mother was still looking at all of us as if she had awakened to find her family turned into werewolves during the night.

—Two hundred and one thousand dollars, my father said when the counting was done. He was shaking his head, looking from one of us to the next as if he needed sympathy. —We'd better get this to the bank.

—Bank? Malissa asked, her eyebrows going up. —What for?

—Bank, Nathan repeated. —You mean we got to telephone London for a numismatist.

—Never mind that, I said. —Dad can take care of the taxes.

It was Malissa's turn to look around for sympathy. It is a sad thing for a pretty young girl to have an idiot brother. —A numismatist, she said quietly, —deals in old coins.

—'Specially like this one, Nathan said, handing me a kind of worn old silver dollar. —It's an 1804 silver dollar.

—That's nice, I said.

Even my father stared at me then. —Eighteen o four? That would be worth—

—Maybe seventy-five thousand by itself, Malissa said evenly. —And we'd lose at least thirty percent trading all this in at the bank. Even the banknotes are worth more than face value. But we need a numismatist.

—Oh sure, my father said. He and mother seemed to have all the starch taken out of them.

Nathan sat frowning, looking at the burdened table. —And maybe you could call a carpenter, too. And whatever you call a man who fills holes.

I choked a little and set twelve thousand dollars in gold certificates down next to my cold coffee.

—I'd do it myself except I have to take Buddy Hobbs' transit back to him.

My father fumbled in his robe and found a match. He tamped his pipe and shrugged at Mother. Just as he was about to strike the match, I remembered. —I wouldn't do that, I said. —There's only a carrot between us and glory if you do.

—Say, Malissa put in brightly. —Maybe you could stay home from work today. And we could all get dressed and—

—Yes, my father said.

—We could go drive out on Fairfield Avenue.

Which is what we did. And that's how we came to live here after the lawsuits and the Internal Revenue and the coin dealers and all were over with. And the nice part is that we never felt like we were outsiders. Because we really belonged on Fairfield Avenue, somebody told my father. After all, we weren't what you'd call new rich, Malissa said. Our money had been in Caddo Parish almost eighty years.

afterword

"The Retrievers" satirizes several attitudes which Corrington and other Southern writers have more often treated seriously. Gently humorous in his approach, Corrington shows a lighter side of such themes as the Southerner's preoccupation with the past, his need to feel rooted in his environment, and his need for respect in the community—in short, his various relationships with tradition.

In this story we see two different responses to Southern tradition. The narrator is fascinated by it and intimately concerned with it; yet, at the same time, he is paralyzed by it. On the other hand, his younger brother and sister have little perceivable concern with tradition, except insofar as they can use it to better their present condition. Moreover, in their dogged refusal to quit in the face of mockery and opposition, they prove themselves to be even closer to the past than is their brother.

questions for general discussion

1. How does the author's attitude toward the past compare with that of Flannery O'Connor?

2. In what way does the character Joe Hobbs contribute to the structure of the story?

3. Why, after they have burned *The Spirit of Saint Louis,* does Malissa cry and Nathan say "something filthy" when their father mentions riding down Fairfield Avenue?

4. Why does the author have Mr. Armistead laughing as he says, "captains of crockery, majors of merchandizing, brigadiers of banking"?

5. Comment on the narrator's reaction to Lafayette's phrase, "Them people have family feeling."

6. What is the significance of the author's using the words "still beautiful" and "impressive" after he has given the description of the decayed Fairfield Avenue?

suggestions for writing

1. Comment on the author's use of the treasure map to reveal character change.

2. How does Corrington make his characters humorous yet sympathetic?

3. Comment on the narrator's tone as it contributes to the overall effect of the story.

4. Comment on what is "retrieved" by the "retrievers."

RALPH ELLISON
battle royal

It goes a long way back, some twenty years. All my life I had been looking for something, and everywhere I turned someone tried to tell me what it was. I accepted their answers too, though they were often in contradiction and even self-contradictory. I was naïve. I was looking for myself and asking everyone except myself questions which I, and only I, could answer. It took me a long time and much painful boomeranging of my expectations to achieve a realization everyone else appears to have been born with: That I am nobody but myself. But first I had to discover that I am an invisible man!

And yet I am no freak of nature, nor of history. I was in the cards, other things having been equal (or unequal) eighty-five years ago. I am not ashamed of my grandparents for having been slaves. I am only ashamed of myself for having at one time been ashamed. About eighty-five years ago they were told that they were free, united with others of our country in everything pertaining to the common good, and, in everything social, separate like the fingers of the hand. And they believed it. They exulted in it. They stayed in their place, worked hard, and brought up my father to do the same. But my grandfather is the one. He was an odd old guy, my grandfather, and I am told I take after him. It was he who caused the trouble. On his deathbed he called my father to him and said, "Son, after I'm gone I want you to keep up the good fight. I never told you, but our life is a war and I have been a traitor all my born days, a spy in the enemy's country ever since I give up my gun back in the Reconstruction. Live with your head in the lion's mouth. I want you to overcome 'em with yeses, undermine 'em with grins, agree 'em to death and destruction, let 'em swoller you till they vomit or bust wide open." They thought the old man had gone out of his mind. He had been the meekest of men. The younger children were rushed from the room, the shades drawn and the flame of the lamp turned so low that it sputtered on the wick like the old man's breathing. "Learn it to the younguns," he whispered fiercely; then he died.

But my folks were more alarmed over his last words than over his dying. It was as though he had not died at all, his words caused so much anxiety. I was warned emphatically to forget what he had said and, indeed, this is the first time it has been mentioned outside the family circle. It had a tremendous effect upon me, however. I could never be sure of what he meant. Grandfather had been a quiet old man who never made any trouble, yet on his deathbed he had called himself a traitor and a spy, and he had spoken of his meekness as a dangerous activity. It became a constant puzzle which lay unanswered in the back of my mind. And whenever things went well for me I remembered my grandfather and felt guilty and uncomfortable. It was as though I was carrying out his advice in spite of myself. And to make it worse, everyone loved me for it. I was praised by the most lily-white men of the town. I was considered an example of desirable conduct—just as my grandfather had been. And what puzzled me was that the old man had defined it as *treachery*. When I was praised for my conduct I felt a guilt that in some way I was doing something that was really against the wishes of the white folks, that if they had understood they would have desired me to act just the opposite, that I should have been sulky and mean, and that that really would have been what they wanted, even though they were fooled and thought they wanted me to act as I did. It made me afraid that some day they would look upon me as a traitor and I would be lost. Still I was more afraid to act any other way because they didn't like that at all. The old man's words were like a curse. On my graduation day I delivered an oration in which I showed that humility was the secret, indeed, the very essence of progress. (Not that I believed this—how could I, remembering my grandfather?—I only believed that it worked.) It was a great success. Everyone praised me and I was invited to give the speech at a gathering of the town's leading white citizens. It was a triumph for our whole community.

It was in the main ballroom of the leading hotel. When I got there I discovered that it was on the occasion of a smoker, and I was told that since I was to be there anyway I might as well take part in the battle royal to be fought by some of my schoolmates as part of the entertainment. The battle royal came first.

All of the town's big shots were there in their tuxedoes, wolfing down the buffet foods, drinking beer and whiskey and smoking black cigars. It was a large room with a high ceiling. Chairs were arranged in neat rows around three sides of a portable boxing ring. The fourth side was clear, revealing a gleaming space of polished floor. I had some misgivings over the battle royal, by the way. Not from a distaste for fighting, but because I didn't care too much for the other fellows who were to take part. They were tough guys who seemed to have no grandfather's curse worrying their minds. No one could mistake their toughness. And besides, I suspected that fighting a battle royal might detract from the dignity of my speech. In those pre-invisible days I visualized myself as a potential Booker T. Washington. But the other fellows didn't care too much for me either, and there were nine of them. I felt superior to them in my way, and I didn't like the manner in which we were all crowded together into the servants' elevator. Nor did they like my being there. In fact, as the warmly lighted floors flashed past the elevator we had words over the fact that I, by taking part in the fight, had knocked one of their friends out of a night's work.

We were led out of the elevator through a rococo hall into an anteroom and told to get into our fighting togs. Each of us was issued a pair of boxing gloves and ushered out into the big mirrored hall, which we entered looking cautiously about us and whispering, lest we might accidentally be heard above the noise of the room. It was foggy with cigar smoke. And already the whiskey was taking effect. I was shocked to see some of the most important men of the town quite tipsy. They were all there—bankers, lawyers, judges, doctors, fire chiefs, teachers, merchants. Even one of the more fashionable pastors. Something we could not see was going on up front. A clarinet was vibrating sensuously and the men were standing up and moving eagerly forward. We were a small tight group, clustered together, our bare upper bodies touching and shining with anticipatory sweat; while up front the big shots were becoming increasingly excited over something we still could not see. Suddenly I heard the school superintendent, who had told me to come, yell, "Bring up the shines, gentlemen! Bring up the little shines!"

We were rushed up to the front of the ballroom, where it smelled even more strongly of tobacco and whiskey. Then we were pushed into place. I almost wet my pants. A sea of faces, some hostile, some amused, ringed around us, and in the center, facing us, stood a magnificent blonde—stark naked. There was a dead silence. I felt a blast of cold air chill me. I tried to back away, but they were behind me and around me. Some of the boys stood with lowered heads, trembling. I felt a wave of irrational guilt and fear. My teeth chattered, my skin turned to goose flesh, my knees knocked. Yet I was strongly attracted and looked in spite of myself. Had the price of looking been blindness, I would have looked. The hair was yellow like that of a circus kewpie doll, the face heavily powdered and rouged, as though to form an abstract mask, the eyes hollow and smeared a cool blue, the color of a baboon's butt. I felt a desire to spit upon her as my eyes brushed slowly over her body. Her breasts were firm and round as the domes of East Indian temples, and I stood so close as to see the fine skin texture and beads of pearly perspiration glistening like dew around the pink and erected buds of her nipples. I wanted at one and the same time to run from the room, to sink through the floor, or go to her and cover her from my eyes and the eyes of the others with my body; to feel the soft thighs, to caress her and destroy her, to love her and murder her, to hide from her, and yet to stroke where below the small American flag tattooed upon her belly her thighs formed a capital V. I had a notion that of all in the room she saw only me with her impersonal eyes.

And then she began to dance, a slow sensuous movement; the smoke of a hundred cigars clinging to her like the thinnest of veils. She seemed like a fair bird-girl girdled in veils calling to me from the angry surface of some gray and threatening sea. I was transported. Then I became aware of the clarinet playing and the big shots yelling at us. Some threatened us if we looked and others if we did not. On my right I saw one boy faint. And now a man grabbed a silver pitcher from a table and stepped close as he dashed ice water upon him and stood him up and forced two of us to support him as his head hung and moans issued from his thick bluish lips. Another boy began to plead to go home. He was the largest of the group, wearing dark red fighting trunks much too small to conceal the erection which projected from him as though in answer to the insinuating low-registered moaning of the clarinet. He tried to hide himself with his boxing gloves.

And all the while the blonde continued dancing, smiling faintly at the big shots who watched her with fascination, and faintly smiling at our fear. I noticed a certain merchant who followed her hungrily, his lips loose and drooling. He was a large man who wore diamond studs in a shirtfront which swelled with the ample paunch underneath, and each time the blonde swayed her undulating hips he ran his hand through the thin hair of his bald head and, with his arms upheld, his posture clumsy like that of an intoxicated panda, wound his belly in a slow and obscene grind. This creature was completely hypnotized. The music had quickened. As the dancer flung herself about with a detached expression on her face, the men began reaching out to touch her. I could see their beefy fingers sink into the soft flesh. Some of the others tried to stop them and she began to move around the floor in graceful circles, as they gave chase, slipping and sliding over the polished floor. It was mad. Chairs went crashing, drinks were spilt, as they ran laughing and howling after her. They caught her just as she reached a door, raised her from the floor, and tossed her as college boys are tossed at a hazing, and above her red, fixed-smiling lips I saw the terror and disgust in her eyes, almost like my own terror and that which I saw in some of the other boys. As I watched, they tossed her twice and her soft breasts seemed to flatten against the air and her legs flung wildly as she spun. Some of the more sober ones helped her to escape. And I started off the floor, heading for the anteroom with the rest of the boys.

Some were still crying and in hysteria. But as we tried to leave we were stopped and ordered to get into the ring. There was nothing to do but what we were told. All ten of us climbed under the ropes and allowed ourselves to be blindfolded with broad bands of white cloth. One of the men seemed to feel a bit sympathetic and tried to cheer us up as we stood with our backs against the ropes. Some of us tried to grin. "See that boy over there?" one of the men said. "I want you to run across at the bell and give it to him right in the belly. If you don't get him, I'm going to get you. I don't like his looks." Each of us was told the same. The blindfolds were put on. Yet even then I had been going over my speech. In my mind each word was as bright as flame. I felt the cloth pressed into place, and frowned so that it would be loosened when I relaxed.

But now I felt a sudden fit of blind terror. I was unused to darkness. It was as though I had suddenly found myself in a dark room filled with poisonous cottonmouths. I could hear the bleary voices yelling insistently for the battle royal to begin.

"Get going in there!"

"Let me at the big nigger!"

I strained to pick up the school superintendent's voice, as though to squeeze some security out of that slightly more familiar sound.

"Let me at those black sonsabitches!" someone yelled.

"No, Jackson, no!" another voice yelled. "Here, somebody, help me hold Jack."

"I want to get at that ginger-colored nigger. Tear him limb from limb," the first voice yelled.

I stood against the ropes trembling. For in those days I was what they called ginger-colored, and he sounded as though he might crunch me between his teeth like a crisp ginger cookie.

Quite a struggle was going on. Chairs were being kicked about and I could hear voices grunting as with a terrific effort. I wanted to see, to see more desperately than ever before. But the blindfold was as tight as a thick skin-puckering scab and when I raised my gloved hands to push the layers of white aside a voice yelled, "Oh, no you don't, black bastard! Leave that alone!"

"Ring the bell before Jackson kills him a coon!" someone boomed in the sudden silence. And I heard the bell clang and the sound of feet scuffling forward.

A glove smacked against my head. I pivoted, striking out stiffly as someone went past, and felt the jar ripple along the length of my arm to my shoulder. Then it seemed as though all nine of the boys had turned upon me at once. Blows pounded me from all sides while I struck out as best I could. So many blows landed upon me that I wondered if I were not the only blindfolded fighter in the ring, or if the man called Jackson hadn't succeeded in getting me after all.

Blindfolded, I could no longer control my motions. I had no dignity. I stumbled about like a baby or a drunken man. The smoke had become thicker and with each new blow it seemed to sear and further restrict my lungs. My saliva became like hot bitter glue. A glove connected with my head, filling my mouth with warm blood. It was everywhere. I could not tell if the moisture I felt upon my body was sweat or blood. A blow landed hard against the nape of my neck. I felt myself going over, my head hitting the floor. Streaks of blue light filled the black world behind the blindfold. I lay prone, pretending that I was knocked out, but felt myself seized by hands and yanked to my feet. "Get going, black boy! Mix it up!" My arms were like lead, my head smarting from blows. I managed to feel my way to the ropes and held on, trying to catch my breath. A glove landed in my midsection and I went over again, feeling as though the smoke had become a knife jabbed into my guts. Pushed this way and that by the legs milling around me, I finally pulled erect and discovered that I could see the black, sweat-washed forms weaving in the smoky-blue atmosphere like drunken dancers weaving to the rapid drum-like thuds of blows.

Everyone fought hysterically. It was complete anarchy. Everybody fought everybody else. No group fought together for long. Two, three, four, fought one, then turned to fight each other, were themselves attacked. Blows landed below the belt and in the kidney, with the gloves open as well as closed, and with my eye partly opened now there was not so much terror. I moved carefully, avoiding blows, although not too many to attract attention, fighting from group to group. The boys groped about like blind, cautious crabs crouching to protect their mid-sections, their heads pulled in short against their shoulders, their arms stretched nervously before them, with their fists testing the smoke-filled air like the knobbed feelers of hypersensitive snails. In one corner I glimpsed a boy violently punching the air and heard him scream in pain as he smashed his hand against a ring post. For a second I saw him bent over holding his hand, then going down as a blow caught his unprotected head. I played one group against the other, slipping in and throwing a punch then stepping out of range while pushing the others into the melee to take the blows blindly aimed at me. The smoke was agonizing and there were no rounds, no bells at three minute intervals to relieve our exhaustion. The room spun round me, a swirl of lights, smoke, sweating bodies surrounded by tense white faces. I bled from both nose and mouth, the blood spattering upon my chest.

The men kept yelling, "Slug him, black boy! Knock his guts out!"

"Uppercut him! Kill him! Kill that big boy!"

Taking a fake fall, I saw a boy going down heavily beside me as though we were felled by a single blow, saw a sneaker-clad foot shoot into his groin as the two who had knocked him down stumbled upon him. I rolled out of range, feeling a twinge of nausea.

The harder we fought the more threatening the men became. And yet, I had begun to worry about my speech again. How would it go? Would they recognize my ability? What would they give me?

I was fighting automatically when suddenly I noticed that one after another of the boys was leaving the ring. I was surprised, filled with panic, as though I had been left alone with an unknown danger. Then I understood. The boys had arranged it among themselves. It was the custom for the two men left in the ring to slug it out for the winner's prize. I discovered this too late. When the bell sounded two men in tuxedoes leaped into the ring and removed the blindfold. I found myself facing Tatlock, the biggest of the gang. I felt sick at my stomach. Hardly had the bell stopped ringing in my ears than it clanged again and I saw him moving swiftly toward me. Thinking of nothing else to do I hit him smash on the nose. He kept coming, bringing the rank sharp violence of stale sweat. His face was a black blank of a face, only his eyes alive—with hate of me and aglow with a feverish terror from what had happened to us all. I became anxious. I wanted to deliver my speech and he came at me as though he meant to beat it out of me. I smashed him again and again, taking his blows as they came. Then on a sudden impulse I struck him lightly and as we clinched, I whispered, "Fake like I knocked you out, you can have the prize."

"I'll break your behind," he whispered hoarsely.

"For *them?*"

"For *me,* sonofabitch."

They were yelling for us to break it up and Tatlock spun me half around with a blow, and as a joggled camera sweeps in a reeling scene, I saw the howling red faces crouching tense beneath the cloud of blue-gray smoke. For a moment the world wavered, unraveled, flowed, then my head cleared and Tatlock bounced before me. That fluttering shadow before my eyes was his jabbing left hand. Then falling forward, my head against his damp shoulder, I whispered,

"I'll make it five dollars more."

"Go to hell!"

But his muscles relaxed a trifle beneath my pressure and I breathed, "Seven?"

"Give it to your ma," he said, ripping me beneath the heart.

And while I still held him I butted him and moved away. I felt myself bombarded with punches. I fought back with hopeless desperation. I wanted to deliver my speech more than anything else in the world, because I felt only these men could judge truly my ability, and now this stupid clown was ruining my chances. I began fighting carefully now, moving in to punch him and out again with my greater speed. A lucky blow to his chin and I had him going too —until I heard a loud voice yell, "I got my money on the big boy."

Hearing this, I almost dropped my guard. I was confused: Should I try to win against the voice out there? Would not this go against my speech, and was not this a moment for humility, for nonresistance? A blow to my head as I danced about sent my right eye popping like a jack-in-the-box and settled my dilemma. The room went red as I fell. It was a dream fall, my body languid and fastidious as to where to land, until the floor became impatient and smashed up to meet me. A moment later I came to. An hypnotic voice said FIVE emphatically. And I lay there, hazily watching a dark red spot of my own blood shaping itself into a butterfly, glistening and soaking into the soiled gray world of the canvas.

When the voice drawled TEN I was lifted up and dragged to a chair. I sat dazed. My eye pained and swelled with each throb of my pounding heart and I wondered if now I would be allowed to speak. I was wringing wet, my mouth still bleeding. We were grouped along the wall now. The other boys ignored me as they congratulated Tatlock and speculated as to how much they would be paid. One boy whimpered over his smashed hand. Looking up front, I saw attendants in white jackets rolling the portable ring away and placing a small square rug in the vacant space surrounded by chairs. Perhaps, I thought, I will stand on the rug to deliver my speech.

Then the M.C. called to us, "Come on up here boys and get your money."

We ran forward to where the men laughed and talked in their chairs, waiting. Everyone seemed friendly now.

"There it is on the rug," the man said. I saw the rug covered with coins of all dimensions and a few crumpled bills. But what excited me, scattered here and there, were the gold pieces.

"Boys, it's all yours," the man said. "You get all you grab."

"That's right, Sambo," a blond man said, winking at me confidentially.

I trembled with excitement, forgetting my pain. I would get the gold and the bills, I thought. I would use both hands. I would throw my body against the boys nearest me to block them from the gold.

"Get down around the rug now," the man commanded, "and don't anyone touch it until I give the signal."

"This ought to be good," I heard.

As told, we got around the square rug on our knees. Slowly the man raised his freckled hand as we followed it upward with our eyes.

I heard, "These niggers look like they're about to pray!"

Then, "Ready," the man said. "Go!"

I lunged for a yellow coin lying on the blue design of the carpet, touching it and sending a surprised shriek to join those rising around me. I tried frantically to remove my hand but could not let go. A hot, violent force tore through my body, shaking me like a wet rat. The rug was electrified. The hair bristled up on my head as I shook myself free. My muscles jumped, my nerves jangled, writhed. But I saw that this was not stopping the other boys. Laughing in fear and embarrassment, some were holding back and scooping up the coins knocked off by the painful contortions of the others. The men roared above us as we struggled.

"Pick it up, goddamnit, pick it up!" someone called like a bass-voiced parrot. "Go on, get it!"

I crawled rapidly around the floor, picking up the coins, trying to avoid the coppers and to get greenbacks and the gold. Ignoring the shock by laughing, as I brushed the coins off quickly, I discovered that I could contain the electricity—a contradiction, but it works. Then the men began to push us onto the rug. Laughing embarrassedly, we struggled out of their hands and kept after the coins. We were all wet and slippery and hard to hold. Suddenly I saw a boy lifted into the air, glistening with sweat like a circus seal, and dropped, his wet back landing flush upon the charged rug, heard him yell and saw him literally dance upon his back, his elbows beating a frenzied tattoo upon the floor, his muscles twitching like the flesh of a horse stung by many flies. When he finally rolled off, his face was gray and no one stopped him when he ran from the floor amid booming laughter.

"Get the money," the M.C. called. "That's good hard American cash!"

And we snatched and grabbed, snatched and grabbed. I was careful not to come too close to the rug now, and when I felt the hot whiskey breath descend upon me like a cloud of foul air I reached out and grabbed the leg of a chair. It was occupied and I held on desperately.

"Leggo nigger! Leggo!"

The huge face wavered down to mine as he tried to push me free. But my body was slippery and he was too drunk. It was Mr. Colcord, who owned a chain of movie houses and "entertainment palaces." Each time he grabbed me I slipped out of his hands. It became a real struggle. I feared the rug more than I did the drunk, so I held on, surprising myself for a moment by trying to topple *him* upon the rug. It was such an enormous idea that I found myself actually carrying it out. I tried not to be obvious, yet when I grabbed his leg, trying to tumble him out of the chair, he raised up roaring with laughter, and, looking at me with soberness dead in the eye, kicked me viciously in the chest. The chair leg flew out of my hand and I felt myself going and rolled. It was as though I had rolled through a bed of hot coals. It seemed a whole century would pass before I would roll free, a century in which I was seared through the deepest levels of my body to the fearful breath within me and the breath seared and heated to the point of explosion. It'll all be over in a flash, I thought as I rolled clear. It'll all be over in a flash.

But not yet, the men on the other side were waiting, red faces swollen as though from apoplexy as they bent forward in their chairs. Seeing their fingers coming toward me I rolled away as a fumbled football rolls off the receiver's fingertips, back into the coals. That time I luckily sent the rug sliding out of place and heard the coins ringing against the floor and the boys scuffling to pick them up and the M.C. calling, "All right, boys, that's all. Go get dressed and get your money."

I was limp as a dish rag. My back felt as though it had been beaten with wires.

When we had dressed the M.C. came in and gave us each five dollars, except Tatlock, who get ten for being last in the ring. Then he told us to leave. I was not to get a chance to deliver my speech, I thought. I was going out into the dim alley in despair when I was stopped and told to go back. I returned to the ballroom, where the men were pushing back their chairs and gathering in groups to talk.

The M.C. knocked on a table for quiet. "Gentlemen," he said, "we almost forgot an important part of the program. A most serious part, gentlemen. This boy was brought here to deliver a speech which he made at his graduation yesterday . . ."

"Bravo!"

"I'm told that he is the smartest boy we've got out there in Greenwood. I'm told that he knows more big words than a pocket-sized dictionary."

Much applause and laughter.

"So now, gentlemen, I want you to give him your attention."

There was still laughter as I faced them, my mouth dry, my eye throbbing. I began slowly, but evidently my throat was tense, because they began shouting, "Louder! Louder!"

"We of the younger generation extol the wisdom of that great leader and educator," I shouted, "who first spoke these flaming words of wisdom: 'A ship lost at sea for many days suddenly sighted a friendly vessel. From the mast of the unfortunate vessel was seen a signal: "Water, water; we die of thirst!" The answer from the friendly vessel came back: "Cast down your bucket where you are." The captain of the distressed vessel, at last heeding the injunction, cast down his bucket, and it came up full of fresh sparkling water from the mouth of the Amazon River.' And like him I say, and in his words, 'To those of my race who depend upon bettering their condition in a foreign land, or who underestimate the importance of cultivating friendly relations with the Southern white man, who is his next-door neighbor, I would say: "Cast down your bucket where you are"—cast it down in making friends in every manly way of the people of all races by whom we are surrounded. . . .' "

I spoke automatically and with such fervor that I did not realize that the men were still talking and laughing until my dry mouth, filling up with blood from the cut, almost strangled me. I coughed, wanting to stop and go to one of the tall brass, sand-filled spittoons to relieve myself, but a few of the men, especially the superintendent, were listening and I was afraid. So I gulped it down, blood, saliva and all, and continued. (What powers of endurance I had during those days! What enthusiasm! What a belief in the rightness of things!) I spoke even louder in spite of the pain. But still they talked and still they laughed, as though deaf with cotton in dirty ears. So I spoke with greater emotional emphasis. I closed my ears and swallowed blood until I was nauseated. The speech seemed a hundred times as long as before, but I could not leave out a single word. All had to be said, each memorized nuance considered, rendered. Nor was that all. Whenever I uttered a word of three or more syllables a group of voices would yell for me to repeat it. I used the phrase "social responsibility" and they yelled:

"What's that word you say, boy?"

"Social responsibility," I said.

"What?"

"Social . . ."

"Louder."

". . . responsibility."

"More!"

"Respon—"

"Repeat!"

"—sibility."

The room filled with the uproar of laughter until, no doubt, distracted by having to gulp down my blood, I made a mistake and yelled a phrase I had often seen denounced in newspaper editorials, heard debated in private.

"Social . . ."

"What?" they yelled.

". . . equality—"

The laughter hung smokelike in the sudden stillness. I opened my eyes, puzzled. Sounds of displeasure filled the room. The M.C. rushed forward. They shouted hostile phrases at me. But I did not understand.

A small dry mustached man in the front row blared out, "Say that slowly, son!"

"What sir?"

"What you just said!"

"Social responsibility, sir," I said.

"You weren't being smart, were you, boy?" he said, not unkindly.

"No, sir!"

"You sure that about 'equality' was a mistake?"

"Oh, yes, sir," I said. "I was swallowing blood."

"Well, you had better speak more slowly so we can understand. We mean to do right by you, but you've got to know your place at all times. All right, now, go on with your speech."

I was afraid. I wanted to leave but I wanted also to speak and I was afraid they'd snatch me down.

"Thank you, sir," I said, beginning where I had left off, and having them ignore me as before.

Yet when I finished there was a thunderous applause. I was surprised to see the superintendent come forth with a package wrapped in white tissue paper, and, gesturing for quiet, address the men.

"Gentlemen, you see that I did not overpraise this boy. He makes a good speech and some day he'll lead his people in the proper paths. And I don't have to tell you that that is important in these days and times. This is a good, smart boy, and so to encourage him in the right direction, in the name of the Board of Education I wish to present him a prize in the form of this . . ."

He paused, removing the tissue paper and revealing a gleaming calfskin briefcase.

". . . in the form of this first-class article from Shad Whitmore's shop."

"Boy," he said, addressing me, "take this prize and keep it well. Consider it a badge of office. Prize it. Keep developing as you are and some day it will be filled with important papers that will help shape the destiny of your people."

I was so moved that I could hardly express my thanks. A rope of bloody saliva forming a shape like an undiscovered continent drooled upon the leather and I wiped it quickly away. I felt an importance that I had never dreamed.

"Open it and see what's inside," I was told.

My fingers a-tremble, I complied, smelling the fresh leather and finding an official-looking document inside. It was a scholarship to the state college for Negroes. My eyes filled with tears and I ran awkwardly off the floor.

I was overjoyed; I did not even mind when I discovered that the gold pieces I had scrambled for were brass pocket tokens advertising a certain make of automobile.

When I reached home everyone was excited. Next day the neighbors came to congratulate me. I even felt safe from grandfather, whose deathbed curse usually spoiled my triumphs. I stood beneath his photograph with my briefcase in hand and smiled triumphantly into his stolid black peasant's face. It was a face that fascinated me. The eyes seemed to follow everywhere I went.

That night I dreamed I was at a circus with him and that he refused to laugh at the clowns no matter what they did. Then later he told me to open my briefcase and read what was inside and I did, finding an official envelope stamped with the state seal; and inside the envelope I found another and another, endlessly, and I thought I would fall of weariness. "Them's years," he said. "Now open that one." And I did and in it I found an engraved document containing a short message in letters of gold. "Read it," my grandfather said. "Out loud."

"To Whom It May Concern," I intoned. "Keep This Nigger-Boy Running."

I awoke with the old man's laughter ringing in my ears.

(It was a dream I was to remember and dream again for many years after. But at that time I had no insight into its meaning. First I had to attend college.)

afterword

"Battle Royal," excerpted from Ellison's novel, *Invisible Man,* presents a nightmarish experience undergone by the protagonist during the time in which he was unaware of his "invisibility." That is, he was unaware of the fact that others viewed him not as a distinct individual with his own needs and ideals, but merely as a stock, less-than-human figure which they called variously "Negro," "Nigger," or "shine." Although, at the smoker described in this story, he had been cruelly mistreated by all the white men whom he had admired, it was apparently only years later that the protagonist realized that his trust in these men was foolish, that his efforts to impress them were futile and self-demeaning, and that his grandfather's lesson about each black man being involved in a war was a sound one. It was later that he realized that, in the words of a dream he had, the desire of all too many whites is to "keep this nigger-boy running."

Ellison was born in 1914 in Oklahoma City, Oklahoma. From 1933 to 1936, he attended Tuskegee Institute in Alabama. Beginning to write seriously in 1939, he subsequently worked on a New York Federal Writer's Project and edited the *Negro Quarterly.* A noted lecturer, he has taught at a number of major universities including the University of Chicago, Rutgers, Yale, and the University of California at Los Angeles. Among the many awards and honors he has received for his writing are the Rosenwald Grant, the National Book Award, and the National Newspaper Publishers Award. In 1963 he was awarded an honorary Doctor of Philosophy in Humane Letters from Tuskegee Institute.

His writings include the novel, *Invisible Man* (1952), and the collected essays, *Shadow and Act* (1964). He is currently engaged in writing another novel.

questions for general discussion

1. Is there any development or change in the character of the protagonist in this story? Does he make any progress toward knowing who he is?

2. What are the implications of the protagonist's statement, "I am not ashamed of my grandparents for having been slaves. I am only ashamed of myself for having at one time been ashamed"?

3. What is the significance of that portion of the protagonist's speech at the

smoker in which he used the quote, "Cast down your bucket where you are"?

4. Contrast the attitudes of the protagonist and Tatlock as they are revealed when Tatlock refuses to "throw" the fight and says he will fight for himself, not for the whites.

5. What is the effect of the scene in which the protagonist sees the nude blonde dancer?

6. What does the scholarship *really* mean to the protagonist?

7. What does Ellison achieve through the lines, "Blindfolded, I could no longer control my motions. I had no dignity"?

suggestions for writing

1. Compare the attitude of the protagonist when he tells the story with his attitude when the events of the story actually took place.

2. Trace and analyze the effects of his grandfather upon the protagonist.

3. Keeping in mind that this story formed part of Ellison's novel, *Invisible Man,* trace and comment on the ways in which various persons—including himself—"see" the protagonist.

4. Comment on the irony in the story. Begin by looking closely at the story's title.

flying home

When Todd came to, he saw two faces suspended above him in a sun so hot and blinding that he could not tell if they were black or white. He stirred, feeling a pain that burned as though his whole body had been laid open to the sun which glared into his eyes. For a moment an old fear of being touched by white hands seized him. Then the very sharpness of the pain began slowly to clear his head. Sounds came to him dimly. He done come to. Who are they? he thought. Naw he ain't, I coulda sworn he was white. Then he heard clearly:

"You hurt bad?"

Something within him uncoiled. It was a Negro sound.

"He's still out," he heard.

"Give 'im time. . . . Say, son, you hurt bad?"

Was he? There was that awful pain. He lay rigid, hearing their breathing and trying to weave a meaning between them and his being stretched painfully upon the ground. He watched them warily, his mind traveling back over a painful distance. Jagged scenes, swiftly unfolding as in a movie trailer, reeled through his mind, and he saw himself piloting a tailspinning plane and landing and landing and falling from the cockpit and trying to stand. Then, as in a great silence, he remembered the sound of crunching bone, and now, looking up into the anxious faces of an old Negro man and a boy from where he lay in the same field, the memory sickened him and he wanted to remember no more.

"How you feel, son?"

Todd hesitated, as though to answer would be to admit an inacceptable weakness. Then, "It's my ankle," he said.

"Which one?"

"The left."

With a sense of remoteness he watched the old man bend and remove his boot, feeling the pressure ease.

"That any better?"

"A lot. Thank you."

He had the sensation of discussing someone else, that his concern was with some far more important thing, which for some reason escaped him.

"You done broke it bad," the old man said. "We have to get you to a doctor."

He felt that he had been thrown into a tailspin. He looked at his watch; how long had he been here? He knew there was but one important thing in the world, to get the plane back to the field before his officers were displeased.

"Help me up," he said. "Into the ship."

"But it's broke too bad. . . ."

"Give me your arm!"

"But, son . . ."

Clutching the old man's arm he pulled himself up, keeping his left leg clear, thinking, "I'd never make him understand," as the leather-smooth face came parallel with his own.

"Now, let's see."

He pushed the old man back, hearing a bird's insistent shrill. He swayed giddily. Blackness washed over him, like infinity.

"You best sit down."

"No, I'm O.K."

"But, son. You jus' gonna make it worse. . . ."

It was a fact that everything in him cried out to deny, even against the flaming pain in his ankle. He would have to try again.

"You mess with that ankle they have to cut your foot off," he heard.

Holding his breath, he started up again. It pained so badly that he had to bite his lips to keep from crying out and he allowed them to help him down with a pang of despair.

"It's best you take it easy. We gon' git you a doctor."

Of all the luck, he thought. Of all the rotten luck, now I have done it. The fumes of high-octane gasoline clung in the heat, taunting him.

"We kin ride him into town on old Ned," the boy said.

Ned? He turned, seeing the boy point toward an ox team browsing where the buried blade of a plow marked the end of a furrow. Thoughts of himself riding an ox through the town, past streets full of white faces, down the concrete runways of the airfield made swift images of humiliation in his mind. With a pang he remembered his girl's last letter. "Todd," she had written, "I don't need the papers to tell me you had the intelligence to fly. And I have always known you to be as brave as anyone else. The papers annoy me. Don't you be contented to prove over and over again that you're brave or skillful just because you're black, Todd. I think they keep beating that dead horse because they don't want to say why you boys are not yet fighting. I'm really disappointed, Todd. Anyone with brains can learn to fly, but then what? What about using it, and who will you use it for? I wish, dear, you'd write about this. I sometimes think they're playing a trick on us. It's very humiliating. . . ." He wiped cold sweat from his face, thinking, What does she know of humiliation? She's never been down South. Now the humiliation would come. When you must have them judge you, knowing that they never accept your mistakes as your own, but hold it against your whole race—that was humiliation. Yes, and humiliation was when you could never be simply yourself, when you were always a part of this old black ignorant man. Sure, he's all right. Nice and kind and helpful. But he's not you. Well, there's one humiliation I can spare myself.

"No," he said, "I have orders not to leave the ship. . . ."

"Aw," the old man said. Then turning to the boy, "Teddy, then you better hustle down to Mister Graves and get him to come. . . ."

"No, wait!" he protested before he was fully aware. Graves might be white. "Just have him get word to the field, please. They'll take care of the rest."

He saw the boy leave, running.

"How far does he have to go?"

"Might' nigh a mile."

He rested back, looking at the dusty face of his watch. But now they know something has happened, he thought. In the ship there was a perfectly good radio, but it was useless. The old fellow would never operate it. That buzzard knocked me back a hundred years, he thought. Irony danced within him like the gnats circling the old man's head. With all I've learned I'm dependent upon this "peasant's" sense of time and space. His leg throbbed. In the plane, instead of time being measured by the rhythms of pain and a kid's legs, the instruments would have told him at a glance. Twisting upon his elbows he saw where dust had powdered the plane's fuselage, feeling the lump form in his throat that was always there when he thought of flight. It's crouched there, he thought, like the abandoned shell of a locust. I'm naked without it. Not a machine, a suit of clothes you wear. And with a sudden embarrassment and wonder he whispered, "It's the only dignity I have. . . ."

He saw the old man watching, his torn overalls clinging limply to him in the heat. He felt a sharp need to tell the old man what he felt. But that would be meaningless. If I tried to explain why I need to fly back, he'd think I was simply afraid of white officers. But it's more than fear . . . a sense of anguish clung to him like the veil of sweat that hugged his face. He watched the old man, hearing him humming snatches of a tune as he admired the plane. He felt a furtive sense of resentment. Such old men often came to the field to watch the pilots with childish eyes. At first it had made him proud; they had been a meaningful part of a new experience. But soon he realized they did not understand his accomplishments and they came to shame and embarrass him, like the distasteful praise of an idiot. A part of the meaning of flying had gone then, and he had not been able to regain it. If I were a prizefighter I would be more human, he thought. Not a monkey doing tricks, but a man. They were pleased simply that he was a Negro who could fly, and that was not enough. He felt cut off from them by age, by understanding, by sensibility, by technology, and by his need to measure himself against the mirror of other men's appreciation. Somehow he felt betrayed, as he had when as a child he grew to discover that his father was dead. Now for him any real appreciation lay with his white officers; and with them he could never be sure. Between ignorant black men and condescending whites, his course of flight seemed mapped by the nature of things away from all needed and natural landmarks. Under some sealed orders, couched in ever more technical and mysterious terms, his path curved swiftly away from both the shame the old man symbolized and the cloudy terrain of white men's regard. Flying blind, he knew but one point of landing and there he would receive his wings. After that the enemy would appreciate his skill and he would assume his deepest meaning, he thought sadly, neither from those who condescended nor from those who praised without understanding, but from the enemy who would recognize his manhood and skill in terms of hate. . . .

He sighed, seeing the oxen making queer, prehistoric shadows against the dry brown earth.

"You just take it easy, son," the old man soothed. "That boy won't take long. Crazy as he is about airplanes."

"I can wait," he said.

"What kinda airplane you call this here'n?"

"An Advanced Trainer," he said, seeing the old man smile. His fingers were like gnarled dark wood against the metal as he touched the low-slung wing.

" 'Bout how fast can she fly?"

"Over two hundred an hour."

"Lawd! That's so fast I bet it don't seem like you moving!"

Holding himself rigid, Todd opened his flying suit. The shade had gone and he lay in a ball of fire.

"You mind if I take a look inside? I was always curious to see. . . ."

"Help yourself. Just don't touch anything."

He heard him climb upon the metal wing, grunting. Now the questions would start. Well, so you don't have to think to answer. . . .

He saw the old man looking over into the cockpit, his eyes bright as a child's.

"You must have to know a lot to work all these here things."

He was silent, seeing him step down and kneel beside him.

"Son, how come you want to fly way up there in the air?"

Because it's the most meaningful act in the world . . . because it makes me less like you, he thought.

But he said: "Because I like it, I guess. It's as good a way to fight and die as I know."

"Yeah? I guess you right," the old man said. "But how long you think before they gonna let you all fight?"

He tensed. This was the question all Negroes asked, put with the same timid hopefulness and longing that always opened a greater void within him than that he had felt beneath the plane the first time he had flown. He felt light-headed. It came to him suddenly that there was something sinister about the conversation, that he was flying unwillingly into unsafe and uncharted regions. If he could only be insulting and tell this old man who was trying to help him to shut up!

"I bet you one thing . . ."

"Yes?"

"That you was plenty scared coming down."

He did not answer. Like a dog on a trail the old man seemed to smell out his fears and he felt anger bubble within him.

"You sho' scared me. When I seen you coming down in that thing with it a-rollin' and a-jumpin' like a pitchin' hoss, I thought sho' you was a goner. I almost had me a stroke!"

He saw the old man grinning, "Ever'thin's been happening round here this morning, come to think of it."

"Like what?" he asked.

"Well, first thing I know, here come two white fellers looking for Mister Rudolph, that's Mister Graves's cousin. That got me worked up right away. . . ."

"Why?"

"Why? 'Cause he done broke outta the crazy house, that's why. He liable to kill somebody," he said. "They oughta have him by now though. Then here you come. First I think it's one of them white boys. Then doggone if you don't fall outta there. Lawd, I'd done heard about you boys but I haven't never seen one o' you-all. Cain't tell you how it felt to see somebody what look like me in a airplane!"

The old man talked on, the sound streaming around Todd's thoughts like air flowing over the fuselage of a flying plane. You were a fool, he thought, remembering how before the spin the sun had blazed bright against the billboard signs beyond the town, and how a boy's blue kite had bloomed beneath him, tugging gently in the wind like a strange, odd-shaped flower. He had once flown such kites himself and tried to find the boy at the end of the invisible cord. But he had been flying too high and too fast. He had climbed steeply away in exultation. Too steeply, he thought. And one of the first rules you learn is that if the angle of thrust is too steep the plane goes into a spin. And then, instead of pulling out of it and going into a dive you let a buzzard panic you. A lousy buzzard!

"Son, what made all that blood on the glass?"

"A buzzard," he said, remembering how the blood and feathers had sprayed back against the hatch. It had been as though he had flown into a storm of blood and blackness.

"Well, I declare! They's lots of 'em around here. They after dead things. Don't eat nothing what's alive."

"A little bit more and he would have made a meal out of me," Todd said grimly.

"They bad luck all right. Teddy's got a name for 'em, calls 'em jimcrows," the old man laughed.

"It's a damned good name."

"They the damnedest birds. Once I seen a hoss all stretched out like he was sick, you know. So I hollers, 'Gid up from there, suh!' Just to make sho! An' doggone, son, if I don't see two ole jimcrows come flying right up outa that hoss's insides! Yessuh! The sun was shinin' on 'em and they couldn't a been no greasier if they'd been eating barbecue."

Todd thought he would vomit, his stomach quivered.

"You made that up," he said.

"Nawsuh! Saw him just like I see you."

"Well, I'm glad it was you."

"You see lots a funny things down here, son."

"No, I'll let you see them," he said.

"By the way, the white folks round here don't like to see you boys up there in the sky. They ever bother you?"

"No."

"Well, they'd like to."

"Someone always wants to bother someone else," Todd said. "How do you know?"

"I just know."

"Well," he said defensively, "no one has bothered us."

Blood pounded in his ears as he looked away into space. He tensed, seeing a black spot in the sky, and strained to confirm what he could not clearly see.

"What does that look like to you?" he asked excitedly.

"Just another bad luck, son."

Then he saw the movement of wings with disappointment. It was gliding smoothly down, wings outspread, tail feathers gripping the air, down swiftly —gone behind the green screen of trees. It was like a bird he had imagined there, only the sloping branches of the pines remained, sharp against the pale stretch of sky. He lay barely breathing and stared at the point where it had disappeared, caught in a spell of loathing and admiration. Why did they make them so disgusting and yet teach them to fly so well? It's like when I was up in heaven, he heard, starting.

The old man was chuckling, rubbing his stubbled chin.

"What did you say?"

"Sho', I died and went to heaven . . . maybe by time I tell you about it they done come after you."

"I hope so," he said wearily.

"You boys ever sit around and swap lies?"

"Not often. Is this going to be one?"

"Well, I ain't so sho', on account of it took place when I was dead."

The old man paused, "That wasn't no lie 'bout the buzzards, though."

"All right," he said.

"Sho' you want to hear 'bout heaven?"

"Please," he answered, resting his head upon his arm.

"Well, I went to heaven and right away started to sproutin' me some wings. Six good ones, they was. Just like them the white angels had. I couldn't hardly believe it. I was so glad that I went off on some clouds by myself and tried 'em out. You know, 'cause I didn't want to make a fool outta myself the first thing. . . ."

It's an old tale, Todd thought. Told me years ago. Had forgotten. But at least it will keep him from talking about buzzards.

He closed his eyes, listening.

". . . First thing I done was to git up on a low cloud and jump off. And doggone, boy, if them wings didn't work! First I tried the right; then I tried the left; then I tried 'em both together. Then Lawd, I started to move on out among the folks. I let 'em see me. . . ."

He saw the old man gesturing flight with his arms, his face full of mock pride as he indicated an imaginary crowd, thinking, It'll be in the newspapers, as he heard, ". . . so I went and found me some colored angels—somehow I didn't believe I was an angel till I seen a real black one, ha, yes! Then I was sho'—but they tole me I better come down 'cause us colored folks had to wear a special kin' a harness when we flew. That was how come they wasn't flyin'. Oh yes, an' you had to be extra strong for a black man even, to fly with one of them harnesses. . . ."

This is a new turn, Todd thought, what's he driving at?

"So I said to myself, I ain't gonna be bothered with no harness! Oh naw! 'Cause if God let you sprout wings you oughta have sense enough not to let nobody make you wear something what gits in the way of flyin'. So I starts to flyin'. Heck, son," he chuckled, his eyes twinkling, "you know I had to let eve'ybody know that old Jefferson could fly as good as anybody else. And I could too, fly smooth as a bird! I could even loop-the-loop—only I had to make sho' to keep my long white robe down roun' my ankles. . . ."

Todd felt uneasy. He wanted to laugh at the joke, but his body refused, as of an independent will. He felt as he had as a child when after he had chewed a sugar-coated pill which his mother had given him, she had laughed at his efforts to remove the terrible taste.

". . . Well," he heard, "I was doing all right 'til I got to speeding. Found out I could fan up a right strong breeze, I could fly so fast. I could do all kin'sa stunts too. I started flying up to the stars and divin' down and zooming roun' the moon. Man, I like to scare the devil outa some ole white angels. I was raisin' hell. Not that I meant any harm, son. But I was just feeling good. It was so good to know I was free at last. I accidentally knocked the tips offa some stars and they tell me I caused a storm and a coupla lynchings down here in Macon County—though I swear I believe them boys what said that was making up lies on me. . . ."

He's mocking me, Todd thought angrily. He thinks it's a joke. Grinning down at me . . . His throat was dry. He looked at his watch; why the hell didn't they come? Since they had to, why? One day I was flying down one of them heavenly streets. You got yourself into it, Todd thought. Like Jonah in the whale.

"Justa throwin' feathers in everybody's face. An' ole Saint Peter called me in. Said, 'Jefferson, tell me two things, what you doin' flyin' without a harness; an' how come you flyin' so fast?' So I tole him I was flyin' without a harness 'cause it got in my way, but I couldn'ta been flyin' so fast, 'cause I wasn't usin' but one wing. Saint Peter said, 'You wasn't flyin' with but one wing?' 'Yessuh,' I says, scared-like. So he says, 'Well, since you got sucha extra fine pair of wings you can leave off yo' harness awhile. But from now on none of that there one-wing flyin', 'cause you gittin' up too damn much speed!' "

And with one mouth full of bad teeth you're making too damned much talk, thought Todd. Why don't I send him after the boy? His body ached from the hard ground and seeking to shift his position he twisted his ankle and hated himself for crying out.

"It gittin' worse?"

"I . . . I twisted it," he groaned.

"Try not to think about it, son. That's what I do."

He bit his lip, fighting pain with counter-pain as the voice resumed its rhythmical droning. Jefferson seemed caught in his own creation.

". . . After all that trouble I just floated roun' heaven in slow motion. But I forgot, like colored folks will do, and got to flyin' with one wing again. This time I was restin' my old broken arm and got to flyin' fast enough to shame the devil. I was comin' so fast, Lawd, I got myself called befo' ole Saint Peter again. He said, 'Jeff, didn't I warn you 'bout that speedin'?' 'Yessuh,' I says, 'but it was an accident.' He looked at me sad-like and shook his head and I knowed I was gone. He said, 'Jeff, you and that speedin' is a danger to the heavenly community. If I was to let you keep on flyin', heaven wouldn't be nothin' but uproar. Jeff, you got to go!' Son, I argued and pleaded with that old white man, but it didn't do a bit of good. They rushed me straight to them pearly gates and gimme a parachute and a map of the state of Alabama . . ."

Todd heard him laughing so that he could hardly speak, making a screen between them upon which his humiliation glowed like fire.

"Maybe you'd better stop awhile," he said, his voice unreal.

"Ain't much more," Jefferson laughed. "When they gimme the parachute ole Saint Peter ask me if I wanted to say a few words before I went. I felt so bad I couldn't hardly look at him, specially with all them white angels standin' around. Then somebody laughed and made me mad. So I tole him, 'Well, you done took my wings. And you puttin' me out. You got charge of things so's I can't do nothin' about it. But you got to admit just this: While I was up here I was the flyinest sonofabitch what ever hit heaven!' "

At the burst of laughter Todd felt such an intense humiliation that only great violence would wash it away. The laughter which shook the old man like a boiling purge set up vibrations of guilt within him which not even the intricate machinery of the plane would have been adequate to transform and he heard himself screaming, "Why do you laugh at me this way?"

He hated himself at that moment, but he had lost control. He saw Jefferson's mouth fall open, "What——?"

"Answer me!"

His blood pounded as though it would surely burst his temples and he tried to reach the old man and fell, screaming, "Can I help it because they won't let us actually fly? Maybe we are a bunch of buzzards feeding on a dead horse, but we can hope to be eagles, can't we? Can't we?"

He fell back, exhausted, his ankle pounding. The saliva was like straw in his mouth. If he had the strength he would strangle this old man. This grinning, gray-headed clown who made him feel as he felt when watched by the white officers at the field. And yet this old man had neither power, prestige, rank, nor technique. Nothing that could rid him of this terrible feeling. He watched him, seeing his face struggle to express a turmoil of feeling.

"What you mean, son? What you talking 'bout . . . ?"

"Go away. Go tell your tales to the white folks."

"But I didn't mean nothing like that. . . . I . . . I wasn't tryin' to hurt your feelings. . . ."

"Please. Get the hell away from me!"

"But I didn't, son. I didn't mean all them things a-tall."

Todd shook as with a chill, searching Jefferson's face for a trace of the mockery he had seen there. But now the face was somber and tired and old. He was confused. He could not be sure that there had ever been laughter there, that Jefferson had ever really laughed in his whole life. He saw Jefferson reach out to touch him and shrank away, wondering if anything except the pain, now causing his vision to waver, was real. Perhaps he had imagined it all.

"Don't let it get you down, son," the voice said pensively.

He heard Jefferson sigh wearily, as though he felt more than he could say. His anger ebbed, leaving only the pain.

"I'm sorry," he mumbled.

"You just wore out with pain, was all. . . ."

He saw him through a blur, smiling. And for a second he felt the embarrassed silence of understanding flutter between them.

"What you was doin' flyin' over this section, son? Wasn't you scared they might shoot you for a crow?"

Todd tensed. Was he being laughed at again? But before he could decide, the pain shook him and a part of him was lying calmly behind the screen of pain that had fallen between them, recalling the first time he had ever seen a plane. It was as though an endless series of hangars had been shaken ajar in the air base of his memory and from each, like a young wasp emerging from its cell, arose the memory of a plane.

The first time I ever saw a plane I was very small and planes were new in the world. I was four-and-a-half and the only plane that I had ever seen was a model suspended from the ceiling of the automobile exhibit at the State Fair. But I did not know that it was only a model. I did not know how large a real plane was, nor how expensive. To me it was a fascinating toy, complete in itself, which my mother said could only be owned by rich little white boys. I stood rigid with admiration, my head straining backwards as I watched the gray little plane describing arcs above the gleaming tops of the automobiles. And I vowed that, rich or poor, someday I would own such a toy. My mother had to drag me out of the exhibit and not even the merry-go-round, the Ferris wheel, or the racing horses could hold my attention for the rest of the Fair. I was too busy imitating the tiny drone of the plane with my lips, and imitating with my hands the motion, swift and circling, that it made in flight.

After that I no longer used the pieces of lumber that lay about our back yard to construct wagons and autos . . . now it was used for airplanes. I built biplanes, using pieces of board for wings, a small box for the fuselage, another piece of wood for the rudder. The trip to the Fair had brought something new into my small world. I asked my mother repeatedly when the Fair would come back again. I'd lie in the grass and watch the sky, and each fighting bird became a soaring plane. I would have been good a year just to have seen a plane again. I became a nuisance to everyone with my questions about airplanes. But planes were new to the old folks, too, and there was little that they could tell me. Only my uncle knew some of the answers. And better still, he could carve propellers from pieces of wood that would whirl rapidly in the wind, wobbling noisily upon oiled nails.

I wanted a plane more than I'd wanted anything; more than I wanted the red wagon with rubber tires, more than the train that ran on a track with its train of cars. I asked my mother over and over again:

"Mamma?"

"What do you want, boy?" she'd say.

"Mamma, will you get mad if I ask you?" I'd say.

"What do you want now? I ain't got time to be answering a lot of fool questions. What you want?"

"Mamma, when you gonna get me one . . . ?" I'd ask.

"Get you one what?" she'd say.

"You know, Mamma; what I been asking you. . . ."

"Boy," she'd say, "if you don't want a spanking you better come on an' tell me what you talking about so I can get on with my work."

"Aw, Mamma, you know. . . ."

"What I just tell you?" she'd say.

"I mean when you gonna buy me a airplane."

"Airplane! Boy, is you crazy? How many times I have to tell you to stop that foolishness. I done told you them things cost too much. I bet I'm gon' wham the living daylight out of you if you don't quit worrying me 'bout them things!"

But this did not stop me, and a few days later I'd try all over again.

Then one day a strange thing happened. It was spring and for some reason I had been hot and irritable all morning. It was a beautiful spring. I could feel it as I played barefoot in the backyard. Blossoms hung from the thorny black locust trees like clusters of fragrant white grapes. Butterflies flickered in the sunlight above the short new dew-wet grass. I had gone in the house for bread and butter and coming out I heard a steady unfamiliar drone. It was unlike anything I had ever heard before. I tried to place the sound. It was no use. It was a sensation like that I had when searching for my father's watch, heard ticking unseen in a room. It made me feel as though I had forgotten to perform some task that my mother had ordered . . . then I located it, overhead. In the sky, flying quite low and about a hundred yards off was a plane! It came so slowly that it seemed barely to move. My mouth hung wide; my bread and butter fell into the dirt. I wanted to jump up and down and cheer. And when the idea struck I trembled with excitement: "Some little white boy's plane's done flew away and all I got to do is stretch out my hands and it'll be mine!" It was a little plane like that at the Fair, flying no higher than the eaves of our roof. Seeing it come steadily forward I felt the world grow warm with promise. I opened the screen and climbed over it and clung there, waiting. I would catch the plane as it came over and swing down fast and run into the house before anyone could see me. Then no one could come to claim the plane. It droned nearer. Then when it hung like a silver cross in the blue directly above me I stretched out my hand and grabbed. It was like sticking my finger through a soap bubble. The plane flew on, as though I had simply blown my breath after it. I grabbed again, frantically, trying to catch the tail. My fingers clutched the air and disappointment surged tight and hard in my throat. Giving one last desperate grasp, I strained forward. My fingers ripped from the screen. I was falling. The ground burst hard against me. I drummed the earth with my heels and when my breath returned, I lay there bawling.

My mother rushed through the door.

"What's the matter, chile! What on earth is wrong with you?"

"It's gone! It's gone!"

"What gone?"

"The airplane . . ."

"Airplane?"

"Yessum, jus' like the one at the Fair. . . . I . . . I tried to stop it an' it kep' right on going. . . ."

"When, boy?"

"Just now," I cried, through my tears.

"Where it go, boy, what way?"

"Yonder, there . . ."

She scanned the sky, her arms akimbo and her checkered apron flapping in the wind as I pointed to the fading plane. Finally she looked down at me, slowly shaking her head.

"It's gone! It's gone!" I cried.

"Boy, is you a fool?" she said. "Don't you see that there's a real airplane 'stead of one of them toy ones?"

"Real . . . ?" I forgot to cry. "Real?"

"Yass, real. Don't you know that thing you reaching for is bigger'n a auto? You here trying to reach for it and I bet it's flying 'bout two hundred miles higher'n this roof." She was disgusted with me. "You come on in this house before somebody else sees what a fool you done turned out to be. You must think these here lil ole arms of you'n is mighty long. . . ."

I was carried into the house and undressed for bed and the doctor was called. I cried bitterly, as much from the disappointment of finding the plane so far beyond my reach as from the pain.

When the doctor came I heard my mother telling him about the plane and asking if anything was wrong with my mind. He explained that I had had a fever for several hours. But I was kept in bed for a week and I constantly saw the plane in my sleep, flying just beyond my fingertips, sailing so slowly that it seemed barely to move. And each time I'd reach out to grab it I'd miss and through each dream I'd hear my grandma warning:

> Young man, young man,
> Yo' arms too short
> To box with God. . . .

"Hey, son!"

At first he did not know where he was and looked at the old man pointing, with blurred eyes.

"Ain't that one of youall's airplanes coming after you?"

As his vision cleared he saw a small black shape above a distant field, soaring through waves of heat. But he could not be sure and with the pain he feared that somehow a horrible recurring fantasy of being split in twain by the whirling blades of a propeller had come true.

"You think he sees us?" he heard.

"See? I hope so."

"He's coming like a bat outa hell!"

Straining, he heard the faint sound of a motor and hoped it would soon be over.

"How you feeling?"

"Like a nightmare," he said.

"Hey, he's done curved back the other way!"

"Maybe he saw us," he said. "Maybe he's gone to send out the ambulance and ground crew." And, he thought with despair, maybe he didn't even see us.

"Where did you send the boy?"

"Down to Mister Graves," Jefferson said. "Man what owns this land."

"Do you think he phoned?"

Jefferson looked at him quickly.

"Aw sho'. Dabney Graves is got a bad name on accounta them killings but he'll call though. . . ."

"What killings?"

"Them five fellers . . . ain't you heard?" he asked with surprise.

"No."

"Everybody knows 'bout Dabney Graves, especially the colored. He done killed enough of us."

Todd had the sensation of being caught in a white neighborhood after dark.

"What did they do?" he asked.

"Thought they was men," Jefferson said. "An' some he owed money, like he do me. . . ."

"But why do you stay here?"

"You black, son."

"I know, but . . ."

"You have to come by the white folks, too."

He turned away from Jefferson's eyes, at once consoled and accused. And I'll have to come by them soon, he thought with despair. Closing his eyes, he heard Jefferson's voice as the sun burned blood-red upon his lips.

"I got nowhere to go," Jefferson said, "an' they'd come after me if I did. But Dabney Graves is a funny fellow. He's all the time making jokes. He can be mean as hell, then he's liable to turn right around and back the colored against the white folks. I seen him do it. But me, I hates him for that more'n anything else. 'Cause just as soon as he gits tired helping a man he don't care what happens to him. He just leaves him stone cold. And then the other white folks is double hard on anybody he done helped. For him it's just a joke. He don't give a hilla beans for nobody—but hisself. . . ."

Todd listened to the thread of detachment in the old man's voice. It was as though he held his words arm's length before him to avoid their destructive meaning.

"He'd just as soon do you a favor and then turn right around and have you strung up. Me, I stays outa his way 'cause down here that's what you gotta do."

If my ankle would only ease for a while, he thought. The closer I spin toward the earth the blacker I become, flashed through his mind. Sweat ran into his eyes and he was sure that he would never see the plane if his head continued whirling. He tried to see Jefferson, what was it that Jefferson held in his hand? It was a little black man, another Jefferson! A little black Jefferson that shook with fits of belly-laughter while the other Jefferson looked on with detachment. Then Jefferson looked up from the thing in his hand and turned to speak, but Todd was far away, searching the sky for a plane in a hot dry land on a day and age he had long forgotten. He was going mysteriously with his mother through empty streets where black faces peered from behind drawn shades and someone was rapping at a window and he was looking back to see a hand and a frightened face frantically beckoning from a cracked door and his mother was looking down the empty perspective of the street and shaking her head and hurrying him along and at first it was only a flash he saw and a motor was droning as through the sun-glare he saw it gleaming silver as it circled and he was seeing a burst like a puff of white smoke and hearing his mother yell, Come along, boy, I got no time for them fool airplanes, I got no time, and he saw it a second time, the plane flying high, and the burst appeared suddenly and fell slowly, billowing out and sparkling like fireworks and he was watching and being hurried along as the air filled with a flurry of white pinwheeling cards that caught in the wind and scattered over the rooftops and into the gutters and a woman was running and snatching a card and reading it and screaming and he darted into the shower, grabbing as in winter he grabbed for snowflakes and bounding away at his mother's, Come on here, boy! Come on, I say! and he was watching as she took the card away, seeing her face grow puzzled and turning taut as her voice quavered, "Niggers Stay From The Polls," and died to a moan of terror as he saw the eyeless sockets of a white hood staring at him from the card and above he saw the plane spiraling gracefully, agleam in the sun like a fiery sword. And seeing it soar he was caught, transfixed between a terrible horror and a horrible fascination.

The sun was not so high now, and Jefferson was calling and gradually he saw three figures moving across the curving roll of the field.

"Look like some doctors, all dressed in white," said Jefferson.

They're coming at last, Todd thought. And he felt such a release of tension within him that he thought he would faint. But no sooner did he close his eyes than he was seized and he was struggling with three white men who were forcing his arms into some kind of coat. It was too much for him, his arms were pinned to his sides and as the pain blazed in his eyes, he realized that it was a straitjacket. What filthy joke was this?

"That oughta hold him, Mister Graves," he heard.

His total energies seemed focused in his eyes as he searched their faces. That was Graves; the other two wore hospital uniforms. He was poised between two poles of fear and hate as he heard the one called Graves saying, "He looks kinda purty in that there suit, boys. I'm glad you dropped by."

"This boy ain't crazy, Mister Graves," one of the others said. "He needs a doctor, not us. Don't see how you led us way out here anyway. It might be a joke to you, but your cousin Rudolph liable to kill somebody. White folks or niggers, don't make no difference. . . ."

Todd saw the man turn red with anger. Graves looked down upon him, chuckling.

"This nigguh belongs in a straitjacket, too, boys. I knowed that the minit

Jeff's kid said something 'bout a nigguh flyer. You all know you cain't let the nigguh git up that high without his going crazy. The nigguh brain ain't built right for high altitudes. . . ."

Todd watched the drawling red face, feeling that all the unnamed horror and obscenities that he had ever imagined stood materialized before him.

"Let's git outta here," one of the attendants said.

Todd saw the other reach toward him, realizing for the first time that he lay upon a stretcher as he yelled.

"Don't put your hands on me!"

They drew back, surprised.

"What's that you say, nigguh?" asked Graves.

He did not answer and thought that Graves's foot was aimed at his head. It landed on his chest and he could hardly breathe. He coughed helplessly, seeing Graves's lips stretch taut over his yellow teeth, and tried to shift his head. It was as though a half-dead fly was dragging slowly across his face and a bomb seemed to burst within him. Blasts of hot, hysterical laughter tore from his chest, causing his eyes to pop and he felt that the veins in his neck would surely burst. And then a part of him stood behind it all, watching the surprise in Graves's red face and his own hysteria. He thought he would never stop, he would laugh himself to death. It rang in his ears like Jefferson's laughter and he looked for him, centering his eyes desperately upon his face, as though somehow he had become his sole salvation in an insane world of outrage and humiliation. It brought a certain relief. He was suddenly aware that although his body was still contorted it was an echo that no longer rang in his ears. He heard Jefferson's voice with gratitude.

"Mister Graves, the Army done tole him not to leave his airplane."

"Nigguh, Army or no, you gittin' off my land! That airplane can stay 'cause it was paid for by taxpayers' money. But you gittin' off. An' dead or alive, it don't make no difference to me."

Todd was beyond it now, lost in a world of anguish.

"Jeff," Graves said, "you and Teddy come and grab holt. I want you to take this here black eagle over to that nigguh airfield and leave him."

Jefferson and the boy approached him silently. He looked away, realizing and doubting at once that only they could release him from his overpowering sense of isolation.

They bent for the stretcher. One of the attendants moved toward Teddy.

"Think you can manage it, boy?"

"I think I can, suh," Teddy said.

"Well, you better go behind then, and let yo' pa go ahead so's to keep that leg elevated."

He saw the white men walking ahead as Jefferson and the boy carried him along in silence. Then they were pausing and he felt a hand wiping his face; then he was moving again. And it was as though he had been lifted out of his isolation, back into the world of men. A new current of communication flowed between the man and boy and himself. They moved him gently. Far away he heard a mockingbird liquidly calling. He raised his eyes, seeing a buzzard poised unmoving in space. For a moment the whole afternoon seemed suspended and he waited for the horror to seize him again. Then like a song within his head he heard the boy's soft humming and saw the dark bird glide into the sun and glow like a bird of flaming gold.

afterword

In "Flying Home," a young black man learns that it is folly for him to turn his back on his race, for in denying his heritage and his people he is, in fact, denying his own identity. Ellison believes that the black man must be aware of, and take pride in, the experience he shares with his fellow blacks if he is effectually to combat the forces which attempt to hold him down. As Ellison shows in his novel, *Invisible Man,* the Negro who tries to be merely what the white man conceives him to be has no identity, is invisible.

The pilot in "Flying Home" has crashed in his actual flight, but symbolically he has successfully completed a different flight, one to a new understanding. Falling back to earth, coming "home" to where he, as a black man in America, began—in a Southern field, tormented by a brutal white master—Todd learns who he is and who his brothers are. Presumably, he will go back to the airfield with a new understanding, a deeper pride, and perhaps a little justified anger.

questions for general discussion

1. Does the title of the story have any ironic implications?

2. Is there more than one conflict involved in the story?

3. What is the climactic scene in the story?

4. What does Ellison mean when he says Todd has a "need to measure himself against the mirror of other men's appreciation"?

5. What is Ellison's purpose in having the old farmer relate his joke about the time he dreamed he was in Heaven?

6. Why does Todd feel that the fumes of high octane gasoline are "taunting" him?

7. In the last line of the story, why is the boy's "soft humming" linked with Todd's seeing "the dark bird glide into the sun and glow like a bird of flaming gold"?

suggestions for writing

1. Write a theme suggesting ways in which Ellison uses the description of physical setting to illuminate the character development of Todd and to cast light on the theme of the story.

2. Compare and contrast some of the physical and psychological traits of Todd with those of the old black farmer who first finds him.

3. Comment on the significance of the reference to the letters Todd has received from his girl. Is Todd's reaction to these letters significant?

4. Comment on the presence or lack of any stereotype characters in the story.

WILLIAM HUMPHREY
a fresh snow

It was silly and a waste of time. School was not even out yet. She could not expect him for half an hour at least. Still she sat at the window watching the corner of the block.

Snow, dingy with soot, lay thick upon the window ledge. The street ran with slush and through the gray light hovering in the street the mass of buildings opposite looked black and close.

As she watched, a few large flakes began to fall. They lighted on the window ledge, and bending forward to look at them, her breath condensing on the glass, she thought of the thrilling, rare snows of her childhood.

She had been five years old when she was wakened in the night to see her first snow. Wrapped in quilts, she and her brother had stood at the window wiping away the steam of their breaths and peering into the blackness, while their father told of the snows he had seen. Two inches fell that night, a good fall, and in the morning the grownups were gay and happy for the children's sake. After breakfast everyone went out with soupbowls. Each looked for a drifted spot to fill his bowl; even so, they had to scrape lightly to keep from picking up dirt. They ate it sprinkled with sugar and flavored with vanilla extract. Her brother came home in midmorning, for school had been let out to celebrate, and through the afternoon they watched the snow disappear. By night it was gone. She was eight before she saw her next.

Otherwise the winters there were fitful times, days of pale sun followed by days of slashing rain. How often she had sat looking out at the dripping trees and the colorless, sodden fields. Seven years before she had sat all day for weeks at the parlor window in her brother Leon's house. Then she was waiting for Donald to be born. Leon had taken her in when she grew too big to work in the confectionery or climb the three flights of the boarding house in town. She had had to stay behind when George was transferred from the camp. There was no housing in California and George was expecting to go overseas any day. Donald was three years old before his father saw him.

She had met George in the confectionery where she was the cashier. The soldiers from the camp were mostly Northern boys and the town mistrusted girls who went out with them. She always rang up their bills and counted out their change with a quickness which discouraged conversation. But George never tried to say more than "thank you." Perhaps it piqued her that her distance suited him that well. In time he grew friendly and she did not remember his former silence against him. One thing right off stood in his favor: he was not an officer. She mistrusted even Southerners who were officers. And once you got to know him George turned out to be a regular tease. She had always enjoyed being gently teased, and when George mimicked her accent, saying, "Yawl fetch it an Ah hep ye tote it," she felt she was being appreciated in a new way. He teased her also with outlandish tales about the North, but she was more impressed when he told her the truth, such as when he described the bolt factory where he worked, which employed more men on each shift than there were in her countyseat. She began to compare him to the local boys whom she knew she might at times have had, and she was glad she had done nothing hasty. To have been forced to settle down with never a glimpse of the world beyond came to seem a dreary life.

What foolish notions she had formed then, and how long ago it seemed. Now she was a regular city dweller. If her kinfolks could see her would they think she was much changed?

A sudden darkening of the light made her turn to the window. The snow was thickening. Down in the street an old bent man was groping along. He was pulling a child's sled on which rode a small carton of groceries. His rapid breath condensed in feeble whiffs and he swayed a little from side to side.

Cities, as she had thought so many times, were no place for old folks. No one had time to help or notice them. Whenever she saw an old man waiting helplessly on a street corner or risking the traffic she was thankful that her poor father had lived and died down South. She was glad she had been with him that last year, glad that he had lived to see Donald and glad she had let him believe that when George came back they were going to settle on the old homeplace. He had liked George. He liked a man, no matter where he was from, who looked you square in the eye, who put something into his handshake, who was not a damned smart aleck. Of course he had felt bound to say something about the Civil War. She remembered well his surprise and her own when George said he did not know whether any of his ancestors had fought in it.

She closed her eyes and saw her father's grave lying under a steady gray rain. She could see the whole family plot and she named them off in order in her mind, with their dates and epitaphs. Another month and it would be graveyard-cleaning time. Surely that old custom had not died out since she went away. It had been such a good time for all, a little melancholy, but not solemn, as you might think. Everyone came early bringing garden rakes and worn-down brooms. It would be the first nice day in spring, still cool enough to work comfortably and make it pleasant to smell the fires of rotted leaves. The children ran and played, being careful not to tread on any graves, of course. It was not thought good taste to clean the graves of your own kin. You cleaned other people's plots and trusted them to clean yours. The children's special chore was to clean and decorate the graves of little children. Each brought a "pretty"—something weatherproof—a china doll or a glass doorknob or a colored bottle, and with these they decorated the graves while they told again the sweetly sad story of each dead child. Then came dinner on the ground. Each woman brought the dish she was famous for and everybody knew without asking whom to compliment on each dish. Her mother always brought pecan pie. It was a time known for forming friendships among the children and courtships among the young. By night the graves had been raked and swept and the headstones straightened, and by then all the men had gone a few times out to the woods where a bottle was kept, so everyone went home feeling tired and happy, pleasantly melancholy, and good friends with the whole community. It seemed you were born knowing the names of every member of every family and when they were born and died, and after a while it came to seem that you had known them all personally all your life and their loss was a personal loss to you.

Often she had wondered where the city dead were buried and how they were looked after, but a feeling of propriety came over her and she hesitated to ask. Surely they could not be as forgotten as they seemed to be. In George's family they never mentioned their dead. You would think they had no kin beyond the living ones.

She saw in her mind the unfinished stone beside her father's grave. It could not be long before her mother would lie there. Would she see her again before that time? What would the date read on that stone? Donald seemed to be losing his memory of his grandmother. Would he see her once more so he could have a memory of her? George would have let her have her mother with her, but her mother would not come. It was just as well, she supposed. It pained her to think how helpless and out of place and lonely her mother would feel, cut off from her old ways, her relatives and old friends. She would feel so lost and frightened, caught up in the shrill, jostling store crowds. She would have sorrowed all day to have been yelled at by the butcher in the chain store.

"Mek up yer mind, lady, mek up yer mind!"

Would her mother find her much changed? She had tried to be a good wife to George. She had believed she ought to try to forget the ways she had been brought up to when they were different from her husband's ways. But there were things she felt she would never get used to. She remembered George's mother asking her right off what nationality she was. If you asked anybody that question back home then you were already sure he was some kind of foreigner, and beneath taking exception.

She looked out for some sight of Donald, but the street was empty. She lay back in her chair and saw herself and him stepping out of the bus in the depot back home. Should she let them know she was coming, or surprise them? If she wrote ahead they would go to a lot of trouble, but, she must admit, that would not have displeased her. They would exclaim over Donald and disagree about which person in the family he looked most like. Strange to realize that many things, so familiar to her, would have to be explained to Donald. In the afternoon they would have people over, relatives and old friends, to sit on the porch and talk. They would tell of births and deaths and talk of the weather and crops, of the things they had always talked about, of life and the afterlife, and stretched out in the porch swing she would feel herself soothed by the warm breeze and by the slow warm liquid flow of Southern voices.

She was startled from her thoughts by the sound of running on the stairs. She had forgotten what she was waiting for and for a moment the sight of the boy in the door awoke no memory in her. She looked at him without recognition. He wore thick snow pants and a padded jacket, heavy rubber boots and a fur cap with large muffs from which his face peeped out red with cold. He was covered with snow. He had dashed in so quickly from outside that flakes still clung to his cheeks and in his brows and lashes.

He closed the door and stamped in, shaking himself like a dog and giving off the smell of cold wool and cold rubber. When he neared her she felt the cold which surrounded him and it seemed to penetrate to her heart. She stood up in an impulse of fear.

"I gotta get my sled. Me and a gang of boys are going to the park," he said. "They're meeting me on the corner in five minutes."

Even his voice seemed stiff with cold. What kind of talk was that, so sharp and nasal? That was not the voice she had given him! She heard the voice of her kin reproach her for bringing up her son in forgetfulness of them.

"No," she cried. "You can't go. Stay with me."

Her strangeness frightened him. He said weakly, "But I told them I would. They've all gone to get their sleds."

But she would not let him go. She made him take off his things. She put cocoa on the range to heat and when it was done she sat him on her lap and rocked him softly, his head against her breast, while she told him all about the South, where he was born.

afterword

William Humphrey, although not unaware of the harshness often found in Southern life, finds in the South a warmth and graciousness which are often lacking in other regions and which grow out of the close relations maintained within families and between members of the same town. There is a sense of shared heritage and, hence, of shared concerns, which frequently makes the exiled Southerner a particularly lonely figure.

In "A Fresh Snow," the coldness of both the climate and people of the North depresses Donald's mother and makes her miss the South. The impersonality and brusqueness of Northern life makes her feel sad and alone. Worse, she fears that her son will know nothing of his Southern background and grow up lacking any awareness of the pleasures of shared communal relationships.

Born in Clarksville, Texas, in 1924, William Humphrey has published stories in a wide assortment of periodicals, including *The New Yorker, Harper's Bazaar,* and the *Sewanee Review.* A collection of short stories, *The Last Husband,* appeared in 1953. His novel, *Home from the Hill,* was received with critical acclaim in 1958; subsequently, the story was made into a motion picture. In 1965 he published a second novel, *The Ordways*. While both novels are set in Humphrey's own region of Southeast Texas, his short stories range widely in setting, character, and tone.

questions for general discussion

1. What is the significance of the title, "A Fresh Snow"?

2. What trait of Donald's frightens his mother shortly following her memory of herself "stretched out in the porch swing . . . soothed by the warm breeze and by the slow warm liquid flow of Southern voices"?

3. Comment on the effect Donald's winter clothing has upon his mother when he comes in from the street. How does she respond to the situation?

4. What is the significance of George's not knowing whether any of his ancestors had fought in the Civil War?

5. What do we learn about Donald's mother from her thought, "Now she was a regular city dweller. If her kinfolks could see her would they think she was much changed"?

suggestions for writing

1. Develop a theme exploring the mother's sense of identity and analyze some reasons for her concern over the effect of environment on Donald.

2. Citing some of the contrasts between the backgrounds of Donald's parents, analyze the effect Humphrey achieves through showing these differences.

3. Comment on Humphrey's use of concrete details as they affect the mood of this story.

4. Comment on the larger social significances of the mother's memory of the customary "graveyard-cleaning time."

ERNEST J. GAINES
the sky is gray

1

Go'n be coming in a few minutes. Coming round that bend down there full speed. And I'm go'n get out my handkerchief and wave it down, and we go'n get on it and go.

I keep on looking for it, but Mama don't look that way no more. She's looking down the road where we just come from. It's a long old road, and far 's you can see you don't see nothing but gravel. You got dry weeds on both sides, and you got trees on both sides, and fences on both sides, too. And you got cows in the pastures and they standing close together. And when we was coming out here to catch the bus I seen the smoke coming out of the cows's noses.

I look at my mama and I know what she's thinking. I been with Mama so much, just me and her, I know what she's thinking all the time. Right now it's home—Auntie and them. She's thinking if they got enough wood—if she left enough there to keep them warm till we get back. She's thinking if it go'n rain and if any of them go'n have to go out in the rain. She's thinking 'bout the hog —if he go'n get out, and if Ty and Val be able to get him back in. She always worry like that when she leaves the house. She don't worry too much if she leave me there with the smaller ones, 'cause she knows I'm go'n look after them and look after Auntie and everything else. I'm the oldest and she say I'm the man.

I look at my mama and I love my mama. She's wearing that black coat and that black hat and she's looking sad. I love my mama and I want put my arm round her and tell her. But I'm not supposed to do that. She say that's weakness and that's crybaby stuff, and she don't want no crybaby round her. She don't want you to be scared, either. 'Cause Ty's scared of ghosts and she's always whipping him. I'm scared of the dark, too, but I make 'tend I ain't. I make 'tend I ain't 'cause I'm the oldest, and I got to set a good sample for the rest. I can't ever be scared and I can't ever cry. And that's why I never said nothing 'bout my teeth. It's been hurting me and hurting me close to a month now, but I never said it. I didn't say it 'cause I didn't want act like a crybaby, and 'cause I know we didn't have enough money to go have it pulled. But,

Lord, it been hurting me. And look like it wouldn't start till at night when you was trying to get yourself little sleep. Then soon 's you shut your eyes—ummm-ummm, Lord, look like it go right down to your heartstring.

"Hurting, hanh?" Ty'd say.

I'd shake my head, but I wouldn't open my mouth for nothing. You open your mouth and let that wind in, and it almost kill you.

I'd just lay there and listen to them snore. Ty there, right 'side me, and Auntie and Val over by the fireplace. Val younger than me and Ty, and he sleeps with Auntie. Mama sleeps round the other side with Louis and Walker.

I'd just lay there and listen to them, and listen to that wind out there, and listen to that fire in the fireplace. Sometimes it'd stop long enough to let me get little rest. Sometimes it just hurt, hurt, hurt. Lord, have mercy.

2

Auntie knowed it was hurting me. I didn't tell nobody but Ty, 'cause we buddies and he ain't go'n tell nobody. But some kind of way Auntie found out. When she asked me, I told her no, nothing was wrong. But she knowed it all the time. She told me to mash up a piece of aspirin and wrap it in some cotton and jugg it down in that hole. I did it, but it didn't do no good. It stopped for a little while, and started right back again. Auntie wanted to tell Mama, but I told her, "Uh-uh." 'Cause I knowed we didn't have any money, and it just was go'n make her mad again. So Auntie told Monsieur Bayonne, and Monsieur Bayonne came over to the house and told me to kneel down 'side him on the fireplace. He put his finger in his mouth and made the Sign of the Cross on my jaw. The tip of Monsieur Bayonne's finger is some hard, 'cause he's always playing on that guitar. If we sit outside at night we can always hear Monsieur Bayonne playing on his guitar. Sometimes we leave him out there playing on the guitar.

Monsieur Bayonne made the Sign of the Cross over and over on my jaw, but that didn't do no good. Even when he prayed and told me to pray some, too, that tooth still hurt me.

"How you feeling?" he say.

"Same," I say.

He kept on praying and making the Sign of the Cross and I kept on praying, too.

"Still hurting?" he say.

"Yes, sir."

Monsieur Bayonne mashed harder and harder on my jaw. He mashed so hard he almost pushed me over on Ty. But then he stopped.

"What kind of prayers you praying, boy?" he say.

"Baptist," I say.

"Well, I'll be—no wonder that tooth is still killing him. I'm going one way and he pulling the other. Boy, don't you know any Catholic prayers?"

"I know 'Hail Mary,' " I say.

"Then you better start saying it."

"Yes, sir."

He started mashing on my jaw again, and I could hear him praying at the same time. And, sure enough, after while it stopped hurting me.

Me and Ty went outside where Monsieur Bayonne's two hounds was and we started playing with them. "Let's go hunting," Ty say. "All right," I say; and we went on back in the pasture. Soon the hounds got on a trail, and me and Ty followed them all 'cross the pasture and then back in the woods, too. And then they cornered this little old rabbit and killed him, and me and Ty made them get back, and we picked up the rabbit and started on back home. But my tooth had started hurting me again. It was hurting me plenty now, but I wouldn't tell Monsieur Bayonne. That night I didn't sleep a bit, and first thing in the morning Auntie told me to go back and let Monsieur Bayonne pray over me some more. Monsieur Bayonne was in his kitchen making coffee when I got there. Soon's he seen me he knowed what was wrong.

"All right, kneel down there 'side that stove," he say. "And this time make sure you pray Catholic. I don't know nothing 'bout that Baptist, and I don't want know nothing 'bout him."

3

Last night Mama say, "Tomorrow we going to town."

"It ain't hurting me no more," I say. "I can eat anything on it."

"Tomorrow we going to town," she say.

And after she finished eating, she got up and went to bed. She always go to bed early now. 'Fore Daddy went in the Army, she used to stay up late. All of us sitting out on the gallery or round the fire. But now, look like soon 's she finish eating she go to bed.

This morning when I woke up, her and Auntie was standing 'fore the fireplace. She say: "Enough to get there and get back. Dollar and a half to have it pulled. Twenty-five for me to go, twenty-five for him. Twenty-five for me to come back, twenty-five for him. Fifty cents left. Guess I get little piece of salt meat with that."

"Sure can use it," Auntie say. "White beans and no salt meat ain't white beans."

"I do the best I can," Mama say.

They was quiet after that, and I made 'tend I was still asleep.

"James, hit the floor," Auntie say.

I still made 'tend I was asleep. I didn't want them to know I was listening.

"All right," Auntie say, shaking me by the shoulder. "Come on. Today's the day."

I pushed the cover down to get out, and Ty grabbed it and pulled it back.

"You, too, Ty," Auntie say.

"I ain't getting no teef pulled," Ty say.

"Don't mean it ain't time to get up," Auntie say. "Hit it, Ty."

Ty got up grumbling.

"James, you hurry up and get in your clothes and eat your food," Auntie say. "What time y'all coming back?" she say to Mama.

"That 'leven o'clock bus," Mama say. "Got to get back in that field this evening."

"Get a move on you, James," Auntie say.

I went in the kitchen and washed my face, then I ate my breakfast. I was having bread and syrup. The bread was warm and hard and tasted good. And I tried to make it last a long time.

Ty came back there grumbling and mad at me.

"Got to get up," he say. "I ain't having no teefes pulled. What I got to be getting up for?"

Ty poured some syrup in his pan and got a piece of bread. He didn't wash his hands, neither his face, and I could see that white stuff in his eyes.

"You the one getting your teef pulled," he say. "What I got to get up for. I bet if I was getting a teef pulled, you wouldn't be getting up. Shucks; syrup again. I'm getting tired of this old syrup. Syrup, syrup, syrup. I'm go'n take with the sugar diabetes. I want me some bacon sometime."

"Go out in the field and work and you can have your bacon," Auntie say. She stood in the middle door looking at Ty. "You better be glad you got syrup. Some people ain't got that—hard 's time is."

"Shucks," Ty say. "How can I be strong."

"I don't know too much 'bout your strength," Auntie say; "but I know where you go'n be hot at, you keep that grumbling up. James, get a move on you; your mama waiting."

I ate my last piece of bread and went in the front room. Mama was standing 'fore the fireplace warming her hands. I put on my coat and my cap, and we left the house.

4

I look down there again, but it still ain't coming. I almost say, "It ain't coming yet," but I keep my mouth shut. 'Cause that's something else she don't like. She don't like for you to say something just for nothing. She can see it ain't coming, I can see it ain't coming, so why say it ain't coming. I don't say it, I turn and look at the river that's back of us. It's so cold the smoke's just raising up from the water. I see a bunch of pool-doos not too far out—just on the other side the lilies. I'm wondering if you can eat pool-doos. I ain't too sure, 'cause I ain't never ate none. But I done ate owls and blackbirds, and I done ate redbirds, too. I didn't want kill the redbirds, but she made me kill them. They had two of them back there. One in my trap, one in Ty's trap. Me and Ty was go'n play with them and let them go, but she made me kill them 'cause we needed the food.

"I can't," I say. "I can't."

"Here," she say. "Take it."

"I can't," I say. "I can't. I can't kill him, Mama, please."

"Here," she say. "Take this fork, James."

"Please, Mama, I can't kill him," I say.

I could tell she was go'n hit me. I jerked back, but I didn't jerk back soon enough.

"Take it," she say.

I took it and reached in for him, but he kept on hopping to the back.

"I can't, Mama," I say. The water just kept on running down my face. "I can't," I say.

"Get him out of there," she say.

I reached in for him and he kept on hopping to the back. Then I reached in farther, and he pecked me on the hand.

"I can't, Mama," I say.

She slapped me again.

I reached in again, but he kept on hopping out my way. Then he hopped to one side and I reached there. The fork got him on the leg and I heard his leg pop. I pulled my hand out 'cause I had hurt him.

"Give it here," she say, and jerked the fork out my hand.

She reached in and got the little bird right in the neck. I heard the fork go in his neck, and I heard it go in the ground. She brought him out and helt him right in front of me.

"That's one," she say. She shook him off and gived me the fork. "Get the other one."

"I can't, Mama," I say. "I'll do anything, but don't make me do that."

She went to the corner of the fence and broke the biggest switch over there she could find. I knelt 'side the trap, crying.

"Get him out of there," she say.

"I can't, Mama."

She started hitting me 'cross the back. I went down on the ground, crying.

"Get him," she say.

"Octavia?" Auntie say.

'Cause she had come out of the house and she was standing by the tree looking at us.

"Get him out of there," Mama say.

"Octavia," Auntie say, "explain to him. Explain to him. Just don't beat him. Explain to him."

But she hit me and hit me and hit me.

I'm still young—I ain't no more than eight; but I know now; I know why I had to do it. (They was so little, though. They was so little. I 'member how I picked the feathers off them and cleaned them and helt them over the fire. Then we all ate them. Ain't had but a little bitty piece each, but we all had a little bitty piece, and everybody just looked at me 'cause they was so proud.) Suppose she had to go away? That's why I had to do it. Suppose she had to go away like Daddy went away? Then who was go'n look after us? They had to be somebody left to carry on. I didn't know it then, but I know it now. Auntie and Monsieur Bayonne talked to me and made me see.

5

Time I see it I get out my handkerchief and start waving. It's still 'way down there, but I keep waving anyhow. Then it come up and stop and me and Mama get on. Mama tell me go sit in the back while she pay. I do like she say, and the people look at me. When I pass the little sign that say "White" and "Colored," I start looking for a seat. I just see one of them back there, but I don't take it, 'cause I want my mama to sit down herself. She comes in the back and sit down, and I lean on the seat. They got seats in the front, but I know I can't sit there, 'cause I have to sit back of the sign. Anyhow, I don't want sit there if my mama go'n sit back here.

They got a lady sitting 'side my mama and she looks at me and smiles little bit. I smile back, but I don't open my mouth, 'cause the wind'll get in and make that tooth ache. The lady take out a pack of gum and reach me a slice, but I shake my head. The lady just can't understand why a little boy'll turn down gum, and she reach me a slice again. This time I point to my jaw. The lady understands and smiles little bit, and I smile little bit, but I don't open my mouth, though.

They got a girl sitting 'cross from me. She got on a red overcoat and her hair's plaited in one big plait. First, I make 'tend I don't see her over there, but then I start looking at her little bit. She make 'tend she don't see me, either, but I catch her looking that way. She got a cold, and every now and then she h'ist that little handkerchief to her nose. She ought to blow it, but she don't. Must think she's too much a lady or something.

Every time she h'ist that little handkerchief, the lady 'side her say something in her ear. She shakes her head and lays her hands in her lap again. Then I catch her kind of looking where I'm at. I smile at her little bit. But think she'll smile back? Uh-uh. She just turn up her little old nose and turn her head. Well, I show her both of us can turn us head. I turn mine too and look out at the river.

The river is gray. The sky is gray. They have pool-doos on the water. The water is wavy, and the pool-doos go up and down. The bus go round a turn, and you got plenty trees hiding the river. Then the bus go round another turn, and I can see the river again.

I look toward the front where all the white people sitting. Then I look at that little old gal again. I don't look right at her, 'cause I don't want all them people to know I love her. I just look at her little bit, like I'm looking out that window over there. But she knows I'm looking that way, and she kind of look at me, too. The lady sitting 'side her catch her this time, and she leans over and says something in her ear.

"I don't love him nothing," that little old gal says out loud.

Everybody back there hear her mouth, and all of them look at us and laugh.

"I don't love you, either," I say. "So you don't have to turn up your nose, Miss."

"You the one looking," she say.

"I wasn't looking at you," I say. "I was looking out that window, there."

"Out that window, my foot," she say. "I seen you. Everytime I turned round you was looking at me."

"You must of been looking yourself if you seen me all them times," I say.

"Shucks," she say, "I got me all kind of boyfriends."

"I got girlfriends, too," I say.

"Well, I just don't want you getting your hopes up," she say.

I don't say no more to that little old gal 'cause I don't want have to bust her in the mouth. I lean on the seat where Mama sitting, and I don't even look that way no more. When we get to Bayonne, she jugg her little old tongue out at me. I make 'tend I'm go'n hit her, and she duck down 'side her mama. And all the people laugh at us again.

6

Me and Mama get off and start walking in town. Bayonne is a little bitty town. Baton Rouge is a hundred times bigger than Bayonne. I went to Baton Rouge once—me, Ty, Mama, and Daddy. But that was 'way back yonder, 'fore Daddy went in the Army. I wonder when we go'n see him again. I wonder when. Look like he ain't ever coming back home. . . . Even the pavement all cracked in Bayonne. Got grass shooting right out the sidewalk. Got weeds in the ditch, too; just like they got at home.

It's some cold in Bayonne. Look like it's colder than it is home. The wind blows in my face, and I feel that stuff running down my nose. I sniff. Mama says use that handkerchief. I blow my nose and put it back.

We pass a school and I see them white children playing in the yard. Big old red school, and them children just running and playing. Then we pass a café, and I see a bunch of people in there eating. I wish I was in there 'cause I'm cold. Mama tells me keep my eyes in front where they belong.

We pass stores that's got dummies, and we pass another café, and then we pass a shoe shop, and that bald-head man in there fixing on a shoe. I look at him and I butt into that white lady, and Mama jerks me in front and tells me stay there.

We come up to the courthouse, and I see the flag waving there. This flag ain't like the one we got at school. This one here ain't got but a handful of stars. One at school got a big pile of stars—one for every state. We pass it and we turn and there it is—the dentist office. Me and Mama go in, and they got people sitting everywhere you look. They even got a little boy in there younger than me.

Me and Mama sit on that bench, and a white lady come in there and ask me what my name is. Mama tells her and the white lady goes on back. Then I hear somebody hollering in there. Soon 's that little boy hear him hollering, he starts hollering, too. His mama pats him and pats him, trying to make him hush up, but he ain't thinking 'bout his mama.

The man that was hollering in there comes out holding his jaw. He is a big old man and he's wearing overalls and a jumper.

"Got it, hanh?" another man asks him.

The man shakes his head—don't want open his mouth.

"Man, I thought they was killing you in there," the other man says. "Hollering like a pig under a gate."

The man don't say nothing. He just heads for the door, and the other man follows him.

"John Lee," the white lady says. "John Lee Williams."

The little boy juggs his head down in his mama's lap and holler more now. His mama tells him go with the nurse, but he ain't thinking 'bout his mama. His mama tells him again, but he don't even hear her. His mama picks him up and takes him in there, and even when the white lady shuts the door I can still hear little old John Lee.

"I often wonder why the Lord let a child like that suffer," a lady says to my mama. The lady's sitting right in front of us on another bench. She's got on a white dress and a black sweater. She must be a nurse or something herself, I reckon.

"Not us to question," a man says.

"Sometimes I don't know if we shouldn't," the lady says.

"I know definitely we shouldn't," the man says. The man looks like a preacher. He's big and fat and he's got on a black suit. He's got a gold chain, too.

"Why?" the lady says.

"Why anything?" the preacher says.

"Yes," the lady says. "Why anything?"

"Not us to question," the preacher says.

The lady looks at the preacher a little while and looks at Mama again.

"And look like it's the poor who suffers the most," she says. "I don't understand it."

"Best not to even try," the preacher says. "He works in mysterious ways—wonders to perform."

Right then little John Lee bust out hollering, and everybody turn they head to listen.

"He's not a good dentist," the lady says. "Dr. Robillard is much better. But more expensive. That's why most of the colored people come here. The white people go to Dr. Robillard. Y'all from Bayonne?"

"Down the river," my mama says. And that's all she go'n say, 'cause she don't talk much. But the lady keeps on looking at her, and so she says, "Near Morgan."

"I see," the lady says.

7

"That's the trouble with the black people in this country today," somebody else says. This one here's sitting on the same side me and Mama's sitting, and he is kind of sitting in front of that preacher. He looks like a teacher or somebody that goes to college. He's got on a suit, and he's got a book that he's been reading. "We don't question is exactly our problem," he says. "We should question and question and question—question everything."

The preacher just looks at him a long time. He done put a toothpick or something in his mouth, and he just keeps on turning it and turning it. You can see he don't like that boy with that book.

"Maybe you can explain what you mean," he says.

"I said what I meant," the boy says. "Question everything. Every stripe, every star, every word spoken. Everything."

"It 'pears to me that this young lady and I was talking 'bout God, young man," the preacher says.

"Question Him, too," the boy says.

"Wait," the preacher says. "Wait now."

"You heard me right," the boy says. "His existence as well as everything else. Everything."

The preacher just looks across the room at the boy. You can see he's getting madder and madder. But mad or no mad, the boy ain't thinking 'bout him. He looks at that preacher just 's hard 's the preacher looks at him.

"Is this what they coming to?" the preacher says. "Is this what we educating them for?"

"You're not educating me," the boy says. "I wash dishes at night so that I can go to school in the day. So even the words you spoke need questioning."

The preacher just looks at him and shakes his head.

"When I come in this room and seen you there with your book, I said to myself, 'There's an intelligent man.' How wrong a person can be."

"Show me one reason to believe in the existence of a God," the boy says.

"My heart tells me," the preacher says.

" 'My heart tells me,' " the boy says. " 'My heart tells me.' Sure, 'My heart tells me.' And as long as you listen to what your heart tells you, you will have only what the white man gives you and nothing more. Me, I don't listen to my heart. The purpose of the heart is to pump blood throughout the body, and nothing else."

"Who's your paw, boy?" the preacher says.

"Why?"

"Who is he?"

"He's dead."

"And your mom?"

"She's in Charity Hospital with pneumonia. Half killed herself, working for nothing."

"And 'cause he's dead and she's sick, you mad at the world?"

"I'm not mad at the world. I'm questioning the world. I'm questioning it with cold logic, sir. What do words like Freedom, Liberty, God, White, Colored mean? I want to know. That's why *you* are sending us to school, to read and to ask questions. And because we ask these questions, you call us mad. No sir, it is not us who are mad."

"You keep saying 'us'?"

" 'Us.' Yes—us. I'm not alone."

The preacher just shakes his head. Then he looks at everybody in the room—everybody. Some of the people look down at the floor, keep from looking at him. I kind of look 'way myself, but soon 's I know he done turn his head, I look that way again.

"I'm sorry for you," he says to the boy.

"Why?" the boy says. "Why not be sorry for yourself? Why are you so much better off than I am? Why aren't you sorry for these other people in here? Why not be sorry for the lady who had to drag her child into the dentist office? Why not be sorry for the lady sitting on that bench over there? Be sorry for them. Not for me. Some way or the other I'm going to make it."

"No, I'm sorry for you," the preacher says.

"Of course, of course," the boy says, nodding his head. "You're sorry for me because I rock that pillar you're leaning on."

"You can't ever rock the pillar I'm leaning on, young man. It's stronger than anything man can ever do."

"You believe in God because a man told you to believe in God," the boy says. "A white man told you to believe in God. And why? To keep you ignorant so he can keep his feet on your neck."

"So now we the ignorant?" the preacher says.

"Yes," the boy says. "Yes." And he opens his book again.

The preacher just looks at him sitting there. The boy done forgot all about him. Everybody else make 'tend they done forgot the squabble, too.

Then I see that preacher getting up real slow. Preacher's a great big old man and he got to brace himself to get up. He comes over where the boy is sitting. He just stands there a little while looking down at him, but the boy don't raise his head.

"Get up, boy," preacher says.

The boy looks up at him, then he shuts his book real slow and stands up. Preacher just hauls back and hit him in the face. The boy falls back 'gainst the wall, but he straightens himself up and looks right back at that preacher.

"You forgot the other cheek," he says.

The preacher hauls back and hit him again on the other side. But this time the boy braces himself and don't fall.

"That hasn't changed a thing," he says.

The preacher just looks at the boy. The preacher's breathing real hard like he just run up a big hill. The boy sits down and opens his book again.

"I feel sorry for you," the preacher says. "I never felt so sorry for a man before."

The boy makes 'tend he don't even hear that preacher. He keeps on reading his book. The preacher goes back and gets his hat off the chair.

"Excuse me," he says to us. "I'll come back some other time. Y'all, please excuse me."

And he looks at the boy and goes out the room. The boy h'ist his hand up to his mouth one time to wipe 'way some blood. All the rest of the time he keeps on reading. And nobody else in there say a word.

8

Little John Lee and his mama come out the dentist office, and the nurse calls somebody else in. Then little bit later they come out, and the nurse calls another name. But fast 's she calls somebody in there, somebody else comes in the place where we sitting, and the room stays full.

The people coming in now, all of them wearing big coats. One of them says something 'bout sleeting, another one says he hope not. Another one says he think it ain't nothing but rain. 'Cause, he says, rain can get awful cold this time of year.

All round the room they talking. Some of them talking to people right by them, some of them talking to people clear 'cross the room, some of them talking to anybody'll listen. It's a little bitty room, no bigger than us kitchen, and I can see everybody in there. The little old room's full of smoke, 'cause you got two old men smoking pipes over by that side door. I think I feel my tooth thumping me some, and I hold my breath and wait. I wait and wait, but it don't thump me no more. Thank God for that.

I feel like going to sleep, and I lean back 'gainst the wall. But I'm scared to go to sleep. Scared 'cause the nurse might call my name and I won't hear her. And Mama might go to sleep, too, and she'll be mad if neither one of us heard the nurse.

I look up at Mama. I love my mama. I love my mama. And when cotton come I'm go'n get her a new coat. And I ain't go'n get a black one, either. I think I'm go'n get her a red one.

"They got some books over there," I say. "Want read one of them?"

Mama looks at the books, but she don't answer me.

"You got yourself a little man there," the lady says.

Mama don't say nothing to the lady, but she must've smiled, 'cause I seen the lady smiling back. The lady looks at me a little while, like she's feeling sorry for me.

"You sure got that preacher out here in a hurry," she says to that boy.

The boy looks up at her and looks in his book again. When I grow up I want be just like him. I want clothes like that and I want keep a book with me, too.

"You really don't believe in God?" the lady says.

"No," he says.

"But why?" the lady says.

"Because the wind is pink," he says.

"What?" the lady says.

The boy don't answer her no more. He just reads in his book.

"Talking 'bout the wind is pink," that old lady says. She's sitting on the same bench with the boy and she's trying to look in his face. The boy makes 'tend the old lady ain't even there. He just keeps on reading. "Wind is pink," she says again. "Eh, Lord, what children go'n be saying next?"

The lady 'cross from us bust out laughing.

"That's a good one," she says. "The wind is pink. Yes sir, that's a good one."

"Don't you believe the wind is pink?" the boy says. He keeps his head down in the book.

"Course I believe it, honey," the lady says. "Course I do." She looks at us and winks her eye. "And what color is grass, honey?"

"Grass? Grass is black."

She bust out laughing again. The boy looks at her.

"Don't you believe grass is black?" he says.

The lady quits her laughing and looks at him. Everybody else looking at him, too. The place quiet, quiet.

"Grass is green, honey," the lady says. "It was green yesterday, it's green today, and it's go'n be green tomorrow."

"How do you know it's green?"

"I know because I know."

"You don't know it's green," the boys says. "You believe it's green because someone told you it was green. If someone had told you it was black you'd believe it was black."

"It's green," the lady says. "I know green when I see green."

"Prove it's green," the boy says.

"Sure, now," the lady says. "Don't tell me it's coming to that."

"It's coming to just that," the boy says. "Words mean nothing. One means no more than the other."

"That's what it all coming to?" that old lady says. That old lady got on a turban and she got on two sweaters. She got a green sweater under a black sweater. I can see the green sweater 'cause some of the buttons on the other sweater's missing.

"Yes ma'am," the boy says. "Words mean nothing. Action is the only thing. Doing. That's the only thing."

"Other words, you want the Lord to come down here and show Hisself to you?" she says.

"Exactly, ma'am," he says.

"You don't mean that, I'm sure?" she says.

"I do, ma'am," he says.

"Done, Jesus," the old lady says, shaking her head.

"I didn't go 'long with that preacher at first," the other lady says; "but now —I don't know. When a person say the grass is black, he's either a lunatic or something's wrong."

"Prove to me that it's green," the boy says.

"It's green because the people say it's green."

"Those same people say we're citizens of these United States," the boy says.

"I think I'm a citizen," the lady says.

"Citizens have certain rights," the boy says. "Name me one right that you have. One right, granted by the Constitution, that you can exercise in Bayonne."

The lady don't answer him. She just looks at him like she don't know what he's talking 'bout. I know I don't.

"Things changing," she says.

"Things are changing because some black men have begun to think with their brains and not their hearts," the boy says.

"You trying to say these people don't believe in God?"

"I'm sure some of them do. Maybe most of them do. But they don't believe that God is going to touch these white people's hearts and change things tomorrow. Things change through action. By no other way."

Everybody sit quiet and look at the boy. Nobody says a thing. Then the lady 'cross the room from me and Mama just shakes her head.

"Let's hope that not all your generation feel the same way you do," she says.

"Think what you please, it doesn't matter," the boy says. "But it will be men who listen to their heads and not their hearts who will see that your children have a better chance than you had."

"Let's hope they ain't all like you, though," the old lady says. "Done forgot the heart absolutely."

"Yes ma'am, I hope they aren't all like me," the boy says. "Unfortunately, I was born too late to believe in your God. Let's hope that the ones who come after will have your faith—if not in your God, then in something else, something definitely that they can lean on. I haven't anything. For me, the wind is pink, the grass is black."

9

The nurse comes in the room where we all sitting and waiting and says the doctor won't take no more patients till one o'clock this evening. My mama jumps up off the bench and goes up to the white lady.

"Nurse, I have to go back in the field this evening," she says.

"The doctor is treating his last patient now," the nurse says. "One o'clock this evening."

"Can I at least speak to the doctor?" my mama asks.

"I'm his nurse," the lady says.

"My little boy's sick," my mama says. "Right now his tooth almost killing him."

The nurse looks at me. She's trying to make up her mind if to let me come in. I look at her real pitiful. The tooth ain't hurting me at all, but Mama say it is, so I make 'tend for her sake.

"This evening," the nurse says, and goes on back in the office.

"Don't feel 'jected, honey," the lady says to Mama. "I been round them a long time—they take you when they want to. If you was white, that's something else; but we the wrong color."

Mama don't say nothing to the lady, and me and her go outside and stand 'gainst the wall. It's cold out there. I can feel that wind going through my coat. Some of the other people come out of the room and go up the street. Me and Mama stand there a little while and we start walking. I don't know where we going. When we come to the other street we just stand there.

"You don't have to make water, do you?" Mama says.

"No, ma'am," I say.

We go on up the street. Walking real slow. I can tell Mama don't know where she's going. When we come to a store we stand there and look at the dummies. I look at a little boy wearing a brown overcoat. He's got on brown shoes, too. I look at my old shoes and look at his'n again. You wait till summer, I say.

Me and Mama walk away. We come up to another store and we stop and look at them dummies, too. Then we go on again. We pass a café where the white people in there eating. Mama tells me keep my eyes in front where they belong, but I can't help from seeing them people eat. My stomach starts to growling 'cause I'm hungry. When I see people eating, I get hungry; when I see a coat, I get cold.

A man whistles at my mama when we go by a filling station. She makes 'tend she don't even see him. I look back and I feel like hitting him in the mouth. If I was bigger, I say; if I was bigger, you'd see.

We keep on going. I'm getting colder and colder, but I don't say nothing. I feel that stuff running down my nose and I sniff.

"That rag," Mama says.

I get it out and wipe my nose. I'm getting cold all over now—my face, my hands, my feet, everything. We pass another little café, but this'n for white people, too, and we can't go in there, either. So we just walk. I'm so cold now I'm 'bout ready to say it. If I knowed where we was going I wouldn't be so cold, but I don't know where we going. We go, we go, we go. We walk clean out of Bayonne. Then we cross the street and we come back. Same thing I seen when I got off the bus this morning. Same old trees, same old walk, same old weeds, same old cracked pave—same old everything.

I sniff again.

"That rag," Mama says.

I wipe my nose real fast and jugg that handkerchief back in my pocket 'fore my hand gets too cold. I raise my head and I can see David's hardware store. When we come up to it, we go in. I don't know why, but I'm glad.

It's warm in there. It's so warm in there you don't ever want to leave. I look for the heater, and I see it over by them barrels. Three white men standing round the heater talking in Creole. One of them comes over to see what my mama want.

"Got any axe handles?" she says.

Me, Mama and the white man start to the back, but Mama stops me when we come up to the heater. She and the white man go on. I hold my hands over the heater and look at them. They go all the way to the back, and I see the white man pointing to the axe handles 'gainst the wall. Mama takes one of them and shakes it like she's trying to figure how much it weighs. Then she rubs her hand over it from one end to the other end. She turns it over and looks at the other side, then she shakes it again, and shakes her head and puts it back. She gets another one and she does it just like she did the first one, then she shakes her head. Then she gets a brown one and do it that, too. But she don't like this one, either. Then she gets another one, but 'fore she shakes it or anything, she looks at me. Look like she's trying to say something to me, but I don't know what it is. All I know is I done got warm now and I'm feeling right smart better. Mama shakes this axe handle just like she did the others, and shakes her head and says something to the white man. The white man just looks at his pile of axe handles, and when Mama pass him to come to the front, the white man just scratch his head and follows her. She tells me come on and we go on out and start walking again.

We walk and walk, and no time at all I'm cold again. Look like I'm colder now 'cause I can still remember how good it was back there. My stomach growls and I suck it in to keep Mama from hearing it. She's walking right 'side me, and it growls so loud you can hear it a mile. But Mama don't say a word.

10

When we come up to the courthouse, I look at the clock. It's got quarter to twelve. Mean we got another hour and a quarter to be out here in the cold. We go and stand 'side a building. Something hits my cap and I look up at the sky. Sleet's falling.

I look at Mama standing there. I want stand close 'side her, but she don't like that. She say that's crybaby stuff. She say you got to stand for yourself, by yourself.

"Let's go back to that office," she says.

We cross the street. When we get to the dentist office I try to open the door, but I can't. I twist and twist, but I can't. Mama pushes me to the side and she twist the knob, but she can't open the door, either. She turns 'way from the door. I look at her, but I don't move and I don't say nothing. I done seen her like this before and I'm scared of her.

"You hungry?" she says. She says it like she's mad at me, like I'm the cause of everything.

"No, ma'am," I say.

"You want eat and walk back, or you rather don't eat and ride?"

"I ain't hungry," I say.

I ain't just hungry, but I'm cold too. I'm so hungry and cold I want to cry. And look like I'm getting colder and colder. My feet done got numb. I try to work my toes, but I don't even feel them. Look like I'm go'n die. Look like

I'm go'n stand right here and freeze to death. I think 'bout home. I think 'bout Val and Auntie and Ty and Louis and Walker. It's 'bout twelve o'clock and I know they eating dinner now. I can hear Ty making jokes. He done forgot 'bout getting up early this morning and right now he's probably making jokes. Always trying to make somebody laugh. I wish I was right there listening to him. Give anything in the world if I was home round the fire.

"Come on," Mama says.

We start walking again. My feet so numb I can't hardly feel them. We turn the corner and go on back up the street. The clock on the courthouse starts hitting for twelve.

The sleet's coming down plenty now. They hit the pave and bounce like rice. Oh, Lord; oh, Lord, I pray. Don't let me die, don't let me die, don't let me die, Lord.

11

Now I know where we going. We going back of town where the colored people eat. I don't care if I don't eat. I been hungry before. I can stand it. But I can't stand the cold.

I can see we go'n have a long walk. It's 'bout a mile down there. But I don't mind. I know when I get there I'm go'n warm myself. I think I can hold out. My hands numb in my pockets and my feet numb, too, but if I keep moving I can hold out. Just don't stop no more, that's all.

The sky's gray. The sleet keeps on falling. Falling like rain now—plenty, plenty. You can hear it hitting the pave. You can see it bouncing. Sometimes it bounces two times 'fore it settles.

We keep on going. We don't say nothing. We just keep on going, keep on going.

I wonder what Mama's thinking. I hope she ain't mad at me. When summer come I'm go'n pick plenty cotton and get her a coat. I'm go'n get her a red one.

I hope they'd make it summer all the time. I'd be glad if it was summer all the time—but it ain't. We got to have winter, too. Lord, I hate the winter. I guess everybody hate the winter.

I don't sniff this time. I get out my handkerchief and wipe my nose. My hands's so cold I can hardly hold the handkerchief.

I think we getting close, but we ain't there yet. I wonder where everybody is. Can't see a soul but us. Look like we the only two people moving round today. Must be too cold for the rest of the people to move round in.

I can hear my teeth. I hope they don't knock together too hard and make that bad one hurt. Lord, that's all I need, for that bad one to start off.

I hear a church bell somewhere. But today ain't Sunday. They must be ringing for a funeral or something.

I wonder what they doing at home. They must be eating. Monsieur Bayonne might be there with his guitar. One day Ty played with Monsieur Bayonne's guitar and broke one of the strings. Monsieur Bayonne was some mad with Ty. He say Ty wasn't go'n ever 'mount to nothing. Ty can go just like Monsieur Bayonne when he ain't there. Ty can make everybody laugh when he starts to mocking Monsieur Bayonne.

I used to like to be with Mama and Daddy. We used to be happy. But they took him in the Army. Now, nobody happy no more. . . . I be glad when Daddy comes home.

Monsieur Bayonne say it wasn't fair for them to take Daddy and give Mama nothing and give us nothing. Auntie say, "Shhh, Etienne. Don't let them hear you talk like that." Monsieur Bayonne say, "It's God truth. What they giving his children? They have to walk three and a half miles to school hot or cold. That's anything to give for a paw? She's got to work in the field rain or shine just to make ends meet. That's anything to give for a husband?" Auntie say, "Shhh, Etienne, shhh." "Yes, you right," Monsieur Bayonne say. "Best don't say it in front of them now. But one day they go'n find out. One day." "Yes, I suppose so," Auntie say. "Then what, Rose Mary?" Monsieur Bayonne say. "I don't know, Etienne," Auntie say. "All we can do is us job, and leave everything else in His hand . . ."

We getting closer, now. We getting closer. I can even see the railroad tracks.

We cross the tracks, and now I see the café. Just to get in there, I say. Just to get in there. Already I'm starting to feel little better.

12

We go in. Ahh, it's good. I look for the heater; there 'gainst the wall. One of them little brown ones. I just stand there and hold my hands over it. I can't open my hands too wide 'cause they almost froze.

Mama's standing right 'side me. She done unbuttoned her coat. Smoke rises out of the coat, and the coat smells like a wet dog.

I move to the side so Mama can have more room. She opens out her hands and rubs them together. I rub mine together, too, 'cause this keep them from hurting. If you let them warm too fast, they hurt you sure. But if you let them warm just little bit at a time, and you keep rubbing them, they be all right every time.

They got just two more people in the café. A lady back of the counter, and a man on this side the counter. They been watching us ever since we come in.

Mama gets out the handkerchief and count up the money. Both of us know how much money she's got there. Three dollars. No, she ain't got three dollars, 'cause she had to pay us way up here. She ain't got but two dollars and a half left. Dollar and a half to get my tooth pulled, and fifty cents for us to go back on, and fifty cents worth of salt meat.

She stirs the money round with her finger. Most of the money is change 'cause I can hear it rubbing together. She stirs it and stirs it. Then she looks at the door. It's still sleeting. I can hear it hitting 'gainst the wall like rice.

"I ain't hungry, Mama," I say.

"Got to pay them something for they heat," she says.

She takes a quarter out the handkerchief and ties the handkerchief up again. She looks over her shoulder at the people, but she still don't move. I hope she don't spend the money. I don't want her spending it on me. I'm hungry, I'm almost starving I'm so hungry, but I don't want her spending the money on me.

She flips the quarter over like she's thinking. She's must be thinking 'bout us walking back home. Lord, I sure don't want walk home. If I thought it'd do any good to say something, I'd say it. But Mama makes up her own mind 'bout things.

She turns 'way from the heater right fast, like she better hurry up and spend the quarter 'fore she change her mind. I watch her go toward the counter. The man and the lady look at her, too. She tells the lady something and the lady walks away. The man keeps on looking at her. Her back's turned to the man, and she don't even know he's standing there.

The lady puts some cakes and a glass of milk on the counter. Then she pours up a cup of coffee and sets it 'side the other stuff. Mama pays her for the things and comes on back where I'm standing. She tells me sit down at the table 'gainst the wall.

The milk and the cakes's for me; the coffee's for Mama. I eat slow and I look at her. She's looking outside at the sleet. She's looking real sad. I say to myself, I'm go'n make all this up one day. You see, one day, I'm go'n make all this up. I want say it now; I want tell her how I feel right now; but Mama don't like for us to talk like that.

"I can't eat all this," I say.

They ain't got but just three little old cakes there. I'm so hungry right now, the Lord knows I can eat a hundred times three, but I want my mama to have one.

Mama don't even look my way. She knows I'm hungry, she knows I want it. I let it stay there a little while, then I get it and eat it. I eat just on my front teeth, though, 'cause if cake touch that back tooth I know what'll happen. Thank God it ain't hurt me at all today.

After I finished eating I see the man go to the juke box. He drops a nickel in it, then he just stand there a little while looking at the record. Mama tells me keep my eyes in front where they belong. I turn my head like she say, but then I hear the man coming toward us.

"Dance, pretty?" he says.

Mama gets up to dance with him. But 'fore you know it, she done grabbed the little man in the collar and done heaved him 'side the wall. He hit the wall so hard he stop the juke box from playing.

"Some pimp," the lady back of the counter says. "Some pimp."

The little man jumps up off the floor and starts toward my mama. 'Fore you know it, Mama done sprung open her knife and she's waiting for him.

"Come on," she says. "Come on. I'll gut you from your neighbo to your throat. Come on."

I go up to the little man to hit him, but Mama makes me come and stand 'side her. The little man looks at me and Mama and goes on back to the counter.

"Some pimp," the lady back of the counter says. "Some pimp." She starts laughing and pointing at the little man. "Yes sir, you a pimp, all right. Yes sir-ree."

13

"Fasten that coat, let's go," Mama says.

"You don't have to leave," the lady says.

Mama don't answer the lady, and we right out in the cold again. I'm warm right now—my hands, my ears, my feet—but I know this ain't go'n last too long. It done sleet so much now you got ice everywhere you look.

We cross the railroad tracks, and soon's we do, I get cold. That wind goes through this little old coat like it ain't even there. I got on a shirt and a sweater under the coat, but that wind don't pay them no mind. I look up and I can see we got a long way to go. I wonder if we go'n make it 'fore I get too cold.

We cross over to walk on the sidewalk. They got just one sidewalk back here, and it's over there.

After we go just a little piece, I smell bread cooking. I look, then I see a baker shop. When we get closer, I can smell it more better. I shut my eyes and make 'tend I'm eating. But I keep them shut too long and I butt up 'gainst a telephone post. Mama grabs me and see if I'm hurt. I ain't bleeding or nothing and she turns me loose.

I can feel I'm getting colder and colder, and I look up to see how far we still got to go. Uptown is 'way up yonder. A half mile more, I reckon. I try to think of something. They say think and you won't get cold. I think of that poem, "Annabel Lee." I ain't been to school in so long—this bad weather—I reckon they done passed "Annabel Lee." by now. But passed it or not, I'm sure Miss Walker go'n make me recite it when I get there. That woman don't never forget nothing. I ain't never seen nobody like that in my life.

I'm still getting cold. "Annabel Lee" or no "Annabel Lee," I'm still getting cold. But I can see we getting closer. We getting there gradually.

Soon 's we turn the corner, I see a little old white lady up in front of us. She's the only lady on the street. She's all in black and she's got a long black rag over her head.

"Stop," she says.

Me and Mama stop and look at her. She must be crazy to be out in all this bad weather. Ain't got but a few other people out there, and all of them's men.

"Y'all done ate?" she says.

"Just finish," Mama says.

"Y'all must be cold then?" she says.

"We headed for the dentist," Mama says. "We'll warm up when we get there."

"What dentist?" the old lady says. "Mr. Bassett?"

"Yes, ma'am," Mama says.

"Come on in," the old lady says. "I'll telephone him and tell him y'all coming."

Me and Mama follow the old lady in the store. It's a little bitty store, and it don't have much in there. The old lady takes off her head rag and folds it up.

"Helena?" somebody calls from the back.

"Yes, Alnest?" the old lady says.

"Did you see them?"

"They're here. Standing beside me."

"Good. Now you can stay inside."

The old lady looks at Mama. Mama's waiting to hear what she brought us in here for. I'm waiting for that, too.

"I saw y'all each time you went by," she says. "I came out to catch you, but you were gone."

"We went back of town," Mama says.

"Did you eat?"

"Yes, ma'am."

The old lady looks at Mama a long time, like she's thinking Mama might be just saying that. Mama looks right back at her. The old lady looks at me to see what I have to say. I don't say nothing. I sure ain't going 'gainst my mama.

"There's food in the kitchen," she says to Mama. "I've been keeping it warm."

Mama turns right around and starts for the door.

"Just a minute," the old lady says. Mama stops. "The boy'll have to work for it. It isn't free."

"We don't take no handout," Mama says.

"I'm not handing out anything," the old lady says. "I need my garbage moved to the front. Ernest has a bad cold and can't go out there."

"James'll move it for you," Mama says.

"Not unless you eat," the old lady says. "I'm old, but I have my pride, too, you know."

Mama can see she ain't go'n beat this old lady down, so she just shakes her head.

"All right," the old lady says. "Come into the kitchen."

She leads the way with that rag in her hand. The kitchen is a little bitty little old thing, too. The table and the stove just 'bout fill it up. They got a little room to the side. Somebody in there laying 'cross the bed—'cause I can see one of his feet. Must be the person she was talking to: Ernest or Alnest—something like that.

"Sit down," the old lady says to Mama. "Not you," she says to me. "You have to move the cans."

"Helena?" the man says in the other room.

"Yes, Alnest?" the old lady says.

"Are you going out there again?"

"I must show the boy where the garbage is, Alnest," the old lady says.

"Keep that shawl over your head," the old man says.

"You don't have to remind me, Alnest. Come, boy," the old lady says.

We go out in the yard. Little old back yard ain't no bigger than the store or the kitchen. But it can sleet here just like it can sleet in any big back yard. And 'fore you know it, I'm trembling.

"There," the old lady says, pointing to the cans. I pick up one of the cans and set it right back down. The can's so light, I'm go'n see what's inside of it.

"Here," the old lady says. "Leave that can alone."

I look back at her standing there in the door. She's got that black rag wrapped round her shoulders, and she's pointing one of her little old fingers at me.

"Pick it up and carry it to the front," she says. I go by her with the can, and she's looking at me all the time. I'm sure the can's empty. I'm sure she could've carried it herself—maybe both of them at the same time. "Set it on the sidewalk by the door and come back for the other one," she says.

I go and come back, and Mama looks at me when I pass her. I get the other can and take it to the front. It don't feel a bit heavier than that first one. I tell myself I ain't go'n be nobody's fool, and I'm go'n look inside this can to see just what I been hauling. First, I look up the street, then down the street. Nobody coming. Then I look over my shoulder toward the door. That little old lady done slipped up there quiet 's mouse, watching me again. Look like she knowed what I was go'n do.

"Ehh, Lord," she says. "Children, children. Come in here, boy, and go wash your hands."

I follow her in the kitchen. She points toward the bathroom, and I go in there and wash up. Little bitty old bathroom, but it's clean, clean. I don't use any of her towels; I wipe my hands on my pants legs.

When I come back in the kitchen, the old lady done dished up the food. Rice, gravy, meat—and she even got some lettuce and tomato in a saucer. She even got a glass of milk and a piece of cake there, too. It looks so good, I almost start eating 'fore I say my blessing.

"Helena?" the old man says.

"Yes, Alnest?"

"Are they eating?"

"Yes," she says.

"Good," he says. "Now you'll stay inside."

The old lady goes in there where he is and I can hear them talking. I look at Mama. She's eating slow like she's thinking. I wonder what's the matter now. I reckon she's thinking 'bout home.

The old lady comes back in the kitchen.

"I talked to Dr. Bassett's nurse," she says. "Dr. Bassett will take you as soon as you get there."

"Thank you, ma'am," Mama says.

"Perfectly all right," the old lady says. "Which one is it?"

Mama nods toward me. The old lady looks at me real sad. I look sad, too.

"You're not afraid, are you?" she says.

"No, ma'am," I say.

"That's a good boy," the old lady says. "Nothing to be afraid of. Dr. Bassett will not hurt you."

When me and Mama get through eating, we thank the old lady again.

"Helena, are they leaving?" the old man says.

"Yes. Alnest."

"Tell them I say good-bye."

"They can hear you, Alnest."

"Good-bye both mother and son," the old man says. "And may God be with you."

Me and Mama tell the old man good-bye, and we follow the old lady in the front room. Mama opens the door to go out, but she stops and comes back in the store.

"You sell salt meat?" she says.

"Yes."

"Give me two bits worth."

"That isn't very much salt meat," the old lady says.

"That's all I have," Mama says.

The old lady goes back of the counter and cuts a big piece off the chunk. Then she wraps it up and puts it in a paper bag.

"Two bits," she says.

"That looks like awful lot of meat for a quarter," Mama says.

"Two bits," the old lady says. "I've been selling salt meat behind this counter twenty-five years. I think I know what I'm doing."

"You got a scale there," Mama says.

"What?" the old lady says.

"Weigh it," Mama says.

"What?" the old lady says. "Are you telling me how to run my business?"

"Thanks very much for the food," Mama says.

"Just a minute," the old lady says.

"James," Mama says to me. I move toward the door.

"Just one minute, I said," the old lady says.

Me and Mama stop again and look at her. The old lady takes the meat out of the bag and unwraps it and cuts 'bout half of it off. Then she wraps it up again and juggs it back in the bag and gives the bag to Mama. Mama lays the quarter on the counter.

"Your kindness will never be forgotten," she says. "James," she says to me.

We go out, and the old lady comes to the door to look at us. After we go a little piece I look back, and she's still there watching us.

The sleet's coming down heavy, heavy now, and I turn up my coat collar to keep my neck warm. My mama tells me turn it right back down.

"You not a bum," she says. "You a man."

afterword

"The Sky Is Gray" deals with one of Ernest J. Gaines' typical themes, that of the attempt to maintain courage and dignity in the midst of deprivation. Although James and his mother have been forced, because of their race, into a life of virtually inescapable poverty and hardship, they refuse to yield to despair. Instead, they endure without complaint, continually sacrificing for each other and asking help from no one. On his long walk through the cold and sleet, young James, observing once again his mother's pride and benefiting from her devotion to him, learns from her, as indeed he has learned from her all his life, what strength of character entails.

Gaines' depiction of courage and selflessness is particularly effective because he conveys his feelings of outrage at the social inequity represented by the plight of James and his mother without resorting to a tone of stridency, which might have turned this account into a diatribe instead of the evocative picture it is of people who are mistreated but not demoralized. Moreover, by using James as his narrator, Gaines evokes a sense of place, a sense of a particular environment inhabited by real people, which imparts to this story an aura of urgency, for the awareness is forced upon the reader that real people are suffering, people who can help themselves if given the smallest opportunity to do so.

Born in 1933 on a cotton and sugar cane plantation near Oscar, Louisiana, Ernest J. Gaines spent his early youth working in the fields, living in the shacks of the deep Southern setting he most often uses in his stories. In his teens, following the pattern of many of his fellow black Americans, he left the South and moved to California. There, working his way, he eventually graduated from San Francisco State College in 1957, and in the following year he won Stanford University's coveted Wallace Stegner Creative Writing Fellowship. Gaines has published two novels, *Catherine Carmier* (1964) and *Of Love and Dust* (1967). His short stories have appeared in the *Sewanee Review, Texas Quarterly,* and *Negro Digest.* A collection of his short stories, *Bloodline,* appeared in 1968. Among the literary prizes he has won is the Joseph Henry Jackson Literary Award, which he received in 1959. Currently, he is at work on a novel entitled *A Short Biography of Miss June Pittman.*

questions for general discussion

1. What is the effect of James' speech, "I smell bread cooking. I look, then I see a baker shop. When we get closer, I can smell it more better. I shut my eyes and make 'tend I'm eating. But I keep them shut too long and I butt up 'gainst a telephone post"?

2. Why is the story divided into numbered sections?

3. Why does the black preacher strike the young black student in the dentist's office? Why does the student react as he does?

4. What is the effect of the young student's statement, "I haven't anything. For me, the wind is pink, the grass is black"?

5. Why does James' mother shop for an axe handle?

6. What is our attitude toward James when he says, "My stomach growls and I suck it in to keep Mama from hearing it. She's walking right 'side me, and it growls so loud you can hear it a mile. But Mama don't say a word"?

suggestions for writing

1. Comment on the various changes of scene in the story and how Gaines appeals to our senses in creating the different settings.

2. Select the most revealing or the most powerful scene in the story and suggest how it contributes to the story's main theme.

3. Comment on the characters in the first scene at the dentist's office. Define and comment on the basic conflict which arises in this scene.

4. Develop a paper on the motives and emotions, obvious and not-so-obvious, revealed in the encounter between James, his mother, and the elderly white couple in the grocery store.

5. Considering the story as one of initiation, compare James' initiation with that of Colonel Sartoris, the boy in Faulkner's "Barn Burning."

GUY OWEN
the flim-flam man
and the tent meeting

Pretty soon after the law chased me and the Flim-Flam Man out of the mountains, I drove our old beat-up truck through the swamps and into the corn and tobacco country. The corn was all eared out and the tobacco was cropped way up the stalks, but the cotton hadn't busted out yet. Only a few bolls was leaking white. The August sun was clear as a bell in the blue sky.

Mr. Jones, he studied his map and we turned off on a bumpy clay road that wasn't even marked and headed back into the sticks, through scraggy pine thickets, back where the owls roost with the chickens. After a mile or so we passed some ramshackly tobacco barns with rusty tin roofs, then we come to a bunch of signs, tacky wooden signs, that was religious. There was one every mile or so, sort of new looking. "Prepare to Meet Thy God," "Are You Saved?", "Repent or Ye Shall Perish." The one I remember best, it was this big red heart that said "Jesus Loves," a sort of six-foot valentine, which some rapscallion had shot twice with a shotgun.

Mr. Jones says, "I hope their religion is more orthodox than their spelling."

I never did take to such ignorant signs nohow. I could maybe stand cluttering up the roads with ads for falsies or toilet paper, even, but not religion, for God's sake. I'm not too religious, I reckon, but that kind of thing bothers me. These crazy bastards had so many signs saying "Prepare to Meet God" you expected to meet Him around the next curve, dressed up maybe in a tux or something. I swear.

Pa was the same way, so I guess I took it after him. He never could stand to see one of them religious signs. He'd cuss and carry on something awful every time he glimpsed one, working himself up into a lather, until he'd just have to haul out his old rusty pistol and shoot it as full of holes as rat cheese. It always seemed to rest him, getting it out of his system that way.

Anyhow, the only thing we met was the Reverend Doakus, not God at all, this poor excuse for a gospel slinger. We spied his little one-horse tent up the road with his gaudy billboard topped by two flags, and all right close to a big country store. A ladder was still leaning against a large sign that said DYNAMITE DOAKUS. It was getting on toward sundown, so we decided to stop there for the night.

210

We went in the store to get a bite to eat, and that's when we met up with old Dynamite, who turned out to be a right lively customer.

I recognized him right off, because his picture was plastered all over his signs and the storefront, only they didn't make him look as bald as he was. He was setting on a nail keg gnawing on a moonpie and drinking a bellywasher. There was a plumpish, sexy-looking brunette eating beside him, with this little lady, Miss Dobbins, that run the store, hovering around them and waiting on them like they was maybe God and the Virgin Mary.

I just bought a box of gingersnaps and a can of vienna sausages and eased away from the counter. All the tacky signs had took my appetite and, besides, I didn't want to get too friendly with Doakus. I didn't like his looks much the first time I saw his picture tacked up back there at Lovick's store by the baboon in the circus poster, and seeing him in the flesh didn't improve matters a speck.

But not Mr. Jones. He didn't do nothing but waltz right over and shake old Dynamite's paw so hard he nearabout dropped his moonpie. I thought Mr. Jones would purely eat the both of them up, from all his sweet talk and glad hand. It would of made me sick, but of course I reasoned he had some cunning scheme behind it all.

Thinks I, You can include me out of this one, old hoss. Me and that kind of religion just don't mix.

But no, he introduced himself as Mr. Jonathan Edwards, shaking hands again, then waved over to me. Said I was Mr. Mather and was working my way through the seminary by helping him sell Bibles during the summer and was a crackerjack salesman and had wide experience playing the guitar and leading the choir at church singings and I don't know what all. I had to nod and grin like a possum, soaking in the prime malarkey. But I wasn't in the mood for it and I went on nibbling at my gingersnaps, setting on a twenty-pound saltlick and leaning against the far counter.

And old Doakus was so flattered and taken in he warmed up and got right sociable. He introduced his lady friend, Miss Letty Queen.

"She takes care of my organ for me," he says in a deep voice, laughing sort of and winking at the Flim-Flam Man. "She's Brother Dynamite's organist."

I'll be hanged if they ain't the exact words he used. And he kept on referring to himself as Brother Dynamite, a habit I've never been exactly mad about. Truth is, the old onionhead looked to me more like a wet firecracker than a stick of dynamite.

I commenced feeling right sorry for the organ lady, her having to listen to him all the time. But I reckon she deserved him and could put up with his rotten mouth. I watched her setting there close by him in a purple silk dress that she'd sweated through, her meaty legs crossed so you could see where her stockings was rolled. She kept a pukey little smile on her face, turning it on me and Mr. Jones. I hate to admit it but she looked sexy as all hell. But built for comfort instead of speed, as the old saying goes.

Mr. Jones, he got wound up then, and it was a pleasure just to hear him stretch his blanket and sling the bull. I can't recall it all, he spread it on so thick. He run on about what a joy it was for him to devote his autumn years to selling Bibles, spreading what little good he could in his humble manner, trying to be a little beacon of positive light in a world of chaos and darkness.

Mr. Jones didn't let old Bogus—that's what my pardner called him, not to his face, naturally—he never let Bogus get a word in edgewise. He went on a mile a minute, every now and then slapping the Bible which anchored his coat pocket. He said he'd been a minister of the gospel once in his life and it was a great disappointment when he had to give it up, one he'd never really recover from until his dying day. Said he'd had a nice little Church of God congregation out in the Midwest.

Then he pointed to his throat and his voice sort of cracked. It was his voice, he said, that forced him into retirement. He had this operation at the Mayo Clinic for cancer of the throat, and after that his voice never could hold up under the strain of a good sermon. Said he wasn't bitter, because taking all things into consideration reviewing his life, he was fortunate to be free and alive, able to do what little service for the people he could.

Which, I had to agree, was true enough.

Well, the upshot of it was old Bogus and the organist expressed their sympathies and the store lady said she'd never been so touched in all her life and wouldn't take a penny for our eats.

Bogus says, "I'd be much obliged if you'd attend our little service tonight."

"We wouldn't miss it for the world, would we, Brother Mather?"

Then the preacher asked Mr. Jones to testify, if he was so moved, and lead in a prayer, and begged me to play.

I told him I had a blister on my thumb.

But Mr. Jones said he would consider it a rare privilege and honor to participate, though his voice would not allow him to testify. He could feel it weakening just from their pleasant conversation. "But you can rely on me, sir. We'll certainly take some part in your revival before it's over."

Thinks I, Amen to that. I knew my pardner hadn't stopped there just to buy a moonpie.

Bogus and Miss Queen stood up to leave and get ready for the tent meeting. He said he didn't think we'd be disappointed. So far he had accomplished a power of good. It was hard to be humble about all the good he had wrought, with the Lord's help, of course.

"I don't claim no special healing powers, Brother Edwards, but at our first meeting Monday an old lady that hadn't seen a speck in ten years, not since her husband died, got back her sight and walked out of my tent right by herself."

"You don't mean it."

"Oh, but he does," says Miss Queen. Kind of snotty.

After they'd left, Miss Dobbins took up and run on about what a ring-tailed miracle it was, the Widow Baldwin suddenly seeing after all them years. The poor soul had died of a heart attack the next night on the way to the tent, but that just went to prove it was even more of a miracle.

Mr. Jones asked if we could park behind the store too, close to Bogus's house trailer. She said we could, she'd be honored to have us. So I went out and drove our red truck around back, out of the common view. We still had a few cases of moonshine left and I judged Mr. Jones aimed to work the tent meeting and get shut of what we wouldn't keep for home consumption, as he called it. There's no place like a tent meeting for peddling panther juice.

Anyhow, about dark we moseyed on over towards the meeting place. Right in front of the tent, near the pasture gate where the cars and wagons drove in, was a big sign. It was topped by two flags and said in big letters: "For All People of All Belief," and under that: "Soul-Stirring Scriptural Gospel Preaching." In even bigger letters it said: "Blazing the Old-Timey Sawdust Trail with Dynamite Doakus."

Mr. Jones whispers, "Now, lad, you'll get an opportunity to observe a real flim-flammer operate. This you have to see to believe." Mr. Jones said he knew because his father had been an evangelist in his day—which was news to me. I never dreamed of the Flim-Flam Man having a bunkshooter for a father.

"I think I've been here before," I says. I remembered all the times I'd been drug to revivals by poor Aunt Doshie—though it never did a particle of good.

We walked under the tent and took a back seat and I gawked a bit. There was mostly old folks inside, men in overalls and women with their hair done up in buns. There was a scattering of young girls, mostly culls, fanning theirselves. It was hot, though both sides of the tent was rolled up as far as they'd go. I felt mighty sorry for all them folks because you could see they was actually looking forward to hearing the evening's message. A pity.

Directly, Old Bogus bounced up on his little platform in a loud checked coat and a blazing tie. He give himself a little time to warm up the crowd, starting out with a few jokes as old as the Bible, just to show he was a regular sort. The crowd didn't laugh much, though. I judged they hadn't *come* to laugh.

Next he had everybody on their feet singing "Amazing Grace" and "Old Time Religion." The sexy organist set down and played the organ, which was close by the pulpit. It looked like she had six or seven pillows on her bench. Why, I don't know, because she had plenty of padding built in of her own. One thing I'll say for Miss Queen though: she could play the hell out of the organ. She naturally made that "Old Time Religion" get up and *hump.*

When Bogus let her, she could play. But he kept hogging the show. He was always breaking in and lining out the verses, begging the folks to put their souls into the next verse, to make the old tent shimmy with some soul-shaking singing. Said it would wake up the Devil and make him mad as fire—and I reckon there was truth in that, too.

By now the crowd was a little more peart. I dare say he judged they was ripe for his message, because all of a sudden he shucked off his checked coat and loosened the knot in his yellow tie and started in. Sweat was already popping out on his face and onion head, and considerable lightning bugs was swirling around his jug ears.

Peering around, he said he saw some new faces under his blessed tent. Maybe some folks there had never heard Brother Dynamite before and he hoped and prayed it would be a real experience for them, one they'd not likely forget.

It was.

Course he hadn't come here to uphold Brother Dynamite. He'd come to divide the Good Book with these simple people and put shame on the horny head of Old Scratch. Amen.

"I don't rightly know what I'm gonna say to you tonight, but I got a notion I'm gonna make some of you stand up in your chairs and grovel on the mourners' bench before you quit this tent."

Then he naturally pitched in and flung himself all over the place. He waved his arms like a windmill gone crazy, and skipped off and on the platform like a goat jumping on and off a barrel. Said he was proud to be a simple instrument of the Lord's. He knew some high-toned folks that give themselves airs and thought he was ridiculous and dog-hauled him for believing in and preaching the old-fashioned gospel. But he wanted to do what he could to save good old-timey religion before it was too late. Before the communists and invisible demons took over and divided the world betwixt them. He was just a simple backwoods preacher, but wherever he pitched his tent, the devil had to pack up his satchel and go.

"Amen!" somebody shouts.

"Glory halleluyah!"

Things begun to get livelier. The preacher got louder and louder, cavorting and prancing about more. He tore into the modernists that was turning the church into a cocktail club and ripped into the evils of strong drink and communism and greed and any other sin he could lay his hands on handy. Oh, he was dead set against sin. Then he snatched up the Bible and divided out a passel of scripture, sweating more and more. Pretty soon things got as lively as a mess of frog legs in a skillet.

Directly, old Bogus called for tithes and offerings, though he said he hated to do it. It was the only part of the ministry that went against his grain. Said he was a humble and poor man and led a simple life, which he urged them all to embrace so they might be happy and simple like him. Then he held up a letter and said it contained about the worst news he'd ever had and called it catastrophic and a calamity. It turned out the rent was due on his home in Queen City and his wife and five little girls was about to be thrown out into the cold street—and he had no one to turn to for succor except them.

He never passed the plate. Old Bogus just held out his hand and asked anybody who was a true Christian to come up and manifest it. And Miss Queen, she struck up "Nearer My God To Thee," and almost all of them poor folks went up the aisle and shelled out. Mr. Jones went up, too, and handed him some folding money. Me, I wouldn't give him one buffalo, old Doakus, and I'm glad now I didn't.

But the way the others forked it over I judge he got a heap more by having them put it right in his paw than he would of by passing the hat. You just naturally couldn't walk up there, with the light shining right on you, and hand him a measly dime.

What happened after that, I can't even hope to tell, and I'm sorely tempted not to try. I'd heard Pa tell of such doings when he was a pup, but I always thought he was stretching it, like he generally did. He used to tell about them old-timey brush arbor meetings—just to aggravate Aunt Doshie. About how the folks all fell out and whooped it up and the young bucks went just to see the girls' tails when they was thrashing their frocks up.

Anyhow, the way the crowd there got religion was a sight to behold in this world. I thought they'd purely shake that little tent down over our ears and suffocate us all. And that's a cold fact. I just hunkered down in a back seat, out of sight sort of, taking it all in next to this whisky-slobbering brother in a blue denim jumper. I reckon my eyes was popping out of my head because Mr. Jones put a finger to his mouth to caution me—quiet. I didn't mean to make fun, mind you. I just set there hunched over, solemn as an owl.

To tell the truth though, they wouldn't of noticed if I'd jumped up and recited the Gettysburg Address ass-backwards. For crying out loud, I could of set the damn tent on *fire,* and they wouldn't of took note of it. A bunch of them was whooping it up over in the Amen Corner to theirselves, and a scattering up front had already sprawled out face down, trembling. They was working their legs and bowed up in knots, and popping their teeth, and quaking like a mule passing briars in a thunderstorm. One old buzzard was circling around on all fours, barking like a dog, uncommonly like a black and tan. A handful was setting bolt upright, their noses flared out like spooked mules and their eyes bulging, and jabbering in some kind of language I couldn't make heads nor tails of.

Mr. Jones said later it was the unknown tongue, and I reckon it was *unknown,* at that. And all of them was making their noises, if it wasn't nothing but to shout "Amen!" every now and then—just to prove they had religion, too, more than likely. I reckon the whippoorwills outside was scared spitless, for I never heard another peep out of them.

And old Dynamite, why, he knocked the socks off any gospel slinger I ever laid eyes on. He was spitting out words so fast you'd of thought he was an auctioneer asking for bids on Beulah Land. The words fairly flew out of his mouth—and considerable spit, too, if you want the whole truth. He spoke so familiar of hell you'd of thought he was born and raised there. I couldn't make much of the words generally—I never tried hard—but he had a right catchy rhythm, and he kept time by bouncing his old bald head up and down like a dang cork and rolling his eyes back till the whites all showed as clean as the girls' drawers—which interested me more.

All of a sudden, when a new candidate keeled off a bench and commenced chewing grass and sawdust, Bogus rushed down and doused the back of their necks with this what-you-may-call-it he had corked up in a glass bottle. Healing oil, he called it. Some sort of sauce. He'd souse them up good and rub it into their necks like it was Vaseline, talking, spewing all the time, never so much as missing a beat.

And if it was a girl needing the oil, he'd lean close over her and maybe give her a goose or two. I didn't *see* him do it, but I wouldn't put it past him, the old ring-tailed rascal. One thing for sure, none of them girls would of cared, the shape they was in, carrying on so—not even if the Devil slipped them a good one, I bet. He never did souse that barking fool, though. He never could run him down and catch him. Come to think of it, I reckon old Bogus was scared the son of a bitch might bite him!

All of a sudden, when things got sort of calm and dull the old baldheaded knocker nearabout broke up the meeting. He was sweating now like a boar chinch in somebody's belly button, mopping his waddled jowls with a snot rag as big as a diaper. By jinks, he ups and cracks his heels together and shouts out, "I'm going to heaven, you all. Watch old Dynamite go through them pearly gates. Look out, Peter, here I come!"

And be swiggered if the old codger didn't climb the tent pole, with the whole crowd singing out "Halleluyah!" at his heels. He'd climb a little stretch, then clamp his knees in and stop and preach some more, with the folks all begging him to go on, shouting encouragement, some of them clapping their hands. And that crazy scudder that thought he was a dog treed him up the pole and barked considerable—though I admit it wasn't much like a hound that's treed. I wouldn't want to exaggerate.

Then Dynamite, he'd snake up the pole a little higher, yelling out at the top of his lungs, "Look out, Peter. Throw them gates open, 'cause Brother Dynamite's on the way!"

Every so often he'd stop and just pant awhile and bulge his eyes out and blow, kind of like a treed possum. Then he'd commence slipping a foot or so, like someone had greased the pole, holding on for dear life. Said it was old Satan dragging him down, and he popped his heels and joggled his feet, trying to fling Old Scratch off. But no, he couldn't shake him and he slid another yard or so. He allowed it was sin weighing him down, dragging like lead, his sins and the sins of all the congregation. And them poor souls groaned and pleaded and I don't know what all.

Directly, he sung out and commenced to climb some more. He mortally tore up the pole like a monkey, jerking his knees up to his chin and yanking up, the way you see a cat do that's chased hellbent for leather up a tree. Only this time he never stopped, just huffed and puffed right on up there. When he reached the top he slapped the canvas and let out a bellow that must of echoed a solid mile. And they pitched in below and capped it until my ears rung.

"It hain't easy," Bogus shouts, "it hain't easy gitting through the narrow gates. It's no soft job for the fainthearted. No, sir. I tell you it takes some get-up-and-go. It takes *humping* to git to Beulah Land." Then he croaks "Glory be, I'm a-coming, I'm a-coming."

I reckon he was, too, the way he was shagging the tent pole.

Then Brother Dynamite up and loosed his grip, sliding down the pole with his eyes shut and his big feet dancing on thin air. Oh, I tell you, it was lively, lively.

Time he struck the ground he bounced back on the platform and took up his sermon again, if you can name it that. He commenced to putting the stopper on it, kindly rounding it off. The shouting and the barking and such like suaged down a trifle, and the unknown tongues, too. Bogus allowed everybody could get to heaven, just like he'd showed them, if they'd follow his example. Then he ripped into Judas, who he didn't seem to admire much and next he climbed over on Peter and flogged him awhile. I saw he intended to wind up with Peter, if his breath didn't fail him.

At last, he mopped his red face again and struck a pose, one arm stretched out and his shadow froze behind him on the tent. He reared back and roars, "Let me leave you with this question. How many Peters are there here tonight?"

I declare, I just set still and waited for the tent to cave in. But no, it just showed what a double-distilled fool I was. Because you could of heard a gnat sneeze. There wasn't a solitary snort and nobody offered to snigger.

Then old Bogus called on Mr. Jones.

The Flim-Flam Man, he stood up and prayed over them a little, and I judged they needed it after all the commotion. There wasn't no flies on his prayer neither, it was short and sweet.

Which was the end of the meeting. Folks got up in a daze and staggered out of the tent, kind of like they was in a dream, or a nightmare. Some rose up from the ground with sawdust and grass stains on their clothes.

There was a dozen or so young bucks waiting at the tent flaps for the girls, and I saw the grins on their faces. They just took them stunned skirts by the arms as they crept out. And wasn't they all ripe for plucking, though?

It didn't seem fair to me somehow. It's like taking advantage of a woman that's stewed with booze, or shooting a dove that's lit on a post. But I wouldn't of been interested nohow. The frizzled-headed gals was pure rutabagas.

But there wasn't time to fret about the mud turtles that was about to be plucked. I gathered me a crowd of young bucks and old farmers and ambled in the dark over to the truck. They wasn't a bit laggard about it. In no time flat I sold about fifty dollars worth of bottled corn, more I'll bet than Bogus's collection come to. Which is no more than right, since Doodle's spirits was even more soul-stirring than old Dynamite's ranting.

afterword

"The Flim-Flam Man and the Tent Meeting" is a satiric view of man's greed and his consequent tendency to be easily bilked and cheated by confidence men. Guy Owen's yarn capitalizes on the same human foibles celebrated by such humorists of the Old Southwest as Mark Twain and George W. Harris. Utilizing hyperbole, slapstick, dialect, and bawdy innuendoes, Owen depicts the same ingredients of the picaresque tradition as seen, for instance, in *The Adventures of Huckleberry Finn,* as he shows the results of a matching of wits between two consummate confidence men.

In this story, the Flim-Flam Man, Mordecai Jones, and his reluctant accomplice, Curley Treadaway, meet up with a figure ubiquitous in the South, the ignorant, ruthless, evangelistic preacher. Curley observes the audacious skulduggery of Brother Dynamite Doakus as he skins for all their worth the local yokels who attend his tent meetings. Satirized throughout the tale are such cliches of Southern literature as illicit sex, fundamentalist religion, moonshine liquor, "testifying of sins," and gospel singing.

Guy Owen was born in 1925 in Clarkton, North Carolina. The author of the novels *Season of Fear* (1960) and *The Ballad of the Flim-Flam Man* (1965), he has published poetry in a number of magazines, including *Saturday Review* and *Poetry,* and has published two collections of poetry, *Cape Fear Country and Other Poems* (1958) and *The White Stallion and Other Poems* (1969). In 1966, a highly successful film version of *The Ballad of the Flim-Flam Man* appeared. A Breadloaf Fellow and a recipient of a Henry Bellamann Foundation Literary Award, Owen now lives in Raleigh, North Carolina, with his wife and two sons, where he is professor of English at North Carolina State University and editor of the *Southern Poetry Review.* A sequel to *The Ballad of the Flim-Flam Man* has been completed, and another novel, *Journey For Joedel,* was published in 1970.

questions for general discussion

1. What is the effect of the specific references to the roadside signs in the opening scene?

2. What is Curley's attitude toward Doakus and his congregation?

3. What is the effect of Owen's paragraphing style in such an example as this:

> . . . Maybe some folks there had never heard Brother Dynamite before and he hoped and prayed it would be a real experience for them, one they'd not likely forget.
> It was.

4. What is the effect of our hearing from Curley rather than from Doakus the preacher's self-characterization, "he wanted to do what he could to save good old-timey religion before it was too late. Before the communists and invisible demons took over and divided the world betwixt them. He was just a simple backwoods preacher, but wherever he pitched his tent, the devil had to pack up his satchel and go"?

suggestions for writing

1. Write an essay comparing and contrasting Curley Treadaway with Huck Finn.

2. Comment on Owen's use of simile, metaphor, and hyperbole as sources of humor.

3. Comment on how Curley's use of specific observations of such things as signs makes his attitudes clear.

4. Write a theme on the role of setting in the story.

GEORGE GARRETT
texarkana was a crazy town

When I went back to the barracks for the last time to pick up my stuff, there was Mooney waiting on me.

"Well," he said. "You feel any better now?"

I didn't answer. I kept busy stuffing things in my duffel bag. I didn't want any trouble with Mooney. I knew how he felt, like I was running out on him.

"How does it feel to be a civilian?"

"How would I know?" I said. "I ain't even been off the post yet."

"You're making a mistake," he said. "You'll be sorry."

"Maybe."

"Maybe nothing!" Mooney said. "Listen here, boy. You've got it made here. You don't know it. You just don't know how it is. You don't know anything else but the Army. It's going to be tough out there for a guy like you, believe me."

"Listen, Mooney," I kidded him, "you came in the Army during the Depression. They had bread lines and all that then. People selling pencils on the street corners. Things are different now."

Mooney grinned. "I may look old," he said, "but I'm not *that* old."

"You look old to me."

"You don't know anything," he said. "What's the matter?"

"We've been all through this before."

"Never mind about before. I want to know."

"I just don't like being pushed around," I said. "And that's all there is to it."

"Who's been pushing you around? You tell me who's been giving you a hard time."

"Nobody," I said. "It's just the idea of the thing. I'm sick of it."

"Jesus Christ!" Mooney said. "That beats all."

Mooney was about the best friend I ever had. I knew him ever since I was seventeen and joined the Army. We had been in the same outfit all along. In the beginning Mooney was my Chief-of-Section on the howitzer. He made a soldier out of me. Now I was a Chief-of-Section and he was the Chief-of-Firing Battery. He could have been First Sergeant if he had wanted to. He turned it down because he wanted to be with the guns. Mooney was what you'd have to call a dedicated man with those guns. He really *cared*. That's why he just couldn't understand why I was leaving.

"What are you going to do?" he asked.

"I don't know."

"Maybe you can make use of your service experience and repair the old cannons in front of American Legion halls."

"Yeah, sure," I said. "And maybe they'll let me fire a salute on the Fourth of July."

"It's too bad you never learned how to play a bugle," Mooney said. "You could double up and play taps on Armistice Day."

"I can always teach dismounted drill to the Boy Scouts. Or maybe I'll open a real highclass professional shoeshine parlor."

"You're crazy."

"I'd rather be crazy than chronic," I said. "You're chronic, Mooney. Nothing but an old chrome-plated chronic."

"Don't go," he said suddenly. "Change your mind."

I was all through packing and I was ready to leave. I didn't want to hang around talking to Mooney all day long. We had been through it all so many times before.

"It's too late," I said. "They already give me my mustering out pay and my permanent grade of PFC—poor freaking civilian."

"What's everything coming to?" Mooney said. "What am I supposed to do for soldiers?"

"Hell, just grab ahold of a couple of those draftees and give them the sales talk. Maybe you'll convert some of them. If you signed up enough of them they might even make you Recruiting NCO and you could get yourself a bonus."

"You got ninety days," he said. "You got ninety days to change your mind. Just remember that."

"Okay," I said. "Just give me ninety days. So long, Mooney."

I stuck out my hand to shake hands with him.

"Don't give me that shit," he said. And he turned his back on me and walked away.

I didn't blame him. I guess I would have been mad too if I was Mooney. I knew how he felt, but that didn't help me a whole lot. He was my friend, a good one, and about the best soldier I ever saw. He was a great guy and you took him for himself. You just forget all about Mooney being a nigger.

I didn't go home. What was the sense in that? I joined the Army in the first place to get away from that. They never would miss me. They've got a houseful anyway. Somebody told me jobs were easy to come by in Houston, Texas, so I went on down there and got a job driving a truck for an ice company. Now you might think in this day and age there wouldn't be a whole lot for an ice man to do. I mean with refrigerators and freezers and all. So did I. I was wrong. There was plenty for me to do all day, and there were plenty of people right there in a great big city who had an old-fashioned ice box.

That job lasted three days. The first day on the job the boss took me aside and told me what was what. There was one special case I had to worry about.

"There's a woman at this address, a real good-looking woman," he said showing me the number on the delivery roster.

"Yeah?"

"Now, when you go in the house, this woman will be in the living room taking a sunbath under a sunlamp, buck naked with the door wide open to the kitchen."

"That's all right with me," I said. "I don't mind if she don't."

"Now you listen to me, sonny boy," he said. "You take the ice in and you put it in the top of the icebox. You don't look left and you don't look right. You don't stop and talk, even if she talks to you. All you do is put the ice in the icebox and get out. If you look, if you stop and talk, she's going to call up the company just as soon as you leave and I'll have to fire you."

"She must be a pretty good customer."

"Yeah," he said. "She's regular."

"Why don't she get herself a refrigerator?" I said. "That woman must be crazy."

"Don't talk like that," he said. "She's my wife."

I think that woman was crazy. She didn't need an icebox even if her husband did run an ice company. They had a nice house with air-conditioning and everything. The kitchen was full of all kinds of machines and appliances. And, to top it all, she had this great big funny old icebox. Well, I put up with it for two days, sneaking in and out of the kitchen like a dog. I couldn't see her, but I could hear the portable radio playing and see the bright glare of the sunlamp out of the corner of my eye and I could feel the heat of it. And I could tell she was just waiting to see what I was going to do.

The third day she tried to trip me up. I got inside and was just putting the ice in the icebox.

"Honey," she called out. "Would you kindly open a can of beer for me and put it by the sink so I can come get it when you leave?"

"Sure," I said.

It was a hot summer day in Houston, really hot and so humid the air seemed to stick to you. I was tired and I wouldn't have minded a beer myself.

"Don't you drink any of it."

"Don't you worry, lady," I said. "When I want to drink a beer, I'll buy it myself."

"You're kind of sassy," she said. "What's your name, honey?"

I came right up to the living room door and leaned against the door frame and just looked at her. She was laying on her stomach facing me, so she couldn't very well move to cover herself up. I'd say she was a pretty nice-looking woman, a little on the heavy side, but nice.

"Pudding Tame, you bitch," I said. I figured I was as good as fired anyway.

"That's no way to talk to a lady," she said.

I lit myself a cigarette and looked around.

"Lady? I don't see no lady."

222   The Southern Experience

"You got a nerve," she said. "I'm going to phone my husband."

"You know what I'd do if I was your husband?"

"No," she said. "What would *you* do?"

"I'd whip your ass good and throw you out in the street where you belong."

I walked over and smacked her fanny so hard I left a print on it, all five fingers included, and then I walked right out of the house with her hollering rape and murder and everything else. I drove straight back to the company and gave the boss the keys to his truck.

"I'm sorry," he said. "But don't say I didn't give you fair warning."

"Mister, you can have this job."

"I'm sorry," he said. "I can't help it. It's just the way things are."

"The hell you can't!" I said. "You ought to knock some sense into that woman. And if she won't shape up, get rid of her."

"I can't help it," he said. "I'm sorry, but that's just the way it is."

"Okay," I said. "Have it your own way."

At the end I almost felt sorry for him. He was just an old guy with a young wife. You know how it goes.

A few days later an oil exploration company hired me to drive a pickup truck for one of their crews. I was really hoping they would send me to South America or Arabia or some place, but they sent me up to Texarkana instead. Texarkana was a crazy town. I don't know how it is now and I couldn't care less, but it was a crazy place then. The state line between Arkansas and Texas ran right up the middle of the street and they said you could break the law on one side and then run across to the other and thumb your nose at the cops if you felt like it. One state, I forget which, was partially dry. You could only buy beer there. If you went across to the other side you could get beer and whiskey and pretty nearly anything else you wanted. Naturally it was heavenly country for bootleggers. On a still calm day you could see the smoke rising up from a half a dozen stills out in the pine woods. The law wouldn't do anything about it or, anyway, I guess they couldn't.

About the time I showed up there was another kind of crime that had everybody worried and worked up. Somebody took to killing off couples parked out in the woods. Whoever it was would sneak up on them in the dark, kill the man, rape the woman and then kill her too. Then he would carve up the bodies with a butcher knife. All the newspapers were full of it. They called him the Phantom Killer and everybody in the area was supposed to be on the lookout to catch him. All this was in the middle of summer when everybody is edgy anyway. Life goes on the same everywhere, with or without no Phantom Killer, but I don't mind telling you it made the town a nervous, kind of suspicious place to be in. It was a tough place to be a stranger.

All that part didn't bother me one way or the other at first, though. I was too busy on the job and getting used to the people I was working with to worry about what kind of a place I was living in. The whole crew lived together in a boarding house. We would be up long before daylight and out on the road, driving miles to wherever we had to work that day. I had to drive a pickup for Pete, the surveyor, and all his gear. We would drive way out in the woods or swamps somewhere and then run a survey for elevation and distance, setting up known locations, stations where the gravity meter crew could come along later and take readings. The driving on those back roads was pretty bad, but I was used to rough driving. The only tough time I had was getting along with Pete. Right from the first day. Part of it was my own fault, I'll admit. He reminded me of my old man. Pete was a little scrawny guy like that and all puffed up with himself like a banty rooster. I guess he figured everybody was against him to start with, so he might as well give everybody else a bad time before they had a chance to do it to him. He went out of his way to let you know right away he thought you were dirt. The first time I ever drove for him he started in on me.

"What did you do before you came to work for us?" he asked me.

"I was in the Army."

"Yeah? I thought so."

I didn't say anything. Plenty of people have plenty of good reasons for not liking the Army. I even have a few good ones myself. When he saw I wasn't about to take his bait, he kept after me.

"Well," he said, "don't try any of your Army tricks around here or you won't last too long."

"Yeah?"

"Yeah. I know how it is. I was in the Army. The idea in the Army is to get out of as much work as you can and let somebody else do it. That's right, isn't it?"

"I wouldn't know."

"Come on now," he said. "You know what I'm talking about."

"I hope you do," I said. "I don't."

"Just don't try any tricks on me."

Like I've said, one of my troubles is I don't like to get pushed around by anybody. And another one is a quick temper sometimes. I pulled the truck off the road and stopped.

"What are you doing?"

"I'm playing my first trick on you," I said.

"I wasn't joking," he said.

"Now listen, you," I said. "I don't want any trouble with you. Let's get everything straight right now. You tell me what to do on this job and I'll do it. Just as good or better than the next guy. But let's just leave the bullshit out of it. They don't pay me to listen to you."

"You talk pretty big for a kid," he said.

"Try me," I said. "I'd just as soon whip your ass as anybody else's. Just try me and find out."

He shut up and we drove on. Later he asked me what rank I had in the Army and I told him sergeant. He said, "I might have known," or something like that. I let it pass. I let him get away with that. He was like my old man. He had to say the last word even if it killed him.

After that Pete didn't give me any trouble for a while. And I didn't bother him. Which is more than the rest of the guys on the crew. They didn't like him either and they always had some practical joke to pull on him. They made him pretty miserable I guess. The hell with it. I just worked with him and let him alone.

We always worked until pretty near dark and then we drove hell for leather back to town. After we got back and cleaned up and had some supper, we would either go over to the cafe across the street and drink beer or else hang around the filling station.

The filling station was run by this one-arm guy that used to be in the Army away back. He had been a mulepack soldier in the days when they still had mules and I liked to go over there and sit around and talk with him about how it had been in the old days. We could talk the same kind of language and I got to where I really liked to hang around there in the evening. Except for one thing. He had this nigger they called Peanuts working for him. Peanuts was tall and skinny and kind of funny-looking with great big loose hands and feet about half a block long. He wasn't very smart, but he was a good-natured simple guy and I got to where I couldn't stand the way they picked on him. Everybody played jokes on Peanuts. They would send him all over town on crazy errands like getting a bucket of polka dot paint or taking the slack out of the state line. He never caught on. Once or twice somebody gave him a bottle of cheap whiskey and got him drunk. He would stagger all around the station singing and hollering and slobbering and carrying on until he just passed out cold. Whiskey put him out of his head. There would be a crowd of the guys to see this happen. They thought it was pretty funny like seeing a pig drunk. In a way I guess it *was* funny too. Except a man is not a pig. So I made up my mind I would rather sit in the cafe and drink beer by myself than to put up with a thing like that.

"What's the matter?" Pete asked me. "You don't hang around with the rest of the guys any more."

"I'd rather drink beer."

"That Delma is a nice piece."

"*Who?*"

"Delma," he said, "the waitress."

"Which one is she?"

"Don't try and fool me," Pete said. "I know what you're up to."

"Well, you know more than I do then."

To tell you the truth Pete put an idea in my head. I hadn't thought about it before, but there was a good-looking waitress working over at the cafe. And I was lonesome and horny as a jack rabbit and I figured that getting tied up with a woman wouldn't be such a bad thing. I never had a whole lot to do with women before I went in the Army. The only women I really knew anything about were the gooks in Japan and Korea. I like them fine, especially the Japanese, but they sure are different from American women.

Delma was a pretty good-looking girl, short and stacked with dark hair and a good smile. Of course they all look good when you want one bad enough. It didn't take long for me to get to know her a little. When business was slack she would come over and sit in the booth with me. She talked a lot and joked. She was full of laughs about everything. She seemed all right.

One night, after I had been around Texarkana for a few weeks, she asked me if I wanted to go out with her.

"Sure," I said. "The only trouble is I don't have a car."

"We can use mine," she said. "I don't feel like working tonight. I feel like going out and having a good time."

She went back to the ladies' room and changed out of her white uniform and into a dress. She looked good in a dress. I never had seen her except in her uniform and so she looked like a different person. She had that clean, kind of shiny look American girls have when they're all dressed up to go somewhere. Like a picture out of a magazine. We got in her car and drove out in the country to some honky-tonk where they had a band.

"I don't dance much," I told her. "I never had much time to learn."

"That's all right," she said. "I'll show you how."

We tried dancing a while, but it didn't work. So we sat down at a table and just drank and listened to the music. That Delma could really drink. I had a hard time keeping up with her.

"This is a pretty rough place," she told me. "A lot of rough guys come here."

"Is that so?"

"You see that big man?" She pointed at a great big guy standing at the bar. "He is one of the toughest men in this part of the country. A big bootlegger."

"What did he do to get so tough?"

"They say he's killed two or three men."

I started to laugh. I don't know why. I just couldn't help it. I was drunk and it struck me funny to hear somebody talk like that, like he was some kind of a hero or something.

"What's so funny?"

"I don't know."

"*Something* must be funny."

"Is that what you have to do to get a name around here—kill somebody?"

"You better not let him catch you laughing at him."

For some reason that made me mad.

"I don't give a damn who catches me laughing," I said. "I'll laugh whenever I damnwell please and take my chances. Listen, I've seen bigger, tougher guys than him break down and pray to Jesus. I've seen plenty of great big tough guys that was as yellow and soft as a stick of butter. It don't take no guts to kill a man. I've seen the yellowest chicken-hearted bastards in the world that would shoot prisoners. I've seen some terrible things. So don't come telling me about no big bad country bootlegger."

While I was sounding off like that she reached across the table and grabbed my hands and squeezed hard. She kept staring at me.

"Finish your drink," she said. "And let's go somewhere."

We went out in the parking lot and got in the car and necked a while. She was all hot and bothered and breathing hard.

"Let's *go* somewhere," she said.

"Where do you want to go?" I said. "Out in the woods?"

"No," she said. "Not out there I'm scared."

"What of?"

"I'm just nervous since all that Phantom Killer stuff has been in the papers."

"All right, you name it."

We drove even farther out the highway to a cheap motel. After I paid the man we went in the cabin and sat down on the bed.

"I've got to have a drink," she said. "Go ask the man for a pint of whiskey. He sells it and don't let him tell you he doesn't."

When I came back to the cabin with the whiskey all the lights were out.

"Hey," I said. "I can't see anything."

"Hurry up and get your clothes off," she said. "I'm so hot I can't stand it."

I climbed in the bed and we drank out of the bottle. You would never believe the first thing she said to me.

"Have you ever killed anybody?" she whispered. "Tell me about it."

I told her I didn't know. The only time I ever shot for real was in Korea, but in the artillery you don't see what you are shooting at most of the time. They telephone or radio back when they have got a target for you to shoot at and then you just keep on shooting until they tell you to quit.

"I don't mean like that," she said. "I mean up close with a knife or something."

The only thing I could figure was she was drunk and had all that Phantom Killer stuff on her mind. I could tell she wanted me to say yes. I don't know why. I guess she wanted to feel bad, dirty maybe. She wanted to pretend she was in bed with some terrible man. Maybe she wanted to pretend that the Phantom Killer was raping her or something. I was drunk enough myself so I didn't care. So I told her yes I had killed a whole lot of gooks with my knife. I made up a couple of long-winded, phony stories and that seemed to excite her. I'll say this for Delma, she was all right in bed even if she did carry on, laughing and crying the whole time until I was afraid the man would throw us out.

Later on, in the early hours of the morning, she got up real quiet and started to get dressed. I sat up in bed.

"What are you doing?"

"Let's go," she said. "It's time to go home."

It was still dark. I snapped the lamp beside the bed and it didn't go on. I tried the bulb and it was tight. I gave the cord a pull and it was free. She must have yanked the plug out while I was out buying the whiskey when we first came in.

"How come you unplugged the light?"

"What do you mean?"

"What's the matter with you?"

"I don't want you to see me," she said.

"I saw you when we came in," I said. "I know who you are."

"Not like this," she said. "You didn't see me like this."

Then she started crying. I thought the hell with it. Just the hell with it all. And I got up and found my clothes and got dressed in the dark. Before we went out the door she took hold of me.

"Aren't you forgetting something?"

"What?"

"It's going to cost you twenty dollars."

"I'll be damn," I said. "I didn't know you were a whore."

"I'm not!" she said. "I'm not a whore. But I've got my kid to think about."

"Your *kid?* I didn't even know you were married."

"Now you know," she said. "And it costs twenty bucks to spend the night with me."

"That's a pretty high price."

Even if I felt bad about being fooled, I went ahead and gave her the money. What was the use of arguing? It was my own fault.

We drove back to town without saying a word. I turned on the radio and picked up some hillbilly music. We finally got to the boarding house and I pulled over to let her take the wheel. I got out and started to walk away. She called to me.

"Listen," she said, "you're not mad, are you?"

"Mad? Why should I be mad?"

"I just want to be sure," she said. "I don't want you to be mad at me."

"What difference does it make?"

"I just wanted to know," she said. "Will I see you again?"

"I don't know," I said. "How would I know?"

"Suit yourself," she said and she drove off.

I just about had time to put on my boots and work clothes before we left for work. I didn't even have time to shave. Pete was already waiting for me when I walked in the house.

"Where the hell have you been?"

"Go on out and wait in the truck," I told him. "I'll be ready in five minutes."

The others left without us. We drove out on the highway alone for an hour or so. Pete just curled up in a corner of the cab and went to sleep. I had a hard time staying awake myself, driving along the long straight road in the first light of the morning. The tires were humming. I nodded and rubbed my eyes and drove on. After a while I turned off on to a back road that led into swamp country where we had been working before. I drove as far as we had worked yesterday. Then I nudged Pete and woke him up.

"Where are the other guys?" I said.

"Where are we?"

He looked around a minute blinking his eyes.

"Godamn!" he said. "You went to the wrong place."

"I thought we were supposed to finish the line we were running."

"Yeah? You thought! Well, it's been changed."

"You could have told me."

"Drive on up the road and see if there's a place we can turn around. I think I remember a shack down the road a piece."

I started up the truck again and drove on.

"Well," Pete said, "while you were out catting around with Delma last night, you missed all the fun."

"What fun?"

"Peanuts," he said. "They beat the living hell out of him."

"Jesus Christ! What did they do that for?"

"They got him drunk last evening, see? Usually when he's drunk he's just funny. But this time he was kind of mean, mean drunk. Some of the boys egged him on and he was just drunk enough to swing at them. They gave that black sonofabitch a real going over. Hell, they had to take him to the hospital when they got through."

"Jesus Christ!"

"You should've been there."

"I can't believe anybody would do anything like that."

I was thinking what a crazy terrible thing it was for some grown men to beat up a poor feeble-minded nigger like that. I was sleepy and hungry and hung over and it was all mixed up in my mind with all that had happened to me last night. Thinking about that married woman, Delma, and how she had to get herself all worked up by pretending she was in bed with some kind of a killer. She couldn't have believed it, but she needed to pretend that she did. Just like those men in town at the station had to pretend that Peanuts had done something to *them* and then beat him up to feel better. I felt so sick about everything in the whole world I wanted to die. I just wanted to fall over dead.

"Hey!" Pete yelled. "Turn in here."

There was a shack all right, just a patch of bare ground with the swamp all around it. It was all falling to pieces, but there were chickens running around the yard and a nigger without a shirt on was sitting on the front stoop picking at a guitar.

"The hell with it," Pete said. "He had it coming."

"Who?"

"Peanuts. They shouldn't let anybody that stupid run around loose."

"For what?" I said. "For what does anybody have awful things coming to him? Answer me that."

"I said the hell with it. Turn the truck around and let's go."

"I'm asking you."

"And I'm telling you to shut up and turn this truck around."

"All right," I said, turning off the engine and putting the keys in my pocket. "It was bound to come to this sooner or later."

"What are you going to do?"

"I'm fixing to beat the hell out of you."

I'll have to say he put up a good fight for a little guy. He was tough. We fought all around the truck and all over the yard, rolling on the ground, kicking and punching each other. I was so tired and sleepy I felt like I was dreaming, but I kept after him and I finally got him down so he couldn't get up. He just lay there panting, all bloody on the ground, and I started kicking at him.

"You going to kill me?"

He looked bad lying there. He was too weak to move. In my blood and my muscles and my bones I never wanted to kill anybody so much. I wanted to tear him into pieces and stamp them in the dust. But I couldn't do it. When he asked me was I going to kill him, all of a sudden I knew what I was doing. I knew what had happened to me and I knew I wasn't a damn bit better than those guys that beat up Peanuts or Delma or Pete or anybody else. I was so sick of myself I felt like I was going to puke.

"I don't know," I told him. "I ought to."

I went up to where I saw a well and hauled a bucket of water and splashed it all over me. The nigger sat there and stared at me with the guitar hanging loose in his hands. I wonder what he thought was going on.

After that I splashed Pete with water too and I put the keys in the truck.

"Drive me back to town," he said.

"Drive yourself," I said. "I'm walking."

I was lucky to get back in my old outfit with my old job. I came into the Battery area on a Sunday afternoon. The barracks was empty except for a few guys on the first floor, broke maybe or without a pass, playing cards on one of the bunks. They were sitting around, smoking, concentrating on the game. When I walked in and went on through they just looked up and looked back down to the game. They were new since I left. They didn't know me and I didn't know them.

I climbed the stairs and went into Mooney's room. He wasn't there but the room had his touch on everything in it. It was bare and clean and neat. The clothes in his wall locker were hanging evenly. The boots under his bed, side by side, were shined up nice, not all spit-shined like some young soldier's, just a nice shine. I made up the empty bunk. I made it up real tight without a wrinkle, so tight you could bounce a quarter off of it if you wanted to. Then I threw all my stuff in the corner and just flopped down in the middle of my bunk. I felt like I was floating on top of water. I lit myself a cigarette and looked at the ceiling.

After a while I heard Mooney climbing up the stairs. He always came up real slow and careful like an old man. Once you heard him walking up stairs you would never mistake it for somebody else. He opened the door and came in.

"How many times do I have to tell you not to smoke in bed," he said. "It's against regulations."

"Don't tell me," I said. "I've heard it all before."

"You think you know it all," he said. "Let me tell you, you got a lot of things to learn."

"Oh yeah? I've been around. I've been outside. I've seen a few things since the last time I seen you."

"Did you learn anything?" he said. "That's what I want to know."

"Not much."

"Nothing?"

"There's one thing, just one thing I've got to find out from you."

He waited for me to ask it.

"Mooney," I said, "how come you're so black?"

Mooney looked at me hard for a minute. Then he leaned back, rocked on his heels. The whole room rattled with his laughter and it was good to hear.

afterword

In the words of one commentator, George Garrett's favorite type of story is "an account of moral change, a fall from innocence into knowledge."* The main character in this story undergoes this sort of process as he leaves the relative security and order of the peacetime Army to enjoy the freedom which he believes exists in civilian society. Unfortunately, though, he finds not real freedom, which always entails self-restraint and self-awareness, but rather violence and irrationality, which evoke similarly dangerous tendencies in himself. Disgusted with society and with himself, for letting society destroy his rationality, he returns to the Army where, paradoxically, things are less violent.

The theme of one man's journey into a world of sickness and hatred—and of his return from it—is not a peculiarly Southern one. However, the particular instances of evil that Garrett points to are ones prevalent in the region, and his emphasis on the idea that violence begets violence is one which is extremely significant for the contemporary South.

George Garrett was born in Orlando, Florida, in 1929. He has been awarded a *Sewanee Review* Fellowship in Poetry and is the poetry editor of the *Transatlantic Review*. Included among his twelve books of poetry and fiction are *The Sleeping Gypsy* and *Do, Lord, Remember Me*. He is the editor of an anthology of short stories entitled *The Girl in the Black Raincoat: Variations on a Theme*. Garrett served as writer in residence at Princeton from 1964 to 1965; he now teaches at Hollins College. He has written a number of screenplays for Hollywood films.

questions for general discussion

1. What is contributed to our understanding of his character when the protagonist asks Pete, "For what? . . . For what does anybody have awful things coming to him? Answer me that"?

---

* William Robinson, "The Fiction of George Garrett," in *Red Clay Reader Two*, ed. Charleen Whisnant (Charlotte, N.C.: Red Clay Reader, 1965), pp. 15–16.

2. What does the protagonist mean when he says to Mooney, "You're chronic, Mooney. Nothing but an old chrome-plated chronic"?

3. Why does the author manipulate the sequence of his story's opening so that several pages elapse before the protagonist says, "He was a great guy and you took him for himself. You just forgot all about Mooney being a nigger"?

4. What is significant about the shirtless Negro with the guitar who sits on the steps and watches the fight between the two white men?

5. What is the protagonist's attitude toward women? Why does he feel this way?

6. Why does the author introduce the episodes of the "Phantom Killer"?

7. Is there any particular significance to the story's title?

suggestions for writing

1. Comment on violence and the various attitudes toward it represented in this story.

2. Comment on the structural unity of the story.

3. Contrast the protagonist's real action with what he wants to believe he is doing when he comments on the mistreatment of Peanuts, "In a way I guess it *was* funny too. Except a man is not a pig. So I made up my mind I would rather sit in the cafe and drink beer by myself than to put up with a thing like that."

4. Comment on the theme of the story.

5. Comment on what the protagonist has, or has not, learned in the brief time he is out of the Army. Comment on the way the author causes us to feel the change. In the end, is he "crazy" or "chronic"?

6. Analyze the two episodes concerning the protagonist's experiences with women, suggesting how they relate to the overall theme of the story.

DIANE OLIVER
neighbors

The bus turning the corner of Patterson and Talford Avenue was full this time of evening. Of the four passengers standing in the rear, she did not recognize any of her friends. Most of the people tucked neatly in the double seats were women, maids and cooks on their way from work or secretaries who had worked late and were riding from the office building at the mill. The cotton mill was out from town, near the house where she worked. She noticed that a few men were riding too. They were obviously just working men, except for one gentleman dressed very neatly in a dark grey suit and carrying what she imagined was a push-button umbrella.

He looked to her as though he usually drove a car to work. She immediately decided that the car probably wouldn't start this morning so he had to catch the bus to and from work. She was standing in the rear of the bus, peering at the passengers, her arms barely reaching the overhead railing, trying not to wobble with every lurch. But every corner the bus turned pushed her head toward a window. And her hair was coming down too, wisps of black curls swung between her eyes. She looked at the people around her. Some of them were white, but most of them were her color. Looking at the passengers at least kept her from thinking of tomorrow. But really she would be glad when it came, then everything would be over.

She took a firmer grip on the green leather seat and wished she had on her glasses. The man with the umbrella was two people ahead of her on the other side of the bus, so she could see him between other people very clearly. She watched as he unfolded the evening newspaper, craning her neck to see what was on the front page. She stood, impatiently trying to read the headlines, when she realized he was staring up at her rather curiously. Biting her lips she turned her head and stared out of the window until the downtown section was in sight.

She would have to wait until she was home to see if they were in the newspaper again. Sometimes she felt that if another person snapped a picture of them she would burst out screaming. Last Monday reporters were already inside the pre-school clinic when she took Tommy for his last polio shot. She didn't understand how anybody could be so heartless to a child. The flashbulb went off right when the needle went in and all the picture showed was Tommy's open mouth.

The bus pulling up to the curb jerked to a stop, startling her and confusing her thoughts. Clutching in her hand the paper bag that contained her uniform, she pushed her way toward the door. By standing in the back of the bus, she was one of the first people to step to the ground. Outside the bus, the evening air felt humid and uncomfortable and her dress kept sticking to her. She looked up and remembered that the weatherman had forecast rain. Just their luck—why, she wondered, would it have to rain on top of everything else?

As she walked along, the main street seemed unnaturally quiet but she decided her imagination was merely playing tricks. Besides, most of the stores had been closed since five o'clock.

She stopped to look at a reversible raincoat in Ivey's window, but although she had a full time job now, she couldn't keep her mind on clothes. She was about to continue walking when she heard a horn blowing. Looking around, half-scared but also curious, she saw a man beckoning to her in a grey car. He was nobody she knew but since a nicely dressed woman was with him in the front seat, she walked to the car.

"You're Jim Mitchell's girl, aren't you?" he questioned. "You Ellie or the other one?"

She nodded yes, wondering who he was and how much he had been drinking.

"Now honey," he said leaning over the woman, "you don't know me but your father does and you tell him that if anything happens to that boy of his tomorrow we're ready to set things straight." He looked her straight in the eye and she promised to take home the message.

Just as the man was about to step on the gas, the woman reached out and touched her arm. "You hurry up home, honey, it's about dark out here."

Before she could find out their names, the Chevrolet had disappeared around a corner. Ellie wished someone would magically appear and tell her everything that had happened since August. Then maybe she could figure out what was real and what she had been imagining for the past couple of days.

She walked past the main shopping district up to Tanner's where Saraline was standing in the window peeling oranges. Everything in the shop was painted orange and green and Ellie couldn't help thinking that poor Saraline looked out of place. She stopped to wave to her friend who pointed the knife to her watch and then to her boyfriend standing in the rear of the shop. Ellie nodded that she understood. She knew Sara wanted her to tell her grandfather that she had to work late again. Neither one of them could figure out why he didn't like Charlie. Saraline had finished high school three years ahead of her and it was time for her to be getting married. Ellie watched as her friend stopped peeling the orange long enough to cross her fingers. She nodded again but she was afraid all the crossed fingers in the world wouldn't stop the trouble tomorrow.

She stopped at the traffic light and spoke to a shrivelled woman hunched against the side of a building. Scuffing the bottom of her sneakers on the curb she waited for the woman to open her mouth and grin as she usually did. The kids used to bait her to talk, and since she didn't have but one tooth in her whole head they called her Doughnut Puncher. But the woman was still, the way everything else had been all week.

From where Ellie stood, across the street from the Sears and Roebuck parking lot, she could see their house, all of the houses on the single street white people called Welfare Row. Those newspaper men always made her angry. All of their articles showed how rough the people were on their street. And the reporters never said her family wasn't on welfare, the papers always said the family lived on that street. She paused to look across the street at a group of kids pouncing on one rubber ball. There were always white kids around their neighborhood mixed up in the games, but playing with them was almost an unwritten rule. When everybody started going to school nobody played together any more.

She crossed at the corner ignoring the cars at the stop light and the closer she got to her street the more she realized that the newspaper was right. The houses were ugly, there were not even any trees, just patches of scraggly bushes and grasses. As she cut across the sticky asphalt pavement covered with cars she was conscious of the parking lot floodlights casting a strange glow on her street. She stared from habit at the house on the end of the block and except for the way the paint was peeling they all looked alike to her. Now at twilight the flaking grey paint had a luminous glow and as she walked down the dirt sidewalk she noticed Mr. Paul's pipe smoke added to the hazy atmosphere. Mr. Paul would be sitting in that same spot waiting until Saraline came home. Ellie slowed her pace to speak to the elderly man sitting on the porch.

"Evening, Mr. Paul," she said. Her voice sounded clear and out of place on the vacant street.

"Eh, who's that?" Mr. Paul leaned over the rail, "What you say, girl?"

"How are you?" she hollered louder. "Sara said she'd be late tonight, she has to work." She waited for the words to sink in.

His head had dropped and his eyes were facing his lap. She could see that he was disappointed. "Couldn't help it," he said finally. "Reckon they needed her again." Then as if he suddenly remembered he turned toward her.

"You people be ready down there? Still gonna let him go tomorrow?"

She looked at Mr. Paul between the missing rails on his porch, seeing how his rolled up trousers seemed to fit exactly in the vacant banister space.

"Last I heard this morning we're still letting him go," she said.

Mr. Paul had shifted his weight back to the chair. "Don't reckon they'll hurt him," he mumbled, scratching the side of his face. "Hope he don't mind being spit on though. Spitting ain't like cutting. They can spit on him and nobody'll ever know who did it," he said, ending his words with a quiet chuckle.

Ellie stood on the sidewalk grinding her heel in the dirt waiting for the old man to finish talking. She was glad somebody found something funny to laugh at. Finally he shut up.

"Goodbye, Mr. Paul," she waved. Her voice sounded loud to her own ears. But she knew the way her head ached intensified noises. She walked home faster, hoping they had some aspirin in the house and that those men would leave earlier tonight.

From the front of her house she could tell that the men were still there. The living room light shone behind the yellow shades, coming through brighter in the patched places. She thought about moving the geranium pot from the porch to catch the rain but changed her mind. She kicked a beer can under a car parked in the street and stopped to look at her reflection on the car door. The tiny flowers of her printed dress made her look as if she had a strange tropical disease. She spotted another can and kicked it out of the way of the car, thinking that one of these days some kid was going to fall and hurt himself. What she wanted to do she knew was kick the car out of the way. Both the station wagon and the Ford had been parked in front of her house all week, waiting. Everybody was just sitting around waiting.

Suddenly she laughed aloud. Reverend Davis' car was big and black and shiny just like, but no, the smile disappeared from her face, her mother didn't like for them to say things about other people's color. She looked around to see who else came, and saw Mr. Moore's old beat up blue car. Somebody had torn away half of his NAACP sign. Sometimes she really felt sorry for the man. No matter how hard he glued on his stickers somebody always yanked them off again.

Ellie didn't recognize the third car but it had an Alabama license plate. She turned around and looked up and down the street, hating to go inside. There were no lights on their street, but in the distance she could see the bright lights of the parking lot. Slowly she did an about face and climbed the steps.

She wondered when her mama was going to remember to get a yellow bulb for the porch. Although the lights hadn't been turned on, usually June bugs and mosquitoes swarmed all around the porch. By the time she was inside the house she always felt like they were crawling in her hair. She pulled on the screen and saw that Mama finally had made Hezekiah patch up the holes. The globs of white adhesive tape scattered over the screen door looked just like misshapen butterflies.

She listened to her father's voice and could tell by the tone that the men were discussing something important again. She rattled the door once more but nobody came.

"Will somebody please let me in?" Her voice carried through the screen to the knot of men sitting in the corner.

"The door's open," her father yelled. "Come on in."

"The door is not open," she said evenly. "You know we stopped leaving it open." She was feeling tired again and her voice had fallen an octave lower.

"Yeah, I forgot, I forgot," he mumbled walking to the door.

She watched her father almost stumble across a chair to let her in. He was shorter than the light bulb and the light seemed to beam down on him, emphasizing the wrinkles around his eyes. She could tell from the way he pushed open the screen that he hadn't had much sleep either. She'd overheard him telling Mama that the people down at the shop seemed to be piling on the work harder just because of this thing. And he couldn't do anything or say anything to his boss because they probably wanted to fire him.

"Where's Mama?" she whispered. He nodded toward the back.

"Good evening, everybody," she said looking at the three men who had not looked up since she entered the room. One of the men half stood, but his attention was geared back to something another man was saying. They were sitting on the sofa in their shirt sleeves and there was a pitcher of ice water on the window sill.

"Your mother probably needs some help," her father said. She looked past him trying to figure out who the white man was sitting on the end. His face looked familiar and she tried to remember where she had seen him before. The men were paying no attention to her. She bent to see what they were studying and saw a large sheet of white drawing paper. She could see blocks and lines and the man sitting in the middle was marking a trail with the eraser edge of the pencil.

The quiet stillness of the room was making her head ache more. She pushed her way through the red embroidered curtains that led to the kitchen.

"I'm home, Mama," she said, standing in front of the back door facing the big yellow sun Hezekiah and Tommy had painted on the wall above the iron stove. Immediately she felt a warmth permeating her skin. "Where is everybody?" she asked, sitting at the table where her mother was peeling potatoes.

"Mrs. McAllister is keeping Helen and Teenie," her mother said. "Your brother is staying over with Harry tonight." With each name she uttered, a slice of potato peeling tumbled to the newspaper on the table. "Tommy's in the bedroom reading that Uncle Wiggily book."

Ellie looked up at her mother but her eyes were straight ahead. She knew that Tommy only read the Uncle Wiggily book by himself when he was unhappy. She got up and walked to the kitchen cabinet.

"The other knives dirty?" she asked.

"No," her mother said, "look in the next drawer."

Ellie pulled open the drawer, flicking scraps of white paint with her fingernail. She reached for the knife and at the same time a pile of envelopes caught her eye.

"Any more come today?" she asked, pulling out the knife and slipping the envelopes under the dish towels.

"Yes, seven more came today," her mother accentuated each word carefully. "Your father has them with him in the other room."

"Same thing?" she asked picking up a potato and wishing she could think of some way to change the subject.

The white people had been threatening them for the past three weeks. Some of the letters were aimed at the family, but most of them were directed to Tommy himself. About once a week in the same handwriting somebody wrote that he'd better not eat lunch at school because they were going to poison him.

They had been getting those letters ever since the school board made Tommy's name public. She sliced the potato and dropped the pieces in the pan of cold water. Out of all those people he had been the only one the board had accepted for transfer to the elementary school. The other children, the members said, didn't live in the district. As she cut the eyes out of another potato she thought about the first letter they had received and how her father just set fire to it in the ashtray. But then Mr. Bell said they'd better save the rest, in case anything happened, they might need the evidence for court.

She peeped up again at her mother, "Who's that white man in there with Daddy?"

"One of Lawyer Belk's friends," she answered. "He's pastor of the church that's always on television Sunday morning. Mr. Belk seems to think that having him around will do some good." Ellie saw that her voice was shaking just like her hand as she reached for the last potato. Both of them could hear Tommy in the next room mumbling to himself. She was afraid to look at her mother.

Suddenly Ellie was aware that her mother's hands were trembling violently. "He's so little," she whispered and suddenly the knife slipped out of her hands and she was crying and breathing at the same time.

Ellie didn't know what to do but after a few seconds she cleared away the peelings and put the knives in the sink. "Why don't you lie down?" she suggested. "I'll clean up and get Tommy in bed." Without saying anything her mother rose and walked to her bedroom.

Ellie wiped off the table and draped the dishcloth over the sink. She stood back and looked at the rusting pipes powdered with a whitish film. One of these days they would have to paint the place. She tiptoed past her mother who looked as if she had fallen asleep from exhaustion.

"Tommy," she called softly, "come on and get ready for bed."

Tommy sitting in the middle of the floor did not answer. He was sitting the way she imagined he would be, crosslegged, pulling his ear lobe as he turned the ragged pages of *Uncle Wiggily at the Zoo*.

"What you doing, Tommy?" she said squatting on the floor beside him. He smiled and pointed at the picture of the ducks.

"School starts tomorrow," she said, turning a page with him. "Don't you think it's time to go to bed?"

"Oh Ellie, do I have to go now?" She looked down at the serious brown eyes and the closely cropped hair. For a minute she wondered if he questioned having to go to bed now or to school tomorrow.

"Well," she said, "aren't you about through with the book?" He shook his head. "Come on," she pulled him up, "you're a sleepyhead." Still he shook his head.

"When Helen and Teenie coming home?"

"Tomorrow after you come home from school they'll be here."

She lifted him from the floor thinking how small he looked to be facing all those people tomorrow.

"Look," he said breaking away from her hand and pointing to a blue shirt and pair of cotton twill pants, "Mama got them for me to wear tomorrow."

While she ran water in the tub, she heard him crawl on top of the bed. He was quiet and she knew he was untying his sneakers.

"Put your shoes out," she called through the door, "and maybe Daddy will polish them."

"Is Daddy still in there with those men? Mama made me be quiet so I wouldn't bother them."

He padded into the bathroom with bare feet and crawled into the water. As she scrubbed him they played Ask Me A Question, their own version of Twenty Questions. She had just dried him and was about to have him step into his pajamas when he asked: "Are they gonna get me tomorrow?"

"Who's going to get you?" She looked into his eyes and began rubbing him furiously with the towel.

"I don't know," he answered. "Somebody I guess."

"Nobody's going to get you," she said, "who wants a little boy who gets bubblegum in his hair anyway—but us?" He grinned but as she hugged him she thought how much he looked like his father. They walked to the bed to say his prayers and while they were kneeling she heard the first drops of rain. By the time she covered him up and tucked the spread off the floor the rain had changed to a steady downpour.

When Tommy had gone to bed her mother got up again and began ironing clothes in the kitchen. Something, she said, to keep her thoughts busy. While her mother folded and sorted the clothes Ellie drew up a chair from the kitchen table. They sat in the kitchen for a while listening to the voices of the men in the next room. Her mother's quiet speech broke the stillness in the room.

"I'd rather," she said making sweeping motions with the iron, "that you stayed home from work tomorrow and went with your father to take Tommy. I don't think I'll be up to those people."

Ellie nodded, "I don't mind," she said, tracing circles on the oil cloth covered table.

"Your father's going," her mother continued. "Belk and Reverend Davis are too. I think that white man in there will probably go."

"They may not need me," Ellie answered.

"Tommy will," her mother said, folding the last dish towel and storing it in the cabinet.

"Mama, I think he's scared," the girl turned toward the woman. "He was so quiet while I was washing him."

"I know," she answered sitting down heavily. "He's been that way all day." Her brown wavy hair glowed in the dim lighting of the kitchen. "I told him he wasn't going to school with Jakie and Bob any more but I said he was going to meet some other children just as nice."

Ellie saw that her mother was twisting her wedding band around and around on her finger.

"I've already told Mrs. Ingraham that I wouldn't be able to come out tomorrow." Ellie paused, "She didn't say very much. She didn't even say anything about his pictures in the newspaper. Mr. Ingraham said we were getting right crazy but even he didn't say anything else."

She stopped to look at the clock sitting near the sink. "It's almost time for the cruise cars to begin," she said. Her mother followed Ellie's eyes to the sink. The policemen circling their block every twenty minutes was supposed to make them feel safe, but hearing the cars come so regularly and that light flashing through the shade above her bed only made her nervous.

She stopped talking to push a wrinkle out of the shiny red cloth, dragging her finger along the table edges. "How long before those men going to leave?" she asked her mother. Just as she spoke she heard one of the men say something about getting some sleep. "I didn't mean to run them away," she said smiling. Her mother half-smiled too. They listened for the sound of motors and tires and waited for her father to shut the front door.

In a few seconds her father's head pushed through the curtain. "Want me to turn down your bed now, Ellie?" She felt uncomfortable staring up at him, the whole family looked drained of all energy.

"That's all right," she answered. "I'll sleep in Helen and Teenie's bed tonight."

"How's Tommy?" he asked looking toward the bedroom. He came in and sat down at the table with them.

They were silent before he spoke. "I keep wondering if we should send him." He lit a match and watched the flame disappear into the ashtray, then he looked into his wife's eyes. "There's no telling what these fool white folks will do."

Her mother reached over and patted his hand. "We're doing what we have to do, I guess," she said. "Sometimes though I wish the others weren't so much older than him."

"But it seems so unfair," Ellie broke in, "sending him there all by himself like that. Everybody keeps asking me why the MacAdams didn't apply for their children."

"Eloise." Her father's voice sounded curt. "We aren't answering for the MacAdams, we're trying to do what's right for your brother. He's not old enough to have his own say so. You and the others could decide for yourselves, but we're the ones that have to do for him."

She didn't say anything but watched him pull a handful of envelopes out of his pocket and tuck them in the cabinet drawer. She knew that if anyone had told him in August that Tommy would be the only one going to Jefferson Davis they would not have let him go.

"Those the new ones?" she asked. "What they say?"

"Let's not talk about the letters," her father said. "Let's go to bed."

Outside they heard the rain become heavier. Since early evening she had become accustomed to the sound. Now it blended in with the rest of the noises that had accumulated in the back of her mind since the whole thing began.

As her mother folded the ironing board they heard the quiet wheels of the police car. Ellie noticed that the clock said twelve-ten and she wondered why they were early. Her mother pulled the iron cord from the switch and they stood silently waiting for the police car to turn around and pass the house again, as if the car's passing were a final blessing for the night.

Suddenly she was aware of a noise that sounded as if everything had broken loose in her head at once, a loudness that almost shook the foundation of the house. At the same time the lights went out and instinctively her father knocked them to the floor. They could hear the tinkling of glass near the front of the house and Tommy began screaming.

"Tommy, get down," her father yelled.

She hoped he would remember to roll under the bed the way they had practiced. She was aware of objects falling and breaking as she lay perfectly still. Her breath was coming in jerks and then there was a second noise, a smaller explosion but still drowning out Tommy's cries.

"Stay still," her father commanded. "I'm going to check on Tommy. They may throw another one."

She watched him crawl across the floor, pushing a broken flower vase and an iron skillet out of his way. All of the sounds, Tommy's crying, the breaking glass, everything was echoing in her ears. She felt as if they had been crouching on the floor for hours but when she heard the police car door slam, the luminous hands of the clock said only twelve-fifteen.

She heard other cars drive up and pairs of heavy feet trample on the porch. "You folks all right in there?"

She could visualize the hands pulling open the door, because she knew the voice. Sergeant Kearns had been responsible for patrolling the house during the past three weeks. She heard him click the light switch in the living room but the darkness remained intense.

Her father deposited Tommy in his wife's lap and went to what was left of the door. In the next fifteen minutes policemen were everywhere. While she rummaged around underneath the cabinet for a candle, her mother tried to hush up Tommy. His cheek was cut where he had scratched himself on the springs of the bed. Her mother motioned for her to dampen a cloth and put some petroleum jelly on it to keep him quiet. She tried to put him to bed again but he would not go, even when she promised to stay with him for the rest of the night. And so she sat in the kitchen rocking the little boy back and forth on her lap.

Ellie wandered around the kitchen but the light from the single candle put an eerie glow on the walls making her nervous. She began picking up pans, stepping over pieces of broken crockery and glassware. She did not want to go into the living room yet, but if she listened closely, snatches of the policemen's conversation came through the curtain.

She heard one man say that the bomb landed near the edge of the yard, that was why it had only gotten the front porch. She knew from their talk that the living room window was shattered completely. Suddenly Ellie sat down. The picture of the living room window kept flashing in her mind and a wave of feeling invaded her body making her shake as if she had lost all muscular control. She slept on the couch, right under that window.

She looked at her mother to see if she too had realized, but her mother was looking down at Tommy and trying to get him to close his eyes. Ellie stood up and crept toward the living room trying to prepare herself for what she would see. Even that minute of determination could not make her control the horror that she felt. There were jagged holes all along the front of the house and the sofa was covered with glass and paint. She started to pick up the picture that had toppled from the book shelf, then she just stepped over the broken frame.

Outside her father was talking and, curious to see who else was with him, she walked across the splinters to the yard. She could see pieces of the geranium pot and the red blossoms turned face down. There were no lights in the other houses on the street. Across from their house she could see forms standing in the door and shadows being pushed back and forth. "I guess the MacAdams are glad they just didn't get involved." No one heard her speak, and no one came over to see if they could help; she knew why and did not really blame them. They were afraid their house could be next.

Most of the policemen had gone now and only one car was left to flash the revolving red light in the rain. She heard the tall skinny man tell her father they would be parked outside for the rest of the night. As she watched the reflection of the police cars returning to the station, feeling sick on her stomach, she wondered now why they bothered.

Ellie went back inside the house and closed the curtain behind her. There was nothing anyone could do now, not even to the house. Everything was scattered all over the floor and poor Tommy still would not go to sleep. She wondered what would happen when the news spread through their section of town, and at once remembered the man in the grey Chevrolet. It would serve them right if her father's friends got one of them.

Ellie pulled up an overturned chair and sat down across from her mother who was crooning to Tommy. What Mr. Paul said was right, white people just couldn't be trusted. Her family had expected anything but even though they had practiced ducking, they didn't really expect anybody to try tearing down the house. But the funny thing was the house belonged to one of them. Maybe it was a good thing her family were just renters.

Exhausted, Ellie put her head down on the table. She didn't know what they were going to do about tomorrow, in the day time they didn't need electricity. She was too tired to think any more about Tommy, yet she could not go to sleep. So, she sat at the table trying to sit still, but every few minutes she would involuntarily twitch. She tried to steady her hands, all the time listening to her mother's sing-songy voice and waiting for her father to come back inside the house.

She didn't know how long she lay hunched against the kitchen table, but when she looked up, her wrists bore the imprints of her hair. She unfolded her arms gingerly, feeling the blood rush to her fingertips. Her father sat in the chair opposite her, staring at the vacant space between them. She heard her mother creep away from the table, taking Tommy to his room.

Ellie looked out the window. The darkness was turning to grey and the hurt feeling was disappearing. As she sat there she could begin to look at the kitchen matter-of-factly. Although the hands of the clock were just a little past five-thirty, she knew somebody was going to have to start clearing up and cook breakfast.

She stood and tipped across the kitchen to her parents' bedroom. "Mama," she whispered, standing near the door of Tommy's room. At the sound of her voice, Tommy made a funny throaty noise in his sleep. Her mother motioned for her to go out and be quiet. Ellie knew then that Tommy had just fallen asleep. She crept back to the kitchen and began picking up the dishes that could be salvaged, being careful not to go into the living room.

She walked around her father, leaving the broken glass underneath the kitchen table. "You want some coffee?" she asked.

He nodded silently, in strange contrast she thought to the water faucet that turned with a loud gurgling noise. While she let the water run to get hot she measured out the instant coffee in one of the plastic cups. Next door she could hear people moving around in the Williams' kitchen, but they too seemed much quieter than usual.

"You reckon everybody knows by now?" she asked, stirring the coffee and putting the saucer in front of him.

"Everybody will know by the time the city paper comes out," he said. "Somebody was here last night from the *Observer*. Guess it'll make front page."

She leaned against the cabinet for support watching him trace endless circles in the brown liquid with the spoon. "Sergeant Kearns says they'll have almost the whole force out there tomorrow," he said.

"Today," she whispered.

Her father looked at the clock and then turned his head.

"When's your mother coming back in here?" he asked, finally picking up the cup and drinking the coffee.

"Tommy's just off to sleep," she answered. "I guess she'll be in here when he's asleep for good."

She looked out the window of the back door at the row of tall hedges that had separated their neighborhood from the white people for as long as she remembered. While she stood there she heard her mother walk into the room. To her ears the steps seemed much slower than usual. She heard her mother stop in front of her father's chair.

"Jim," she said, sounding very timid, "what we going to do?" Yet as Ellie turned toward her she noticed her mother's face was strangely calm as she looked down on her husband.

Ellie continued standing by the door listening to them talk. Nobody asked the question to which they all wanted an answer.

"I keep thinking," her father said finally, "that the policemen will be with him all day. They couldn't hurt him inside the school building without getting some of their own kind."

"But he'll be in there all by himself," her mother said softly. "A hundred policemen can't be a little boy's only friends."

She watched her father wrap his calloused hands, still splotched with machine oil, around the salt shaker on the table.

"I keep trying," he said to her, "to tell myself that somebody's got to be the first one and then I just think how quiet he's been all week."

Ellie listened to the quiet voices that seemed to be a room apart from her. In the back of her mind she could hear phrases of a hymn her grandmother used to sing, something about trouble, her being born for trouble.

"Jim, I cannot let my baby go." Her mother's words, although quiet, were carefully pronounced.

"Maybe," her father answered, "it's not in our hands. Reverend Davis and I were talking day before yesterday how God tested the Israelites, maybe he's just trying us."

"God expects you to take care of your own," his wife interrupted. Ellie sensed a trace of bitterness in her mother's voice.

"Tommy's not going to understand why he can't go to school," her father replied. "He's going to wonder why, and how are we going to tell him we're afraid of them?" Her father's hand clutched the coffee cup. "He's going to be fighting them the rest of his life. He's got to start sometime."

But he's not on their level. Tommy's too little to go around hating people. One of the others, they're bigger, they understand about things."

Ellie still leaning against the door saw that the sun covered part of the sky behind the hedges and the light slipping through the kitchen window seemed to reflect the shiny red of the table cloth.

"He's our child," she heard her mother say. "Whatever we do, we're going to be the cause." Her father had pushed the cup away from him and sat with his hands covering part of his face. Outside Ellie could hear a horn blowing.

"God knows we tried but I guess there's just no use." Her father's voice forced her attention back to the two people sitting in front of her. "Maybe when things come back to normal, we'll try again."

He covered his wife's chunky fingers with the palm of his hand and her mother seemed to be enveloped in silence. The three of them remained quiet, each involved in his own thoughts, but related, Ellie knew, to the same thing. She was the first to break the silence.

"Mama," she called after a long pause, "do you want me to start setting the table for breakfast?"

Her mother nodded.

Ellie turned the clock so she could see it from the sink while she washed the dishes that had been scattered over the floor.

"You going to wake up Tommy or you want me to?"

"No," her mother said, still holding her father's hand, "let him sleep. When you wash your face, you go up the street and call Hezekiah. Tell him to keep up with the children after school, I want to do something to this house before they come home."

She stopped talking and looked around the kitchen, finally turning to her husband. "He's probably kicked the spread off by now," she said. Ellie watched her father, who without saying anything walked toward the bedroom.

She watched her mother lift herself from the chair and automatically push in the stuffing underneath the cracked plastic cover. Her face looked set, as it always did when she was trying hard to keep her composure.

"He'll need something hot when he wakes up. Hand me the oatmeal," she commanded, reaching on top of the icebox for matches to light the kitchen stove.

afterword

The family described in Diane Oliver's story, "Neighbors," are defeated by social conditions which are too much for them. Confronting the timidity and indifference of their own people and the hostility of the whites proves ultimately to be too arduous a task for them to undertake alone. For the time being, at least, beaten by outside forces, they find solace only in their withdrawal into their small family circle. Written in the mid-sixties, this story reveals some of the reasons why Negroes have recently encouraged black solidarity in their struggle against racism.

Diane Oliver was born in 1943 in Charlotte, North Carolina. Before her untimely death in a motorcycle accident in 1967, she published short stories in the *Negro Digest,* the *Red Clay Reader,* and the *Sewanee Review.* In 1965, she was a writing fellow in the State University of Iowa Writers' Workshop.

questions for general discussion

1. What is the effect of the sentence describing the door: "The globs of white adhesive tape scattered over the screen door looked just like misshapen butterflies"?

2. Give some examples of foreshadowing in the story.

3. What is the effect of the mother's statement at the end of the story, "He'll need something hot when he wakes up. Hand me the oatmeal"?

4. Is the story's title ambiguous or ironic?

5. What is the effect on the reader of seeing Tommy reading his Uncle Wiggily book?

6. What is the protagonist's relationship with her parents? With her world?

suggestions for writing

1. Write a theme on the protagonist's perception of reality in the story.

2. Comment on the use of concrete details in the establishment of setting and atmosphere.

3. Write an essay suggesting two different ways of viewing the story's ending, supporting both views with specific references.

4. Comment on the theme of the story.

5. Comment on those aspects of this story which make it singularly a story of Negro life. Suggest ways in which it is, or might be, a story of human—not just racial—hatred.

EUDORA WELTY

where is the voice coming from?

I says to my wife, "You can reach and turn it off. You don't have to set and look at a black nigger face no longer than you want to, or listen to what you don't want to hear. It's still a free country."

I reckon that's how I give myself the idea.

I says, I could find right exactly where in Thermopylae that nigger's living that's asking for equal time. And without a bit of trouble to me.

And I ain't saying it might not be because that's pretty close to where *I* live. The other hand, there could be reasons you might have yourself for knowing how to get there in the dark. It's where you all go for the thing you want when you want it the most. Ain't that right?

The Branch Bank sign tells you in lights, all night long even, what time it is and how hot. When it was quarter to four, and 92, that was me going by in my brother-in-law's truck. He don't deliver nothing at that hour of the morning.

So you leave Four Corners and head west on Nathan B. Forrest Road, past the Surplus & Salvage, not much beyond the Kum Back Drive-In and Trailer Camp, not as far as where the signs starts saying "Live Bait," "Used Parts," "Fireworks," "Peaches," and "Sister Peebles Reader and Adviser." Turn before you hit the city limits and duck back towards the I.C. tracks. And his street's been paved.

And there was his light on, waiting for me. In his garage, if you please. His car's gone. He's out planning still some other ways to do what we tell 'em they can't. I *thought* I'd beat him home. All I had to do was pick my tree and walk in close behind it.

I didn't come expecting not to wait. But it was so hot, all I did was hope and pray one or the other of us wouldn't melt before it was over.

Now, it wasn't no bargain I'd struck.

I've heard what you've heard about Goat Dykeman, in Mississippi. Sure, everybody knows about Goat Dykeman. Goat he got word to the Governor's Mansion he'd go up yonder and shoot that nigger Meredith clean out of school, if he's let out of the pen to do it. Old Ross turned *that* over in his mind before saying him nay, it stands to reason.

I ain't no Goat Dykeman, I ain't in no pen, and I ain't ask no Governor Barnett to give me one thing. Unless he wants to give me a pat on the back for the trouble I took this morning. But he don't have to if he don't want to. I done what I done for my own pure-D satisfaction.

As soon as I heard wheels, I knowed who was coming. That was him and bound to be him. It was the right nigger heading in a new white car up his driveway towards his garage with the light shining, but stopping before he got there, maybe not to wake 'em. That was him. I knowed it when he cut off the car lights and put his foot out and I knowed him standing dark against the light. I knowed him then like I know me now. I knowed him even by his still, listening back.

Never seen him before, never seen him since, never seen anything of his black face but his picture, never seen his face alive, any time at all, or anywheres, and didn't want to, need to, never hope to see that face and never will. As long as there was no question in my mind.

He had to be the one. He stood right still and waited against the light, his back was fixed, fixed on me like a preacher's eyeballs when he's yelling "Are you saved?" He's the one.

I'd already brought up my rifle, I'd already taken my sights. And I'd already got him, because it was too late then for him or me to turn by one hair.

Something darker than him, like the wings of a bird, spread on his back and pulled him down. He climbed up once, like a man under bad claws, and like just blood could weigh a ton he walked with it on his back to better light. Didn't get no further than his door. And fell to stay.

He was down. He was down, and a ton load of bricks on his back wouldn't have laid any heavier. There on his paved driveway, yes sir.

And it wasn't till the minute before, that the mockingbird had quit singing. He'd been singing up my sassafras tree. Either he was up early, or he hadn't never gone to bed, he was like me. And the mocker he'd stayed right with me, filling the air till come the crack, till I turned loose of my load. I was like him. I was on top of the world myself. For once.

I stepped to the edge of his light there, where he's laying flat. I says, "Roland? There was one way left, for me to be ahead of you and stay ahead of you, by Dad, and I just taken it. Now I'm alive and you ain't. We ain't never now, never going to be equals and you know why? One of us is dead. What about that, Roland?" I said. "Well, you seen to it, didn't you?"

I stood a minute—just to see would somebody inside come out long enough to pick him up. And there she comes, the woman. I doubt she'd been to sleep. Because it seemed to me she'd been in there keeping awake all along.

It was mighty green where I skint over the yard getting back. That nigger wife of his, she wanted nice grass! I bet my wife would hate to pay her water bill. And for burning her electricity. And there's my brother-in-law's truck, still waiting with the door open.

"No Riders"—that didn't mean me.

There wasn't a thing I been able to think of since would have made it to go any nicer. Except a chair to my back while I was putting in my waiting. But going home, I seen what little time it takes after all to get a thing done like you really want it. It was 4:34, and while I was looking it moved to 35. And the temperature stuck where it was. All that night I guarantee you it had stood without dropping, a good 92.

My wife says, "What? Didn't the skeeters bite you?" She said, "Well, they been asking that—why somebody didn't trouble to load a rifle and get some of these agitators out of Thermopylae. Didn't the fella keep drumming it in, what a good idea? The one that writes a column ever' day?"

I says to my wife, "Find *some* way I don't get the credit."

"He says do it for Thermopylae," she says. "Don't you ever skim the paper?"

I says, "Thermopylae never done nothing for me. And I don't owe nothing to Thermopylae. Didn't do it for you. Hell, any more'n I'd do something or other for them Kennedys! I done it for my own pure-D satisfaction."

"It's going to get him right back on TV," says my wife. "You watch for the funeral."

I says, "You didn't even leave a light burning when you went to bed. So how was I supposed to even get me home or pull Buddy's truck up safe in our front yard?"

"Well, hear another good joke on you," my wife says next. "Didn't you hear the news? The N. double A.C.P. is fixing to send somebody to Thermopylae. Why couldn't you waited? You might could have got you somebody better. Listen and hear 'em say so."

I ain't but one. I reckon you have to tell *somebody*.

"Where's the gun, then?" my wife says. "What did you do with our protection?"

I says, "It was scorching! It was scorching!" I told her, "It's laying out on the ground in rank weeds, trying to cool off, that's what it's doing now."

"You dropped it," she says. "Back there."

And I told her, "Because I'm so tired of ever'thing in the world being just that hot to the touch! The keys to the truck, the doorknob, the bedsheet, ever'thing, it's all like a stove lid. There just ain't much going that's worth holding onto it no more," I says, "when it's a hundred and two in the shade by day and by night not too much difference. I wish *you'd* laid *your* finger to that gun."

"Trust you to come off and leave it," my wife says.

"Is that how no-'count I am?" she makes me ask. "*You* want to go back and get it?"

"You're the one they'll catch. I say it's so hot that even if you get to sleep you wake up feeling like you cried all night!" says my wife. "Cheer up, here's one more joke before time to get up. Heard what *Caroline* said? Caroline said, 'Daddy, I just can't wait to grow up big, so I can marry *James Meredith*.' I heard that where I work. One richbitch to another one, to make her cackle."

"At least I kept some dern teen-ager from North Thermopylae getting there and doing it first," I says. "Driving his own car."

On TV and in the paper, they don't know but half of it. They know who Roland Summers was without knowing who I am. His face was in front of the public before I got rid of him, and after I got rid of him there it is again—the same picture. And none of me. I ain't ever had one made. Not ever! The best that newspaper could do for me was offer a five-hundred-dollar reward for finding out who I am. For as long as they don't know who that is, whoever shot Roland is worth a good deal more right now than Roland is.

But by the time I was moving around uptown, it was hotter still. That pavement in the middle of Main Street was so hot to my feet I might've been walking the barrel of my gun. If the whole world could've just felt Main Street this morning through the soles of my shoes, maybe it would've helped some.

Then the first thing I heard 'em say was the N. double A.C.P. done it themselves, killed Roland Summers, and proved it by saying the shooting was done by a expert (I hope to tell you it was!) and at just the right hour and minute to get the whites in trouble.

You can't win.

"They'll never find him," the old man trying to sell roasted peanuts tells me to my face.

And it's so hot.

It looks like the town's on fire already, whichever ways you turn, ever' street you strike, because there's those trees hanging them pones of bloom like split watermelon. And a thousand cops crowding ever'where you go, half of 'em too young to start shaving, but all streaming sweat alike. I'm getting tired of 'em.

I was already tired of seeing a hundred cops getting us white people nowheres. Back at the beginning, I stood on the corner and I watched them new babyface cops loading nothing but nigger children into the paddy wagon and they come marching out of a little parade and into the paddy wagon singing. And they got in and sat down without providing a speck of trouble, and their hands held little new American flags, and all the cops could do was knock them flagsticks a-loose from their hands, and not let 'em pick 'em up, that was all, and give 'em a free ride. And children can just get 'em more flags.

Everybody: It don't get you nowhere to take nothing from nobody unless you make sure it's for keeps, for good and all, for ever and amen.

I won't be sorry to see them brickbats hail down on us for a change. Pop bottles too, they can come flying whenever they want to. Hundreds, all to smash, like Birmingham. I'm waiting on 'em to bring out them switchblade knives, like Harlem and Chicago. Watch TV long enough and you'll see it all to happen on Deacon Street in Thermopylae. What's holding it back, that's all?—Because it's *in* 'em.

I'm ready myself for that funeral.

Oh, they may find me. May catch me one day in spite of 'emselves. (But I grew up in the country.) May try to railroad me into the electric chair, and what that amounts to is something hotter than yesterday and today put together.

But I advise 'em to go careful. Ain't it about time us taxpayers starts to calling the moves? Starts to telling the teachers *and* the preachers *and* the judges of our so-called courts how far they can go?

Even the President so far, he can't walk in my house without being invited, like he's my daddy, just to say whoa. Not yet!

Once, I run away from my home. And there was a ad for me, come to be printed in our county weekly. My mother paid for it. It was from her. It says: "SON: You are not being hunted for anything but to find you." That time, I come on back home.

But people are dead now.

And it's so hot. Without it even being August yet.

Anyways, I seen him fall. I was evermore the one.

So I reach me down my old guitar off the nail in the wall. 'Cause I've got my guitar, what I've held onto from way back when, and I never dropped that, never lost or forgot it, never hocked it but to get it again, never give it away, and I set in my chair, with nobody home but me, and I start to play, and sing a-Down. And sing a-down, down, down, down. Sing a-down, down, down, down. Down.

afterword

Like many of Eudora Welty's stories, "Where Is the Voice Coming From?" centers upon an individual who, feeling rebuffed by society, falls back on himself in order to create a private version of reality in which he is somehow significant, and who then reaches out to attack those who refuse to acknowledge this significance. In her stories, Miss Welty exposes some of the dangers latent in the Southern emphasis on individualism as she presents characters who frequently render themselves ludicrous, vicious, and pathetic while attempting to assert their worth.

The question "Where Is the Voice Coming From?" manifests Miss Welty's difficulty in viewing her self-alienated protagonist as part of the world of men. Her question, her emphasis on the heat in the murderer's environment, and the last words of the story seem to indicate that the voice is coming from some infernal region far removed from our world. Yet Miss Welty emphasizes the specificities of her setting and her plot closely parallels an actual murder (that of Medgar Evers), to make clear that the hell she is portraying is one that exists in America now, frequently, but not exclusively, in the South.

Born in Jackson, Mississippi, in 1909, Eudora Welty was educated in public schools there. Later she studied at Mississippi State College for Women, and took a B.A. degree from the University of Wisconsin in 1929. After a year of studying advertising at Columbia University, she returned to Jackson, where she worked in journalism. Miss Welty has spent most of her life in Mississippi, and that state is the setting for most of her work. Her stories first appeared in several little magazines in the South. Publication of her works in such national magazines as *The Atlantic Monthly* and *Harper's Bazaar* was followed by the first collection of her short stories, *A Curtain of Green* (1941). Subsequent books include *The Robber Bridegroom* (1942), *Delta Wedding* (1946), *The Golden Apples* (1949), *The Ponder Heart* (1954), and *The Bride of Innisfallen* (1955). Among other literary prizes she has won two O. Henry Memorial Awards.

questions for general discussion

1. What, finally, is your attitude toward the speaker? Is it one of anger or pity?

2. What is the significance of the birds mentioned by the speaker as he stands near his "sassafras tree"?

3. What is Welty's purpose in closing the story with the guitar and the song?

4. What is significant about the speaker's explanation to his wife of how he left his rifle behind?

5. What are some obvious contrasts between Roland Summers' life and that of the speaker?

6. What effect is achieved when the speaker says to his wife, "I didn't do it for you. I did it for my own pure-D satisfaction"?

suggestions for writing

1. Develop a theme suggesting ways in which Miss Welty employs details of the setting to affect our attitudes toward the speaker in the story.

2. Discuss the speaker's motives for doing what he does.

3. Comment on the ways in which the speaker reveals attitudes of which he, himself, may be unconscious.

4. Trace and analyze some of the elements by which Miss Welty creates the atmosphere of her story.

EDWARD J. CABBELL
the soul's sting

It was five o'clock in the morning and I found myself walking the streets in Harlem. A gush of wind whirled out of the hot July sky and licked into my face and clothes. I squinted my eyes as bits of paper and dirt whirled around me. The coolness of the wind sent a chill over my sweating body, as the sweat dried too quickly. I took refuge in the closest open dive I saw. The heated odor of liquor, beer, cigarettes, and body funk soon returned the sweat to my tiring body. The darkness of the place was interrupted by the gay colors of the jukebox and the bright lights behind the crowded, semicircular bar. I pushed my way past the twisting bodies of black men and women to reach the bar. The bartender shouted curses above the roar of the jukebox at a giggling girl who was slumped over the counter. A short, black man retorted to the bartender and lowered his hand around the woman. The bartender threatened to kick them both out. All of the tired black and brown faces surrounding the bar laughed except one. He was a tall, lanky boy. His black face showed a bitter pity for these men and women as they went from cursing to laughter, to anger, to lust. His sweat-stained shirt clung to his back, revealing the hard, stingy leanness of his compact muscles. "He must be a boy from the old country," I said. He had that green look I had seen on so many Southern migrants who packed into Harlem every day. They had hopes of finding a better life here. I knew them for I had been one of them. I had fled Biloxi for Harlem one winter morning four long-ago years. Hungry and tired, I found myself free in a rat race of sex, liquor, and good times. I soon found that my new freedom was a curse. I could never become a full member of this den of men and women who talked, laughed, and fought together from day to day. "We live it up every day," a harsh voiced woman told me. "Hell, it's the only way to live. You stop and think where you is and that's it. . . . You worry yo'self to death." Her words had a deep meaning for me. They became even deeper as I fought rats, hunger, men, and women to keep alive.

I landed a job with a small dance band—Murphy Mason and the Cold Sweats. We would never make the Copa but we tried like hell to land in the Apollo. Anyway, I was eating regularly and I made enough to rent an apartment in which I could sleep without waking up with chinch bites all over me or facing a rat attack during the night. After awhile I was able to buy some flashy clothes like the "in" crowd—high-hitched pants, gay colored Nehru jackets, and fancy ankle-height boots. It didn't take long for me to accept my new world.

I still had the dangerous habit of walking the streets for hours after the band had finished a ten 'til two spot. Occasionally, I would drift into a dive, as the joints here were called, and lose myself in the crowd of muddy-eyed and muddy-faced men and harsh-voiced women in bright, tight dresses, giggling up at their grinning escorts. Usually, I'd spot some lonely woman with a cigarette between her fingers or hanging out of the corner of her mouth. I would give her the eye and she would wiggle over to the bar. Next I found myself with the others—enjoying liquor, sex, and good times. Perhaps this was the reason I was out tonight. I never stopped to think.

I knew this boy before me and his look of dismay. I had seen him a thousand times. I had once been him. I wanted to tell him to go back home—if he had one—just get out now. There was nothing here good for him. He could only receive hunger and pain—a stinging pain of discovery. Here you could easily find yourself for there were too many YOUS all around —each one with a powerful sting of body and soul. "Get out, boy," I almost forced myself to scream but I couldn't. I was too distant from him. I had no right to destroy his innocence or his hopes. My mother's words, "Every man is entitled to his dreams," came to me as I walked toward him.

"Drinking?" I questioned him, sounding slightly drunk.

He nodded his head as a grin inched across his suspicious face. His clothes were wrinkled and dusty. I figured he had arrived about two or three days ago. His neck was stiff and a strong body odor made it clear that he had neither eaten nor rested since he arrived.

"Two regulars, J.B.," I yelled at the bartender, still sounding slightly drunk.

I cautiously watched the boy as he drank the vodka. He wasn't used to drinking. He acted as if a wave of pain was shooting through him. Then he grabbed his stomach. Yeah . . . the boy was hungry. I knew that look.

"You oughtta know better than to drink on an empty belly," I said, forgetting about my phoney drunk tone. I sort of let my thoughts speak out loud.

He nodded his head. An almost embarrassed look was now on his face. "Jest cause you brought that damn drink don't give ya no reason to go preachin' ta me," he shouted in anger, losing his suspicious look for a moment.

" 'scuse me, shotgun," I snapped, "I didn't know you was loaded and exploding."

The boy turned to walk away. I could tell he was weak from hunger by the way he moved. "Wait a minute, boy," I called without thinking.

"Boy plays with Tarzan. I play with Jane and you know she's a white woman!" he snapped.

"Look b . . . o . . . y," I mocked, "let's stop playin' games. You're hungry and you know it. There's no sense in gettin' uppity here. These barflies don't give a damn about you. Most of them are too drunk to hear or understand what I'm saying or how damn ignorant you're acting. Come on off your high horse, boy. Let's git outta here and find some food somewhere."

The boy looked as if he were lost in a fog of fear. He didn't even move.

"I ain't out for no fag pickup or nothing. . . . What's wrong with you? . . . This ain't the village, you know," I interrupted his slight trance. "I know what you're going through . . . I'm a Southern refugee, too," I added as I walked out the door. "Oh, what the hell. . . ." I pushed my way through the crowd again as I headed toward the door.

Reaching the street, I was met by the hotness of the odorous mass of men, trash, and rats. I hated the obscenity of all of them.

After I had walked about two or three blocks I sensed someone following me. Several beatings and petty robberies had taught me not to look back or waste time now. I speeded up a little and ducked into a small all-night restaurant. A few seconds after I entered the restaurant I saw the boy through the window. I motioned for him to come on in. He joined me. He still had that embarrassed look on his face and a hint of fear. I ordered a breakfast for him and a cup of coffee for myself. It was four o'clock in the morning—too early for anyone to eat unless he were hungry, drunk, or at a party combining the two.

In a short time the boy was eating, smiling and talking freely. He was Jason Thomas. He was from a farm near Auburn, Alabama. He had gotten into some freedom movement trouble and was rushed out of Auburn. His parents were sharecroppers. He and several of the younger boys had organized a strike against the man up in the "big house" for higher wages or a fairer deal than they were getting. Several croppers on other farms were talking about doing the same to their "bosses." It wasn't long before the leaders were singled out. Jason's parents and friends could barely scrape up enough money to get him a safe distance from Auburn. He made it to Mobile and worked from town to town heading north. He had always heard about the good times in Harlem. He worked odd jobs and hitchhiked to get here. He had lived through hate, fear, and hopelessness only to have a repeat performance.

As Jason talked I understood him all too well. I knew his life of pathos and tragedy. I knew him all too well. That was the stinging thing. I was an eight-year veteran in this struggle of crossing the "cotton curtain." I knew this boy's situation. I could see myself through this boy's gaudy chaos. Yet, I felt he was better off than I was—he had hope. Yeah, I was like this boy . . . once . . . truly like him.

I had left Biloxi filled with the humiliation, degradation, frustration, and resentment of too many bitter migrants before me. My mother had worked herself to death in a white man's kitchen while I prowled the streets in search of meaning among people too desperate to understand the horrible sting that daily mounted within my body and soul. I was led from one tumultuous experience to another—each one more obscene than the last one. My mother beat me until I was almost unconscious every day of the week. Then she would force me to go to church every Sunday. I hated every minute of listening to the moans and groans of the brothers and sisters, as they called themselves. They danced, screamed, and spoke in unknown tongues every Sunday before a pulpit full of bald-headed men who roared messages of deliverance and salvation until sweat poured down their black faces and stained the collars of their white shirts. I also knew these men too well. I had met them sneaking in bootleggers and joints. I knew the brothers and sisters, too. The same sweat which now covered their pain-racked bodies was only a return of that which I had seen on them on Saturday night. Most of them were no better than the "sinners" they condemned to torment. I had decided that hell couldn't be any worse than the life I or most of the so-called saints lived. And there was little we could really do about it. We were all huddled into a strange ghetto of corruption.

After constant pushing by my mother I reluctantly joined the saints. I was called converted after stomping and rolling on the floor at the height of the emotionalism one night during a spring revival. I was a good boy as long as I joined in with the saints on Sunday and didn't raise too much hell during the week. After my mother's funeral I never went back to the church. I was called a backslider. Someone was either backsliding or being reinstated nearly every Sunday. When I found life unbearable in Biloxi I fled to Harlem.

I knew my father was supposed to be in the big city of New York. Harlem was a reasonable place to start looking for him. My desire to find him was motivated more by hate than anything else. I wanted to destroy him. He was responsible for the debauchery of my mother. He had destroyed her sixteen-year chastity and deserted her, leaving her and her family humiliated. When the frustration and agony became unbearable she escaped to a two-room shanty in Biloxi, where I spent the first eighteen years of my life. My mother never mentioned him to me but my Aunt Martha, who visited us too often, threw it up all the time when she was angry at me. I often heard my mother crying at night. I knew it was over him. I left home determined to find him and make him pay for what he had done. But my blood-pounding experiences in Harlem didn't allow me the time to go on a manhunt. I had to fight to survive.

As Jason talked I reminisced. The agony of this nineteen-year-old boy demanded a fresh self-examination of my unforgettable experiences. The compassionate eloquence of this innocent boy hit me with the impact of a harsh and savage power. He was the boy my mother had wanted. I couldn't let him destroy himself here.

It was almost six o'clock when we finished talking. The streets were becoming busy as black men and women made their way downtown to work. I invited Jason to my apartment to get some rest. He was slightly reluctant but he consented. We rushed through the crowding streets trying to reach the subway before the mainstream of the crowd.

With a quick jerk we were off for my apartment. After several backsnapping stops and starts we were at the Hime's Apartments and in my three-room flat on the fifth floor.

I pulled out the sofa bed for Jason. He went out like a light on the foam cushioning. It wasn't long before I was asleep in the other room. The phone woke me up around two-thirty, Murphy was calling for me to come to practice. On the run, I went in the bathroom for a quick shave and some fast grooming and finished dressing in the bedroom. Jason was still asleep when I left. I wrote him a note and left him a few bucks for lunch and dinner.

Murphy was furious when I arrived for rehearsal. He had landed a trial booking at the Apollo. An agent was coming to the Flamingo tonight to hear us play. If we were good enough the booking would be solid—maybe a few weeks of backgrounding and a minor attraction billing. I grabbed up my sax and joined in the swinging rhythm of *Soul Jump*. Murphy had recently composed the song for me. It was rather unusual for an alto sax to take the lead over the tenor. The exotic tones had cast a mystic spell over the audiences in the small spots. Now we'd have a chance to try it at the Apollo—if everything went off okay tonight.

As the mellow notes blurted from the sax I was proud of my high school band instructor and his patience with me. I probably would never have graduated if it hadn't been for him. The band was my only link with school but I couldn't afford an instrument. He had loaned me his sax. I did odd jobs around his house in return. He also tutored me in my weak classes—enough for me to pass them. I struggled with his beautiful shiny metal with its silver valves and bell piece all plated with gold on its inside. He said I was a natural with it. By my junior year I had started a rhythm band. We called ourselves the Silver Sounds. I had made just enough money to buy my own sax when the band broke up. We were always fussing and fighting about one thing or another. I lost interest in bands after that but I never stopped practicing. My sax was my only means of expression. I played it from deep within—from my soul, Murphy said the night I was wailing away in a bar.

I was making the sounds for petty cash. I also needed something to eat and a place to rest. I jazzed up some old church tunes I remembered and picked up a buck or two around the dives. Murphy heard me one night and hired me.

As I played tonight Murphy calmed down. We didn't practice long—about two hours—before we took a break. After several more hours of practice I had to go home. I kept thinking about Jason. If I hurried I'd have a couple of hours to devote to my lost self before the dance started.

When I arrived at the apartment Jason was gone, so was the note and money. He was probably out eating. I shined my shoes and aired out my band costume as I waited for him. He hadn't returned by nine-thirty. The dance would begin in half an hour. At least it was scheduled that way—we usually started about half an hour later. Murphy called at ten—he was worried that I would hold him up as usual and he didn't want anything to go wrong tonight. I told him I was waiting for Jason and tried to explain the situation hurriedly. He began to curse and threatened me if I messed up things. He had threatened me countless times before but this time he really sounded serious—his ambition was at stake. "You'd betta be here!" he had nervously concluded. I would be lucky if I reached the club by ten-thirty.

I was locking the apartment door when the phone rang again. It was J.B. "A kid's been hurt here," he said. "He's bleedin' kinda bad. . . . He keeps calling your name and he has a note of yours. . . . He was in here mouthin' off . . . some damn fool's done 'bout sliced him to death," J.B. explained fervidly.

I dashed over to J.B.'s place. When I got there Jason was sprawled out in a pool of blood. He was surrounded by anguished and passionate black faces. J.B. reluctantly called the police. I told them all I knew about Jason. They took me down to headquarters for some kind of statement.

As I walked away from the precinct a fierce energy shot through my body. I felt like walking. I must have walked for miles. I passed flashy black studs with brightly clad gals giggling at their sides. I passed by unkept buildings with half-naked women shouting chants from windows and their pimps advertising for them in the streets. I passed devastated apartments with overturned trash cans and dim lights passing through cheap window shades. I could hear curses as too-loud televisions and radios blasted through the thin-walled rooms. Here and there some brave man or woman—more often both together—was sleeping on a fire escape to get away from the odorous heat inside their unbearable rooms. Finally I passed a store-front church with THE GLORIOUS TEMPLE OF GOD THROUGH CHRIST JESUS painted across its huge window. I could hear the familiar sounds of tambourines, drums, and cymbals almost drowning out the voices of the saints.

A black curtain prevented me from seeing them. I had seen them too often, anyway. The brothers dressed in cheap suits, probably the only ones they owned, would A-men and Yeah while white-clad sisters would belt the spirituals. I began to pat my foot to their rhythm:

> He's a well of water
>   in my soul
> He's a well of living water
>   in my soul

The words *in my soul* had an overwhelming power over me. As they rang in my ears I could see Jason's body lying in the pool of blood with the anguished and passionate black faces surrounding him. I could see the police questioning them, then me. The murderer had gotten away as usual—no one would tell. The police would close the joint down for the night. Closing the dive would be the only tribute the boy would receive.

He probably had done no more than gaze too hard at some tight-dressed barfly. Maybe he had insulted her. She had to be protected by her escort, who had beaten her unmercifully last week or last night. Perhaps he had just let that high temper of his fly off at some drunk.

I could only see an innocent boy destroyed. They had destroyed his body but they couldn't have destroyed his soul. No, they hadn't known him long enough to invade his soul.

I listened to the saints:

> He's a well of water
>   in my soul

He's a well of living water
  in my soul

Their words began to draw me into the church. I took a seat in the back. I didn't want to attract too much attention. I had on my gold Nehru jacket and the rest of my flashy band costume.

Three or four of the sisters began to dance to the rhythm. A few more were speaking in unknown tongues. The rest of the saints repeated the chorus with added vigor.

A single tear dropped from my eyes followed by a flood of tears. I tried but I just couldn't stop them. I soon found myself stomping around the floor. I fell before the altar and continued to cry. I felt a fire burning within me. Then I blacked out. When I came to I was surrounded by a mass of tired black and brown faces. The saints were shouting, "Turn him loose Satan! . . . Turn him loose! . . . You done had his body. . . . You cain't have his soul. . . . Turn him loose!"

In the dark cloud of faces I saw one which was a duplicate of my own. It was older and showed more signs of worry and stress. Beneath the face was a preacher's collar and dirty, wrinkled clothes. Balls of sweat were flowing down the muddy face. A dingy handkerchief protected the muddy eyes from the salty sweat. The fierce energy returned to my body as he reached out and grasped my hand. He bent his pain-racked body and said, "Thank the Lawd, son."

afterword

"The Soul's Sting" describes the plight of many of those Negroes who go North in an attempt to have a better chance than the one they feel is available to them in the South. All too often, though, they experience in the urban ghettoes of the North a life of bitterness and frustration as shattering as anything they have left behind. Their world frequently becomes one of desperate pleasures as they compulsively seek to erase their sense of the futility of their efforts, but, as their random acts of violence and self-destruction indicate, even the pleasures do not allow them to forget.

Before Jason's death, Cabbell's narrator finds some satisfaction in the hedonistic life he has found for himself in Harlem. Although he seems to realize that it is a distinctly limited existence, indeed a trap, into which social inequality has led him, he refuses to admit this to himself. With the murder of Jason, though, he is forced to acknowledge the futility of his life in Harlem, and he attempts to run from that life, only to find himself back where he began, in a transplanted Southern fundamentalist church. Apparently, Cabbell is saying that his narrator has gone full cycle and found only defeat.

Edward J. Cabbell was born in a coal camp near Eckman, West Virginia, in 1946. He graduated from nearby Concord College in Athens, West Virginia, with a B.S. in Education, concentrating in Social Studies. He is presently employed by Concord College, as assistant director of the Upward Bound Project and resides in Princeton, West Virginia, with his wife and two daughters. His short stories and poems have appeared in *Phylon, The Negro History Bulletin,* and other college and literary magazines. He is a black studies enthusiast, with particular interests in literature.

questions for general discussion

1. Comment on the significance of the last line in the story.

2. Why is it significant that the narrator sees the old preacher's face as "one which was a duplicate of my own. It was older and showed more signs of worry and stress"?

3. Why does the narrator not keep his appointment with Murphy for the audition for the Apollo?

4. Could the story's ending be conceived as an optimistic one?

5. Is there any possible significance in the young man's name being Jason?

suggestions for writing

1. Comment on the evolution of the narrator's image of himself between the time of his meeting Jason and his meeting the preacher.

2. Write a theme on the narrator's use of references to jazz and spirituals to establish character, tone, and setting.

3. Write an essay articulating the theme of the story, utilizing the significance of the title.